Central Asia in Focus: Political and Economic Issues

CENTRAL ASIA IN FOCUS: POLITICAL AND ECONOMIC ISSUES

LYDIA M. BUYERS (EDITOR)

Nova Science Publishers, Inc.
New York

Senior Editors: Susan Boriotti and Donna Dennis
Coordinating Editor: Tatiana Shohov
Office Manager: Annette Hellinger
Graphics: Wanda Serrano
Editorial Production: Maya Columbus, Vladimir Klestov, Matthew Kozlowski, and Tom Moceri
Circulation: Ave Maria Gonzalez, Vera Popovic, Luis Aviles, Raymond Davis, Melissa Diaz, Magdalene Nunez, Marlene Nunez and Jeannie Pappas
Communications and Acquisitions: Serge P. Shohov
Marketing: Cathy DeGregory

Library of Congress Cataloging-in-Publication Data
Available Upon Request

ISBN: 1-59033-153-2.

400 Oser Ave, Suite 1600
Hauppauge, New York 11788-3619
Tele. 631-231-7269 Fax 631-231-8175
e-mail: Novascience@earthlink.net
Web Site: http://www.novapublishers.com

Printed in the United States of America

CONTENTS

PREFACE

Neglect is usually accompanied by either a dim light or no light whatsoever. Central Asia, until quite recently, was a part of the world known to only a few scholars of the obscure. Cold War opponents dropped their lukewarm interest in the area like a sack of hot coals. All of a sudden, this part of the world is being touted as terribly significant to everyone; America, Europe, Asia and all Muslim countries. This book presents important political and economic information valuable to learning more about the region.

INTRODUCTION*

Glenn E. Curtis

In 1991 the five Soviet Republics of Central Asia--Kazakhstan, Kyrgyzstan, Tajikistan, Turkmenistan, and Uzbekistan--were faced for the first time with the prospect of existence as independent states. In critical respects, they were unprepared for this event: their economies all had performed specific tasks in the Soviet system, mainly the supply of raw materials; only outdated Soviet-era political structures remained behind in the five republics, with no tradition of national political institutions; and the end of the union fragmented the armed forces units of the former Soviet Union that remained on the republics' territory. In the 1990s, the progress of the five republics toward resolving these problems has been quite uneven. The republics with the richest natural resources--Kazakhstan, Turkmenistan, and Uzbekistan--have developed the strongest economies--albeit with serious defects in each case--and have attracted substantial Western investment. In all cases, movement away from the Soviet model of strong, one-party central government has been extremely slow. Some degree of military autonomy has appeared in all republics save Tajikistan, which still is bedeviled by rebel forces and a porous southern border. At the same time, the strategic doctrine of all Central Asian countries remains based on protection from Russia's military.

The total area of the five republics is approximately 3.9 million square kilometers, slightly more than 40 percent of the area of the United States and less than one-quarter of the area of Russia. The region stretches from the Caspian Sea in the west to China in the east, and from central Siberia in the north to Afghanistan, Iran, and Pakistan in the south. The area of the republics varies greatly: Kazakhstan, by far the largest, occupies about 2.7 million square kilometers, more than two-thirds of the region. The smallest republic, Kyrgyzstan, occupies only 198,500 square kilometers. The Central Asian republics also feature quite different topographies, varying from the wide expanses of desert in primarily flat Kazakhstan and Turkmenistan to the steep slopes and river valleys of mountainous Tajikistan and Kyrgyzstan.

The region contains enormous natural and agricultural resources. All five republics have favorable agricultural regions and some combination of attractive minerals and fuels. Their industrial bases include trained workers, and their populations have relatively high

* Excerpted from the Library of Congress Country Studies Website at: http://lcweb2.loc.gov/frd/cs/cshome.html.

educational levels and literacy rates. Unfortunately, the moribund, highly inefficient system through which the Soviet Union exploited those resources has proved very difficult to disassemble. The Central Asians have suffered all the typical transitional ills of former communist states moving toward a market economy: erratic supply of critical industrial inputs, increased unemployment, sharply increased inflation, declining capacity utilization and output by industry, and acute shortages of goods. In response, all five governments have pledged meaningful reform, but obstacles such as unworkable government structure, ethnic rivalries, and a variety of social tensions have made all five move cautiously.

Central Asia has a rich history to which numerous tribes and nationalities have contributed over at least 2,500 years. A vital factor in the history of the southern part of the region was its location astride the most direct trade route between China and Europe, the so-called Silk Route, which began to develop in the heyday of the Roman Empire (see fig. 3). Cities such as Samarqand (Samarkand) and Bukhoro (Bukhara), founded by Iranians, became powerful cultural and commercial centers as East-West trade increased. That prosperity made part or all of the region the object of many conquests (including those by the Arabs in the eighth century A.D., several Turkic groups beginning in the ninth century, and the Mongols in the early thirteenth century). The Arabs and the Turks brought Islam to much of Central Asia. Meanwhile, the northern part of the region was inhabited by nomadic herding peoples, including the Turkic predecessors of the Kazaks and Kyrgyz, who also fell under the control of the Mongols.

In the sixteenth century, the Uzbeks established powerful khanates along the Silk Route. Those entities flourished until the nineteenth century, when they were overtaken gradually by the traders and settlers of the expanding Russian Empire. The Russians moved southward from the steppes of Kazakhstan in search of trade and later of the cotton that could be grown in present-day Tajikistan, Turkmenistan, and Uzbekistan. In the ensuing decades, cotton became the vital economic magnet for increased Russian occupation, and large tracts of the region were devoted to that crop to supply Russia's domestic needs.

In 1917 the region passed from the Russian Empire to the Soviet Union, with little participation by its inhabitants. Full Soviet control did not occur until the mid-1920s, as guerrilla bands continued to resist Soviet authority. In the 1920s, four of the five republics came into existence for the first time as Soviet authorities drew borders in anticipation of reordering all of Central Asian society. (Kyrgyzstan gained full republic status in 1936.) In the 1930s, the primarily agricultural region was traumatized by the forced collectivization campaign of Joseph V. Stalin's regime; episodes of widespread famine were common. (By 1900 the Kazak, Kyrgyz, and Turkmen nomads already had suffered massive disruption of their traditional lifestyles as a result of Russian settlers taking their grazing land for farms.)

Throughout the Soviet period, the Central Asian republics participated in the life of the union in a rather peripheral sense, and many phases of cultural life were unaffected by Soviet rule. Local communist parties suffered the same purges as those in other republics, but they exercised little political influence in Moscow. Regional economies were stunted by increased demands for production of cotton and other specifically assigned items. As was discovered in the 1980s, decades of Soviet intensive cultivation caused massive pollution, from which the region still suffers. Interrepublican animosities over access to scarce resources went largely ignored by Soviet authorities. The more liberal Soviet regime of Mikhail S. Gorbachev (in office 1985-91) saw increased airing of grievances that long had been withheld by the peoples of the Central Asian republics, but before 1991 no organized movement for independence had evolved from that discontent.

The five post-Soviet states of Central Asia still are defined by the arbitrary borders created in the early years of the Soviet era, and the demarcation among them still fails to correspond to the ethnic and linguistic situation of the region. Thus, Kyrgyzstan and Turkmenistan have substantial Uzbek minorities, and Tajikistan and Uzbekistan have large numbers of their respective neighbor's people. Kazakhstan has few Central Asian people of other nationalities; its largest minorities are Russian, Ukrainian, and German.

Until the 1990s, the Soviet Central Asian states were viewed from the outside world largely as parts of a single, homogeneous region. Since 1991, however, the Western world has begun to discover substantial differences in almost all aspects of those new nations. The West also has discovered the possibility of commercial gain from oil, natural gas, gold, and other natural resources abundant in the region. The presence of these materials was known in the Soviet era, but they were accessible only by way of Moscow.

In responding to their neighbors in the new independence period, the policy makers of the five states have moved in two contrary directions: toward establishing common goals and greater unity in a regional grouping, and toward individual economic and political development and identification with countries outside the region. The philosophical ideal of Pan-Turkism, an ethnically based unity concept that originated among Central Asian intellectuals in the nineteenth century, still receives support, but relatively few concrete steps have been taken to realize the ideal. Furthermore, the people of Tajikistan are of predominantly Persian rather than Turkic origin. Meanwhile, Central Asians have placed special emphasis on ethnic self-differentiation as a belated reaction against the stereotyping of non-Slavs that was common practice in the Soviet Union. That ethnic generalization continues in the Russian Federation, which still exerts enormous influence in the Central Asian republics.

The most important single cultural commonality among the republics is the practice of Sunni Islam, which is the professed religion of a very large majority of the peoples of the five republics and which has experienced a significant revival throughout the region in the 1990s. Propaganda from Russia and from the ruling regimes in the republics identifies Islamic political activity as a vague, monolithic threat to political stability everywhere in the region. However, the role of Islam in the five cultures is far from uniform, and its role in politics has been minimal everywhere except in Tajikistan. For Kazaks, Kyrgyz, and Turkmen, whose society was based on a nomadic lifestyle that carried on many traditional tribal beliefs after their nominal conversion, Islam has had a less profound influence on culture than for the sedentary Tajik and Uzbek Muslims, who have a conventional religious hierarchy.

Regional economic cooperation, another type of unity that has received substantial lip service in the 1990s, has failed to materialize on a large scale. All five republics joined the Economic Cooperation Organization (ECO--see Glossary) shortly after independence, and Kazakhstan, Kyrgyzstan, and Uzbekistan established a limited common market in 1994. But Uzbekistan vetoed the membership of unstable Tajikistan, and Turkmenistan refused to join. Existing arrangements within the free-trade zone have not significantly promoted large-scale commerce within the group of three. For all five republics, Russia remains the top trading partner because much of the emphasis in their agricultural and industrial infrastructures remains the same as when the republics had assigned roles in supplying Moscow. Those roles and dependence on Russian trade are changing slowly in the mid-1990s, however, as diversification occurs.

Several factors encourage economic rivalry rather than cooperation. Water, a crucial resource for agriculture and power generation, has been the object of bitter bilateral and multilateral disputes both before and after independence. In the 1990s, the republics at the headwaters of major rivers, Kyrgyzstan and Tajikistan, have chafed at apportionment of water consumption favoring downstream consumers Turkmenistan and Uzbekistan, and Turkmenistan has complained about excessive water consumption by the Uzbekistanis upstream. Kyrgyzstan and Uzbekistan have come close to conflict over water in the Fergana Valley, where vital agricultural reform and land privatization programs are endangered by unresolved water disputes.

The republics still offer a similar range of commodities for trade. Their common emphasis on cotton, natural gas, and oil limits the potential for advantageous commerce within the group and fosters rivalry in trade with outside customers. Some of the commercial relationships that have developed--such as the sale of fuels to Kyrgyzstan and Tajikistan by the other three fuel-rich republics--have been one-sided and subject to shutdown in response to nonpayment or in attempts to gain economic and political leverage.

The five republics have several major problems in common. All remain in the economic, military, and political shadow of their giant neighbor to the north. In the mid-1990s, Russian policy makers, encouraged by a very vocal nationalist faction in the federation, speak openly of recapturing influence in the "near abroad"; Central Asia usually is the first region cited as an example. In the first two years of independence, the five republics remained in the ruble zone (see Glossary), their monetary activities restricted by the nonconvertibility of the old Soviet ruble that remained the currency of that grouping. In 1993 all but Tajikistan introduced new currencies with limited convertibility. Russia had attempted to keep Kazakhstan and Uzbekistan in a new Russian ruble zone, but ruble distribution problems and harsh conversion conditions forced those republics to follow the independent course of Kyrgyzstan and Turkmenistan. The Tajikistani ruble (for value of the Tajikistani ruble--see Glossary) introduced in 1995 remained closely connected with its Russian counterpart. In 1996 Kazakhstan and Kyrgyzstan established a new customs union and other economic ties with Russia and Belarus, hoping to gain selected advantages while avoiding large-scale concessions that would increase Russian influence.

The Soviet legacy includes an economic infrastructure in which all republics depend heavily on other republics for vital inputs. A complex Soviet-designed system of pipelines and electric cables connects the five republics. Pending completion of Turkmenistan's new line to Iran, only one railroad line leading out of Central Asia connects the region with a destination other than Russia (the one line goes only to the Xinjiang Uygur Autonomous Region in China). Heavy industry in all five republics also has depended heavily on local Russian skilled labor.

The Central Asian republics also suffer common geographic disadvantages. All are landlocked and located far from potential markets outside the Commonwealth of Independent States (CIS--see Glossary) and the Middle East. Nations such as Azerbaijan and Afghanistan, through which goods must travel overland to reach Western markets, still are quite unstable, and others such as China and Russia are powerful neighbors with a history of taking advantage of weaker nations that need commercial favors. Kazakhstan and Turkmenistan, both in need of a route to move oil and gas to Western customers, have been especially frustrated by Russia's failure to support new pipelines. The landlocked position also presents a national security obstacle.

Although the region is blessed with ample arable land, most of that land becomes useful only when irrigated. Large-scale irrigation, in turn, has taken a huge toll on the hydrological systems of the region--in the most obvious case, the system that feeds the fast-disappearing Aral Sea. Regional cooperation on the Aral Sea problem, recognized as one of the most serious environmental crises in the world, received much lip service and little action in the first half of the 1990s. By 1995 an estimated 36,000 square kilometers of the sea's bed had been exposed, and an estimated 3 million inhabitants of nearby Turkmenistan, Uzbekistan, and Kazakhstan had developed chronic health problems associated with that process. In October 1995, a United Nations (UN)-sponsored regional conference produced the Nukus Declaration, which resulted in the promise of intensified joint efforts to stabilize the sea and a pledge of US$200 million from the UN and the World Bank (see Glossary) for regional development and aid.

When independence was declared in 1991, none of the five republics had experienced an independence movement or had a corps of leaders who had considered how such a change might be managed. Five years after independence, in four of the states political leadership remains in the hands of the same individual as in the last years of the Soviet Union: Nursultan Nazarbayev in Kazakhstan, Askar Akayev in Kyrgyzstan, Saparmyrat Niyazov in Turkmenistan, and Islam Karimov in Uzbekistan. President Emomali Rakhmanov of Tajikistan was not president in 1991, but, like his cohorts, his roots are in his republic's pre-1992 political world. Political power in all five republics is based on clan and regional groupings that make national coalitions risky and fragile. Clan rivalries have played a particular role in the civil war of Tajikistan and in Akayev's difficulties in unifying Kyrgyzstan behind a reform program.

Although all the republics had adopted new constitutions by 1995, the three government branches prescribed by those documents are severely imbalanced in favor of the executive. In all five cases, the political opposition of the early 1990s has been virtually extinguished in the name of preserving stability and preventing the putative onset of Islamic politicization. Although the new constitutions of the republics specify independent judicial branches, the concept of due process has not been established consistently anywhere.

All five republics have suffered increasing rates of crime in the liberalized atmosphere of the postindependence years. Drug trafficking, official corruption, and white-collar crime have increased most noticeably. All republics lack the resources to equip and train qualified police and specialized forces, and their judicial systems are not sufficiently removed from their Soviet antecedents to deal equitably with new generations of criminals. Evaluation and quantification of crime in post-Soviet Central Asia have been hampered by changes in responsible agencies, by irregularities in reporting procedures, and by lack of control and responsiveness in law enforcement agencies, particularly in Tajikistan. Statistics for the years 1990 and 1994 from Kazakhstan and Kyrgyzstan show dramatic increases in every type of crime, although those from the other three republics, where record keeping is known to be substantially less comprehensive, show considerable drops in many categories. In 1995 and 1996, Kazakhstan and Uzbekistan set up new, specialized police units to deal with economic and organized crime.

Kazakhstan

By far the largest of the Central Asian republics, Kazakhstan extends almost 2,000 kilometers from the Caspian Sea in the west to the border of China in the east and nearly 1,300 kilometers from central Siberia in the north to eastern Uzbekistan in the south. Despite its size, in population Kazakhstan is a distant second to Uzbekistan among the Central Asian republics. With the lowest birth rate and the highest emigration rate in the region, Kazakhstan's population has remained virtually stable for the past ten years. Kazakhstan has by far the largest non-Asian population (45 percent in 1994, equaling the Kazak population) and the smallest population of other Central Asian ethnic groups (for example, only 2 percent are Uzbek).

The largest minority in Kazakhstan is its Russian population (36 percent in 1994), which until the 1990s was the plurality group. The status of the Russians, whose number includes many irreplaceable technical experts, has been one of Kazakhstan's burning post-Soviet issues. The government has resisted making Russian an official second language, although Russian is understood by most Kazaks and used in most official communications. In May 1996, a treaty established the status of Kazak and Russian citizens in Russia and Kazakhstan, respectively, ending a long disputed aspect of the nationality issue.

Of the five Central Asian republics, Kazakhstan played the most important industrial role in the Soviet system because of the abundant coal and oil deposits in the northern sector of the republic, closest to Russia. Although the Soviet Union developed specific sectors of industry such as chemicals, metals, and military equipment, the republic also inherited an antiquated industrial infrastructure geared to feed materials into the Soviet economy. Energy industries, which also played a large part in the economy, have suffered from substantial reductions in Russia's post-Soviet demand, as have other industries that remain dependent on Russian markets.

In 1996 most of Kazakhstan's economy was still state-owned and lacked fundamental restructuring, despite large-scale privatization of smaller enterprises in the preceding years. Some large firms have been sold to solid international companies (such as the Republic of Korea's (South Korea's) Samsung, which now manages the Zhezqazghan Nonferrous Metallurgy complex and refinery), but many were awarded to unknown companies whose contracts later were cancelled. In June 1996, the government sold the country's largest oil refinery at Shymkent, Yuzhneftegaz, one of its largest oil enterprises, and the Vasilevskoye gold mine, one of the largest in the world, by public tender to foreign companies. Those sales, together worth an estimated US$1 billion, were a major departure from previous policy and were aimed at improving the confidence of international investors.

In 1996 the healthiest parts of the economy were the oil, gas, and mineral extraction industries. However, infrastructural decay and slow structural reform have delayed the recovery of those sectors from post-Soviet lethargy. Many of the state enterprises concentrated in northern Kazakhstan are far in debt and unable to pay wages to their workers. The transfer of the national capital from Almaty along the border of Uzbekistan to Aqmola in the industrial north, planned for 1998, is an attempt to revive that zone, as well as to retain the cadre of Russian technical experts who continue to leave the country.

Foreign investment in Kazakhstan has been frustrated by complex bureaucratic rules, and the domestic consumer market is restricted by the very low average wage of US$96 per month. The Western oil companies Chevron and Mobil have invested heavily in the Tengiz oil fields offshore in the Caspian Sea, but they have been frustrated by a long dispute with the consortium of Kazakhstan, Oman, and Russia over the structure of a new delivery pipeline. The common customs regime established with Russia in 1995 has accelerated trade, but conditions favored Russia in the first year.

The Central Bank of Kazakhstan, President Nazarbayev, and the Council of Ministers play a strong role in economic policy making. The bank has advocated market reform and inflation control the most strongly of the three. Experts rate Nazarbayev's economic initiatives as erratic. Government goals for 1996 included reducing inflation to 28 percent (the 1995 rate was 60 percent), reducing the budget deficit to about 3.3 percent of the gross domestic product (GDP--see Glossary); and limiting devaluation of the tenge (for value of the tenge--see Glossary) to a 10 percent decline against the dollar.

The exchange rate of the tenge against the United States dollar has improved steadily, allowing upper-class Kazaks to expand foreign goods purchases. For 1997 the Economist Intelligence Unit forecasts significant stabilization and recovery, with overall GDP growth of 1 percent and consumer price inflation of 45 percent. Substantial aid was expected from the International Monetary Fund (IMF--see Glossary) in 1996. Full membership in the Islamic Development Bank, achieved in mid-1996, brought Kazakhstan additional aid for trade operations, personnel training, and infrastructure improvements.

Despite the abundance of fuel in Kazakhstan, in 1996 the republic continued to be plagued by its Soviet-era transportation system, which failed to connect population centers with distant hydrocarbon deposits within the country. As a result, in the winter of 1996-97 Almaty and others cities suffered severe shortages of electric power and heat.

In December 1996, Russia finally stopped blocking a multinational agreement to build an export pipeline that would allow Kazakhstan to sell its abundant oil directly to Western customers. Because the pipeline will not be available until 1999 or later, in 1997 Kazakhstan began shipping oil across the Caspian Sea for resale in Iran--a procedure that risked Western condemnation because of the ongoing economic embargo of Iran.

As the Soviet Union faced dissolution late in 1991, Nazarbayev was one of the last advocates of the union's preservation in some form. Since that time, he has pursued a careful foreign policy aimed at preserving both close relations with Russia and as much as possible of his nation's economic and political independence. In domestic politics, he nominally expanded some of the republic's democratic institutions, pushing through a new constitution and a popularly elected parliament. However, Nazarbayev also consolidated his executive power steadily in the mid-1990s. Parliaments were dissolved in 1993 and 1995, and Nazarbayev made numerous changes in the personnel and structure of his cabinets, all in an effort to obtain cooperation in his reform programs. In April 1995, a referendum overwhelmingly extended the president's term to 2000, canceling the 1995 presidential election. Decrees by Nazarbayev in December 1995 and April 1996 further extended the president's powers. Nazarbayev also dissolved the Constitutional Court in 1995 and replaced members of the Supreme Court in 1996.

Party politics in Kazakhstan have not worked well, although a substantial opposition movement exists. Despite efforts by the ruling People's Unity Party (SNEK) to minimize opposition activity, the top three opposition parties gained twenty-two of sixty-seven seats in the lower house (Majilis) of parliament in the December 1995 elections, and another fourteen seats went to independent candidates. Indicating the inferior role of parliament in the Kazakhstani government, however, was the lack of competition in those elections; only forty-nine candidates vied for the forty Senate (upper-house) seats being contested. In both houses, Kazaks outnumbered Russians, by forty-two to nineteen in the Majilis and by twenty-nine to fifteen in the Senate (the president appoints seven senators).

In the Soviet era, Semipalatinsk (now Semey) in northeastern Kazakhstan was the world's largest and most frequently used test site for nuclear weapons. During the long Cold-War period of nuclear weapons testing, an estimated 1.5 to 2 million people were affected by radioactive pollution in northern Kazakhstan. Demonstrations against nuclear testing began in 1989, and a major environmental movement sprang from that opposition.

When the Soviet Union dissolved, Kazakhstan was one of four republics possessing nuclear weapons and materials. In November 1994, the United States completed Project Sapphire, which involved the purchase and removal of more than 600 kilograms of weapons-grade plutonium from Kazakhstan, whose insecure storage facilities and possible nuclear sales to Libya and Iran had aroused international concern. In May 1995, the last of Kazakhstan's nuclear weapons was destroyed, removing a major shadow from the Soviet past. The United States has promised aid in permanently sealing the Semey test site.

In the 1990s, Kazakhstan's foreign policy has continued Nazarbayev's early support of a federation among the former Soviet states, now loosely united in the CIS. Because the country's industrial and energy bases are located close to Russia's southern border, experts have identified Kazakhstan as the former Soviet republic most likely to experience Russian pressure toward reunification. Despite the strains caused by the uncertain status of the large Russian minority in his republic, Nazarbayev has maintained close relations with Russia; in early 1996, he brought Kazakhstan into a new commercial confederation with Belarus, Russia, and Kyrgyzstan. In June 1996, Prime Minister Akezhan Kazhegeldin reiterated Kazakhstan's full support for additional CIS integration (while preserving member-state sovereignty) and for the reelection of Boris N. Yeltsin as president of Russia. Meanwhile, Kazakhstan worked with Kyrgyzstan and Uzbekistan to extend the activities of the Central Asian Economic Union, which was established in 1993. At the Bishkek summit of January 1997, a treaty of "eternal friendship" guaranteed mutual security assistance among the three member nations; the summit also discussed mutual convertibility of the three currencies.

Kyrgyzstan.

Kyrgyzstan, the second-smallest of the Central Asian republics in both area and population, is located between two giants: Kazakhstan to its north and China to its south and east. The rural population, already the largest by percentage in Central Asia, is growing faster than the cities. Like Kazakhstan, Kyrgyzstan has a minority population of Russians (22 percent in 1994) whose accelerated emigration threatens the country's technological base. The country's legal and political systems give clear priority to the Kyrgyz majority, alienating not only Russians but also the large Uzbek minority concentrated in the Osh region of southwestern Kyrgyzstan. Friction persists over control of the scarce land of the Fergana Valley, which overlaps the territory of three republics: Kyrgyzstan, Tajikistan, and Uzbekistan. The regime of President Askar Akayev (first elected in 1990) has attempted to balance sorely needed national reform programs with the demands of ethnic groups and clans that still exercise strong influence on the country's political and social structures.

Kyrgyzstan, ranked as the second-poorest republic in Central Asia, possesses a more limited range of natural resources than its neighbors. In the Soviet era, Kyrgyzstan contributed a specific group of minerals--antimony, gold, and mercury--to Moscow's economic plan. Of the three, only gold is a valuable asset in the post-Soviet world; it has attracted several Western investor companies. Kyrgyzstan has only limited amounts of coal and oil. The major energy resource is water power from the republic's fast-moving rivers. However, despite a government program of increased emphasis on hydroelectric power, Kyrgyzstan must import a large proportion of its energy supply. Kyrgyzstan's industry, which had been specialized to serve the Soviet military-industrial complex, suffered heavily when that demand disappeared; conversion has proven very difficult.

After independence, Kyrgyzstan suffered one of the worst economic declines among the CIS states (particularly in industrial output), despite a reform program that was deployed more rapidly than most others. Statistically, privatization was very effective, but because meaningful economic change did not occur after privatization, inefficient state enterprises continued to drag down the economy. Government and commercial corruption also diluted the effects of economic reform.

In the mid-1990s, official measurements of Kyrgyzstan's economic performance were very negative; they were, however, not completely accurate. By 1996 an estimated 30 percent of real GDP came from the "black economy"--independent, unregistered entrepreneurs selling their wares on the street or in private shops--while state-owned enterprises continued to go bankrupt or failed to pay their employees. However, even official GDP bottomed out in 1995; it dropped 6.2 percent after slumping by 26 percent in the previous year. The Economist Intelligence Unit forecast GDP rises of 1 percent in 1996 and 2.5 percent in 1997, the latter spurred by the opening of the Canadian joint-venture gold mine at Kumtor. In 1995 the volume of industrial production dropped 12.5 percent, and consumer goods production dropped 25.4 percent, but agriculture improved by 38.8 percent.

Other indicators are more positive, however. By early 1996, the inflation rate, which had reached 1,400 percent in 1993, was about 1 percent per month. The government's goal was to halve the end-of-1995 rate by the end of 1996. The exchange rate of the som (for value of the som--see Glossary) remained stable in 1996 at eleven to US$1. The budget deficit remained high at about 12 percent of GDP, with foreign loans applied to make up the shortfall.

Foreign investment remained very sparse in 1996. Many joint ventures with Turkey have failed, and the sale of Kyrgyzstani firms to foreign investors has provided embarrassingly little revenue for the government. International loans continue, but Kyrgyzstan already has fallen behind in repayments to Russia and Turkey. Repayment of pending international debts inevitably will raise the national debt. Debt and the failure of foreign investment have forced Kyrgyzstan to rely more heavily on Russia. The customs union that Kyrgystan joined with Belarus, Kazakhstan, and Russia early in 1996 will add to Moscow's power over Kyrgyzstan's trade policy.

At the same time, Kyrgyzstan's parliament has resisted reform legislation that would modernize the tax code and privatization of large state enterprises in energy, telecommunications, mining, and aviation. According to a government estimate, as many as 70 percent of privatized enterprises were bankrupt in 1996 because, under existing economic conditions, they simply lacked customers. A limited capital market includes the Kyrgyzstan Stock Exchange, which opened in early 1995, and some independent brokerage houses, but because there is no legal framework or government regulation for capital exchange, cash transactions were few in 1996.

Although President Akayev began his regime with ideals of multiparty democracy, strong opposition stymied his reform programs and moved him gradually closer to the authoritarian positions of his four Central Asian colleagues. Power struggles between the legislative and executive branches of government promoted Akayev's expansion of executive power. In the mid-1990s, two elections--the first reelecting Akayev by a huge margin in December 1995 and the second giving 95 percent approval in a referendum on extending his power in February 1996--were approved by international observers as free and fair, although the opposition claimed otherwise. The referendum empowers the president to conduct domestic and foreign policy and to name and dismiss cabinet ministers and judges without consulting parliament. The parliament retains approval rights over the presidential appointment of the prime minister, Supreme Court judges, and other officials, but the president may dissolve parliament if it fails three times to approve a nominee. Akayev had argued that centralizing presidential power was necessary to speed economic, political, and legal reform and to reduce the influence of regional political centers. In March 1996, he exercised his new power by securing the resignation of the government, naming four new ministers, and redesignating the positions of five others. He also reorganized local government to reduce the power of provincial leaders and assign them direct responsibility for enactment of national reforms.

In May 1996, a new government document described social conditions and listed goals for social programs in the ensuing years. Kyrgyzstan, which has made earnest efforts to maintain social support programs in the lean years of the 1990s, is emphasizing job creation and prevention of unemployment, reorganization of social insurance and pension systems, and reforms in education and health care. The official unemployment figure in mid-1996 was 76,600; about 60 percent of the unemployed received unemployment benefits. The government goal is to keep unemployment below 100,000 while mounting a new, long-term job creation program. In 1996 a proposal was made for a government-controlled social fund to run a uniform state insurance and pension system that would remove the severe inequities of Kyrgyzstan's current system.

Meanwhile, nearly one-third of the population (1.257 million) are estimated to live below the poverty line, and the 14,000 refugees arriving annually from Tajikistan create additional social pressures. Kyrgyzstan became a preferred refugee destination when Kazakhstan and Uzbekistan tightened their migration controls in 1993.

In the 1990s, Kyrgyzstan's foreign policy has been shaped by the small country's reliance on Russia for national security. In 1996 President Akayev reiterated that Kyrgyzstan always would view Russia as a natural ally and partner. At the same time, Kyrgyzstan has appealed to the North Atlantic Treaty Organization (NATO--see Glossary) and the Organization for Security and Cooperation in Europe (OSCE--see Glossary) to replace the CIS force in Tajikistan and, in fact, to guarantee the security of the entire region--a position at odds with Russia's strong opposition to NATO influence anywhere in the former Warsaw Pact regions. However, in early 1997 Akayev backed Russia's opposition to NATO expansion in Europe. In 1996-97 Kyrgyzstan diversified its national security policy somewhat by participating in the Central Asian peacekeeping battalion under the aegis of the Central Asian Economic Union.

Difficult relations with Central Asian neighbors increase the need for an outside source of security. Uzbekistan, which has a 13 percent minority population in western Kyrgyzstan, has flexed its muscles by shutting off fuel supplies. Kyrgyzstan depends heavily on the

Kazakhstani capital, Almaty, for air traffic in the absence of a first-class domestic airport. Unresolved border issues and a continuing flow of civil war refugees have inflamed relations with Tajikistan. Greatly expanded trade relations with China also have brought large numbers of Chinese merchants who threaten to stifle domestic commerce in some Kyrgyzstani cities. Kyrgyzstan has expressed the need to balance its policy between China and Russia, and has praised China for its relative restraint in exerting influence over Central Asia.

Tajikistan

Located on the western slopes of the Pamir Mountains, Tajikistan occupies one of the most rugged and topographically divided regions in the world. Possessing extremely convoluted frontiers, it borders Uzbekistan to the west, China to the east, Afghanistan to the south, and Kyrgyzstan to the north. Tajikistan is the smallest in area and third-largest in population of the Central Asian republics. Unlike the ethnically dominant groups of the other four republics, the Tajiks have a culture and a language based on Iranian rather than Turkic roots. Despite their differing cultural backgrounds, the Tajiks and the Uzbeks did not consider themselves separate until the Soviet Union's artificial demarcation of the republics in the 1920s. (Until 1929 the Autonomous Republic of Tajikistan was part of the Soviet Socialist Republic of Uzbekistan.)

The Soviet Union brought Tajikistan significant advancement in education, industry, and infrastructure compared with the primitive conditions of 1917. In the mid-1990s, however, the country remained the most backward of the Central Asian republics, partly because of specifically focused Soviet development policies and partly because of topographical factors that enormously complicate exploitation of existing resources.

In the Soviet system, the Tajikistani economy was designed to produce cotton, aluminum, and a few other mineral products, including uranium and gold. Waged across a large portion of the republic, the civil war has caused great and lasting damage to the national economy. In 1994 damage to industry was estimated at about US$12 billion. Production levels in all industries had dropped an estimated 60 percent in 1994 compared with 1990. Many Germans and Russians, a high percentage of the country's key technical personnel, fled the civil war. The rate of inflation was steep in 1992-93.

In 1996 Tajikistan's economy still was in desperate condition. It remains the least attractive of the former Soviet republics for foreign investment. Only the export of cotton and aluminum has brought significant profits. A joint cotton venture with the United Arab Emirates was scheduled to begin in mid-1996. In 1995 the Regar (Tursunzoda) aluminum plant produced 230,000 tons of primary aluminum, about half its capacity but enough to make aluminum the second-largest export product. As it was earlier in the 1990s, aluminum production has been limited by continued reliance on imported raw materials and energy. Tajikistani industry remains handicapped in general by the country's inability to pay foreign energy suppliers.

Some movement toward economic reform was seen in 1996, although the unreliability of performance statistics makes evaluation difficult. Prime minister Yahyo Azimov, who took office in February 1996, has stressed the need for quick privatization and assistance from the IMF and the World Bank. In early 1996, controls were lifted on bread prices, a move that led to riots in some cities but that was considered a sign of commitment to market reform. The

Azimov government set a 1996 budget deficit cap of 6 percent of GDP. In mid-1996 the World Bank was considering a loan of US$50 million, but the IMF withheld aid pending improvement of foreign exchange and other conditions. The privatization target for the end of 1996 was 50 percent of total enterprises, after only 8 percent of the country's enterprises were privatized in the first four years of independence. The Economist Intelligence Unit forecast additional GDP reductions of 12.4 percent in 1996 and 10 percent in 1997.

In 1996 and 1997, Tajikistan attempted to join regional organizations that would improve its economic position. The customs union of Belarus, Kazakhstan, Kyrgzstan, and Russia considered Tajikistan for membership, but the Central Asian Economic Union of Kazakhstan, Kyrgyzstan, and Uzbekistan refused Tajikistan's overtures.

Some improvements were made in 1995-96 in Tajikistan's woefully shabby infrastructure. The Daewoo firm of South Korea modernized the telephone system, and United States, German, and Turkish firms were scheduled to add new features. The Dushanbe Airport still needs modernization, although in the mid-1990s regular flights were established to Moscow, India, and some other points.

Especially in comparison with the stable regimes that have dominated the other republics since 1991, the political scene in Tajikistan has been unsettled from the day of independence onward. Throughout the 1990s, an old guard with roots in the Soviet era parried the efforts of various opposition groups to share or monopolize power. In 1992 a short-lived coalition government broke down, sending the country into a civil war that was won nominally when the old guard forces captured Dushanbe and named Emomali Rakhmanov chief executive. But conflict persisted, based partly on the geographical and clan divisions of the country and partly on the political question of reform versus reaction. Between 1993 and 1996, fighting flared, mostly in limited engagements, in several regions of Tajikistan and across the border in Afghanistan. In 1993 a multinational CIS force, dominated by Russian units, entered the country with the primary mission of enforcing the southern border, across which opposition forces had received substantial support. In early 1994, the UN arranged a first round of peace talks, and five more rounds followed over the next two years. None of the talks led to an agreement on peace terms, however.

In 1996 Tajikistan's political situation remained as unstable as it had been for the previous three years. The Rakhmanov regime was unable to defeat rebel forces or to compromise enough to reach a satisfactory agreement with them. As it had in the previous three years, Russia failed to bring the government and the opposition to the peace table. Meanwhile, continued instability provided Russia the pretext for maintaining substantial "peacekeeping" forces in a key region of the former Soviet Union. The situation has led some outsiders to doubt the sincerity of Russia's efforts to bring peace to the area.

In early June 1996, the civil war in Tajikistan intensified once again, and observers saw similarities between Russia's military activity there and its occupation of Chechnya. Russian air attacks on opposition villages in south-central Tajikistan contravened the latest three-month extension of the UN-sponsored cease-fire (originally signed in 1994), which had been set in May. In a new campaign apparently coordinated with Moscow, Tajikistani troops moved with Russian air support eastward into the country's narrow central corridor toward opposition strongholds. Meanwhile, in May the Rakhmanov regime refused to reconvene UN-sponsored talks as scheduled, and the UN Observer Mission in Tajikistan (UNMOT) was refused access to the combat zone. In August 1996, opposition troops moved close to Dushanbe amid intensified fighting that ended yet another cease-fire agreement.

In the fall of 1996, the government's military position was unfavorable as rebel forces drove from Afghanistan into central and eastern Tajikistan. In December Rakhmanov signed a peace agreement with Sayed Abdullo Nuri, leader of the opposition Islamic Rebirth Party. The agreement called for a National Reconciliation Council that would be a forum to negotiate the terms of a permanent peace. In the months that followed, the Rakhmanov government negotiated with the United Tajikistan Opposition to reintegrate the political and military organizations of the two sides. Scattered fighting continued into the spring of 1997, however.

According to a Russian report in May 1996, the Tajikistani army was lacking 40 percent of its nominal officer cadre, and only 40 percent of those in service, many of them callups from the reserves, had a military education. The Tajikistani force was evaluated as inferior to its opposition in training and armament. Instances of troop mutiny reinforced that opinion, paralleling the situation in Afghanistan during the 1980s. In both Tajikistan and Afghanistan, Russian troops operated in a highly unstable civil war atmosphere, and the opposing sides were deeply divided within themselves.

As the civil war continued, the Rakhmanov regime took steps to avoid internal sources of opposition. Although the new constitution approved in November 1994 contained substantial guarantees of human rights (also staples of all the Soviet-era constitutions), prescribed legislative and review functions for the legislature, and mandated an independent judiciary, in fact the country's governance amounted to one-man rule based on declarations of emergency executive powers extended from 1993 and 1994. The result has been imprisonment, exile, and assassination of opposition political figures and some foreign observers. Rakhmanov won a decisive victory in the presidential election of 1994, with opposition only from a second hard-line politician of similar background, in what was generally labeled a rigged outcome. The unicameral legislature offers decisive majority support for Rakhmanov's programs, and the judiciary is fully under the control of the president, who has the power to dismiss any judge. The Gorno-Badakhshan Autonomous Province, which accounts for nearly 45 percent of the republic's territory, has disputed status and is a main stronghold of separatist opposition forces.

Tajikistan's foreign policy increasingly has sought the economic and military security of close relations with Russia. In Tajikistan, the Russian minority enjoys a more liberal set of privileges than it finds in any other Central Asian republic. For example, Russians are allowed dual citizenship and Russian remains an official language. In April 1996, Rakhmanov appointed the Russian mayor of Dushanbe, Yuriy Ponosov, as first deputy prime minister, continuing the policy of granting high government positions to ethnic Russians. Despite favorable treatment of the Russian minority, Russians have fled Tajikistan steadily since 1992. In early 1996, only about 80,000 of the 500,000 Russians identified in the 1989 Soviet census remained. Most have complained that Russian government authorities did not afford them adequate aid or security in Tajikistan, leaving them no choice but to leave.

Turkmenistan

Turkmenistan was known for most of its history as a loosely defined geographic region of independent tribes. Now it is a landlocked, mostly desert nation of only about 3.8 million people (the smallest population of the Central Asian republics in the second-largest land mass). The country remains quite isolated on the eastern shore of the Caspian Sea, largely occupied by the Qizilqum (Kyzyl Kum) Desert. Traditional tribal relationships still are a fundamental base of society, and telecommunications service from the outside world has only begun to have an impact. Like the Kazaks and the Kyrgyz, the Turkmen peoples were nomadic herders until the second half of the nineteenth century, when the arrival of Russian settlers began to deprive them of the vast expanses needed for livestock.

Agriculture contributes about half of Turkmenistan's GDP, whereas industry accounts for only about one-fifth. However, irrigation is necessary for nearly all the republic's arable land. In the early 1990s, government subsidies protected consumers from the shock of leaving the insulated Soviet system. Nevertheless, the standard of living protected by those subsidies had been among the lowest in the Soviet Union, and it deteriorated further in the 1990s. Although the Niyazov regime launched ambitious privatization programs in 1992 and 1993--with energy, transportation, agriculture, and communications to remain under state control--only minor progress had been made toward the programs' goals by the mid-1990s. Progress also has been quite slow in the reform of commercial and banking legislation.

Turkmenistan played a vital role in the Soviet system as a natural gas supplier. In the post-Soviet period, Russia remained the republic's top trade partner, with Turkey moving into second place in the mid-1990s. A crucial rail link with Iran also was an important commercial improvement.

The single most important mineral resource is natural gas; Turkmenistan's reserves may be among the largest in the world, with estimates as high as 15 trillion cubic meters. Nearly all the republic has been identified as potentially productive, and important offshore reserves exist in the Caspian Sea. The second major resource is petroleum, of which Turkmenistan has an estimated 63 billion tons. However, the range of the republic's mineral resources is small: sulfur, mineral salts, and clays complete the list.

In the mid-1990s, Turkmenistan's economic policy continued to rely heavily on the West's demand for natural gas. But, for a nation isolated along the east coast of the Caspian Sea, gas sales depend strictly on pipeline movement. Existing lines, built to serve the Turkmenistan-Russia north-south axis, cannot fill this need. New lines moving from east to west have been planned, but all plans encounter strong geopolitical opposition from a regional power or from the United States. Until the pipeline problem is solved, Turkmenistan can sell gas only to the same customers it served in the Soviet era, who now are its impoverished fellow members of the CIS. Armenia and Ukraine, major CIS customers, have been chronically late in paying. In February 1996, Turkmenistan made a long-term agreement to sell as much as 15 billion cubic meters of gas per year to Turkey between 1998 and 2020. Turkey also received development rights for a field in Turkmenistan believed to contain 20 million tons of oil.

Many recent economic indicators can only be approximated because Turkmenistan has not issued precise statistics. The national currency, the manat (for value of the manat--see Glossary), was devalued in late 1995 from a ratio of 500 to US$1 to 2,100 to US$1; it has remained non-convertible. It is believed that inflation in 1995 exceeded 1,000 percent; the 1996 annual rate, 140 percent, still was the highest in Central Asia. Exports for 1995 were about US$1.9 billion and imports about US$1.5 billion in official estimates. However, Turkmenistan conducts much barter trade, and payment failures of gas customers further undermine the application of cash trade figures. For 1996 the Economist Intelligence Unit forecast a 5 percent reduction of GDP following a drop of 15 percent in 1995. It also forecast a reduction in inflation in 1996 to 800 percent and a further drop in the value of the manat to a rate of 3,000 to US$1.

The state still strongly dominates the national economy. Little private enterprise occurs without some form of government approval or support, and about 90 percent of the work force is in state enterprises. In 1996 plans called for modernization of tax and business laws, including joint-venture conditions for the oil and gas industries. Pending those developments, foreign investors face a mass of state bureaucracy.

Foreign investment has been small, and experts predict no short-term improvement, partly because of the republic's insufficient legal and bureaucratic infrastructure, and partly because the very small and impoverished population provides little market opportunity. (The official average monthly wage was US$7 in early 1996.) The European Bank for Reconstruction and Development (EBRD) and other international banks are funding a textile complex, and Ashgabat Airport will be modernized with a loan of US$31 million from the British Export Credit Agency. However, for 1996 total direct investment was only US$32 million, with another US$61 million in joint ventures and US$161 million in foreign loans.

Turkmenistan has pursued the most independent and pragmatic foreign policy of the five Central Asian republics. The overall goal has been to form advantageous regional relationships without becoming involved in regional conflicts such as the Tajikistani civil war. In December 1996, Turkmenistan passed legislation declaring permanent neutrality and prohibiting membership in any military or political-military alliance entailing responsibilities for collective action by its members.

President Niyazov has run the country's foreign policy personally; he has faced little pressure at home to orient policy in a particular direction. Thus, he has been able to form ties with diverse foreign nations, maintaining economic advancement as the primary goal. Through the mid-1990s, Iran has been the top regional partner, although national security relations with Russia also have been a high priority during that period. In 1995 Turkmenistan signed a series of bilateral agreements with Russia, expanding economic and political cooperation and proclaiming the two nations "strategic partners" through 2000.

Turkmenistan has explicitly avoided multilateral arrangements, most of them sponsored by Uzbekistan, with the other Central Asian republics. It refused membership in the Central Asian customs union established by Kazakhstan, Kyrgyzstan, and Uzbekistan in 1994, and in the Central Asian Economic Union that sprang from the initial agreement. Turkmenistan also contributed nothing to the CIS peacekeeping force sent to Tajikistan by those three nations and Russia in 1993. Substantial tension has arisen with Uzbekistan over water consumption, competition on the world cotton market, the Uzbek minority population's potential for unrest, and resentment of Uzbekistan's ambitions for regional leadership. By the end of 1995, tensions with Uzbekistan were so high that Turkmenistan boycotted all regional meetings. However, in January 1996 a meeting of the two nations' presidents produced a package of economic cooperation agreements, and new agreements on road and railroad transportation were discussed in the first half of 1996.

Uzbekistan

Uzbekistan is the third-largest of the Central Asian republics in area and the first in population (estimated at 23 million in 1994 and growing at the fastest rate in Central Asia).

Uzbekistan is completely landlocked between Kazakhstan to the north, Turkmenistan to the south, and Kyrgyzstan and Tajikistan to the east. It shares the Aral Sea, and hence the environmental problems of that area, with Kazakhstan. The territory of modern Uzbekistan was at the center of the rich cultural and commercial developments that occurred in Central Asia over a period of two millennia, especially along the axis defined by the Silk Route between Europe and China. Included in Uzbekistan are the three chief Silk Route outposts of Bukhoro (Bukhara), Khiva, and Samarqand (Samarkand).

Besides the agricultural base that yields cotton, vegetables, and grain, Uzbekistan's economy is blessed with gold, several other valuable minerals, and substantial reserves of energy resources, especially natural gas. In the mid-1990s, the economy still is based primarily on agriculture, following substantial increases in irrigation-dependent output in the 1970s and 1980s. Cotton remains the most valuable crop, and Uzbekistan is the fourth-largest cotton producer in the world.

Uzbekistan has suffered from high inflation, mainly because the state has continued Soviet-era social protection programs, bank credits for unprofitable enterprises, budget deficits, and price supports that require expanding the supply of money. As inflation has redistributed wealth, many Uzbekistanis have suffered substantial losses of real income. By 1994 annual inflation reached 1,300 percent, but government restrictions in 1995 lowered the year-end figure to 77 percent.

Throughout the post-Soviet period, a primary goal of Uzbekistan's economic reform policy has been to avoid the disruptions associated with rapid transition. While proclaiming the eventual goal of a market economy, economic planners have moved very slowly in privatization and in the creation of a Western-style financial sector that would offer economic incentives and encourage private entrepreneurial initiative. This strategy has succeeded in reducing the transition shocks experienced by other post-Soviet societies. Since independence, Uzbekistan's GDP has fallen about 20 percent, compared with the Central Asian average of 50 percent. Part of that moderation results from Uzbekistan's initially more favorable situation in 1992. Because the cotton monoculture gave Uzbekistan a commodity with sales value worldwide (in 1995 some 75 percent of cotton exports went outside the CIS) and because Uzbekistan was less dependent on foreign trade and imported energy supplies than the other Central Asian countries, the end of the Soviet Union imposed fewer economic hardships. The 1995 cotton crop, expected to set a record, was significantly below forecast levels, however. Meanwhile, in 1996 the republics of the region continued nominal efforts to improve the Aral Sea environmental disaster, amid significant doubts that Uzbekistan would sacrifice cotton irrigation water from Aral tributaries to achieve that goal.

In late 1995, the IMF lent the regime US$260 million for economic reform, the first money accepted by Karimov from the IMF. In its evaluation at that time, the IMF noted that Uzbekistan's structural reform had been slow, notably in the banking sector, but that its tight monetary policy had slowed the economy's previous runaway inflation and liberalization of foreign exchange had been effective. Inflation for 1995 was 77 percent; the IMF year-end inflation target for 1996 was 21 to 25 percent; the exchange rate of the Uzbekistani som (for value of the som--see Glossary) fell from thirty to the United States dollar in 1995 to thirty-five to the dollar in 1996. The Economist Intelligence Unit forecast a 1996 drop in GDP of 1 percent, followed by growth of 1 percent in 1997. The projected budget deficit for 1996 was 3.5 percent of GDP, which conforms with IMF loan guidelines. An IMF credit of US$124 million was granted in December 1995.

Uzbekistan's economy is one of the most stable in the Central Asian region, and foreign investment activity there has been the highest in the region. In December 1995, the United States Overseas Private Investment Corporation agreed to provide US$500 million to convert the Soviet-era military industry, and United States oil companies committed US$1.3 billion of long-term investments in the oil and gas industry. Uzbekistan is the regional distribution center for electronic and domestic appliances from Dubai, based on a favorable tariff system that places no tax on most imports **Error! Bookmark not defined.**(a 15 percent tariff was levied on electronics in 1996). A large Daewoo (South Korean) television and videocassette plant in Tashkent is the most visible foreign electronics enterprise. The British Massey-Ferguson firm plans an agricultural machinery plant at some future date, and the British Quickstop supermarket chain opened outlets in Tashkent in 1996. Although some improvement has been made in Uzbekistan's tax and legal system, the dominance of the state bureaucracy continues to complicate foreign investment.

In 1996 the Karimov regime became noticeably less cautious in its approach to economic reform. Karimov criticized some bureaucrats for hindering execution of reform decrees, and the president began advocating private enterprise as the surest path to individual and national prosperity.

Overall foreign trade goals still include expanded commercial agreements with East Asia and the West, but by 1996 Uzbekistan had expressed willingness to join a customs union with Belarus, Kazakhstan, and Russia, which already had reached a series of commercial accommodations early in 1996. Self-sufficiency in oil, gained for the first time in 1996, has freed Uzbekistan from dependence on Russia in a key area.

Uzbekistan's position as the only Central Asian state bordering all the other four has combined with other advantages (the largest population in the region and significant natural resources) to advance its claim as the leader and potential unifying force of the Central Asians. That putative role also has gained Uzbekistan considerable distrust among the other four republics, each of which has a significant Uzbek minority population and each of which has felt the impact of Uzbekistan's drive for supremacy in different ways. In 1992 Uzbekistani troops--the best-equipped in Central Asia--were instrumental in the triumph of Emomali Rakhmanov's communist forces in Tajikistan, and since that time Uzbekistan has participated in the CIS force attempting to keep the peace in that country. In tandem with its drive for Western economic ties and privatization, in 1996 Uzbekistan intensified its promotion of regional economic and security agreements. Partly as a counterweight to Russia's influence in the region, Uzbekistan has encouraged broader activities by the Central Asian Economic Union, which it shares with Kazakhstan and Kyrgyzstan. In 1996 the most notable departure from dependency on Russia was establishment of the Central Asian peacekeeping battalion, which held an initial exercise in the United States under the auspices of the NATO Partnership for Peace program. In January 1997, the economic union's members signed a treaty of "eternal friendship" that included mutual security guarantees.

The armed forces, which had inherited a substantial infrastructure from the Soviet period, were the best-equipped force in the region by 1996, after developing steadily in the interim years. In 1996, Uzbekistan's armed forces numbered 30,000 persons, including 25,000 ground and 4,000 air force troops. At that time, the government announced that ethnic Uzbeks constituted 80 percent of the country's armed forces, compared with 6 percent in the former Soviet force of 1992.

After independence, much of Uzbekistan's political structure remained essentially unchanged. Although some impetus had existed toward more democratic governance prior to independence, Karimov set the tone for political activity by winning a rigged presidential election in 1991. The new constitution approved in December 1992 prescribed a secular, multiparty democracy with full observance of human rights. However, the trial and harassment of opposition political figures and the restriction of the media began immediately; international protests in the next few years achieved scant results. Only two parties, Karimov's and a token opposition group, were permitted to participate in the parliamentary election of 1994. In March 1995, a rigged referendum extended the presidency of Karimov until 2000. Shortly thereafter, Karimov sentenced seven leaders of the political opposition to prison terms. Although the stable atmosphere fostered by Karimov's regime had tended to soften international criticism, Uzbekistan's human rights record still left much to be desired. In 1995 and 1996, however, a general improvement in government observation of human rights was noted; the government apparently has attempted to attract Western investors by responding to criticism of its handling of human rights cases. Two new political parties were formed and registered officially in mid-1995.

Uzbekistan's relations with Russia have been characterized by a combination of resentment and dependence, representing one of the few areas where the Karimov regime does not exercise full control. Although Karimov has strongly encouraged business activities by Western countries, especially Germany, he has been careful not to alienate Russia's commercial interests. In 1994 and 1995, Uzbekistan signed commercial treaties with a variety of CIS countries, but Russia always was the primary partner in such deals.

The issue of dual citizenship for the Russian minority in Uzbekistan, strongly pressed by Russia in the early 1990s, has caused serious irritation, as did Russia's unsuccessful pressure for Uzbekistan to remain in the ruble zone in 1993. Like the other Central Asian republics, Uzbekistan has suffered a rapid loss of its Russian technocrat population. Since independence, an estimated 500,000 Russians (out of the 1.65 million in 1989) have left, and the emigration of Germans, Jews, and Koreans further depleted the republic's base of technical know-how.

Just beyond the borders of Central Asia, Uzbekistan has established new relationships with Iran, Pakistan, and Turkey, based chiefly on economic exchanges. Stimulated by the economic stability of Uzbekistan, international lenders such as the EBRD and the IMF have offered fairly generous loans. The United States, conscious of human rights violations, has offered less generous assistance to Uzbekistan than to other Central Asian countries.

The republics of Central Asia emerged from the Soviet Union with a combination of assets and handicaps. Their geographic isolation has complicated establishment of commercial relationships, and even name recognition, in the West. The complete lack of democratic tradition has kept the republics from complying with Western legal and commercial standards, and the expression of political dissent has been erratic and sometimes costly to dissenters. Serious deterioration of the Soviet-era education systems in all five countries threatens to diminish the capabilities of the next generation to contribute to the national economies at a time when those economies may be ready to flourish. At the same time, ample natural resources hold out the prospect that at least the republics most blessed in this way--Kazakhstan, Turkmenistan, and Uzbekistan--may ultimately enrich their economies and hence the standard of living of their people. The prospect of full regional cooperation remains only theoretical, in spite of numerous bilateral and trilateral agreements. And relations with Russia, traditionally the dominant outside force in Central Asia's geopolitical situation, remain close and vital, although fraught with misgivings. In early 1997, the future of the region remained nearly as unclear as it was in 1991, the year of independence.

Chapter 1

UZBEKISTAN: CURRENT DEVELOPMENTS AND U.S. INTERESTS[1]

James P. Nichol

SUMMARY

The United States views Uzbekistan as an emerging Central Asian regional power by virtue of its relatively large population, important energy and other resources, and political prominence, and urges it to play a stabilizing and responsible regional role. Although Uzbekistan has made some progress in economic reforms, scant democratization and human rights abuses continue to be U.S. concerns.

U.S. POLICY

According to Ambassador-at-Large to the New Independent States (NIS) Stephen Sestanovich, the United States has a "significant interest" in seeing Uzbekistan implement democratic and economic reforms, uphold human rights, and play a "key" stabilizing and cooperative role in enhancing the independence and security of the Central Asian states. The United States seeks to develop military cooperation "to orient Uzbekistan's sizable military toward cooperation with NATO, the United States, and Uzbekistan's own neighbors," and to support "U.S. global and security objectives." Other goals include fostering economic and democratic reforms that are viewed as contributing to stability and to U.S. trade and investment. (*State Department, Congressional Presentation on Foreign Operations*, FY2000 and FY2001). In late 1997, the United States and Uzbekistan formed a joint commission to pursue a widening range of security, political, and regional interests, headed at the undersecretary level. Karimov visited the United States in 1996 and met with political and business leaders. USCENTOCOM Commander-in-Chief Tommy Franks visited Uzbekistan

[1] Sources include Foreign Broadcast Information Service, *Daily Report: Central Eurasia*; RFE/RL *Newsline*; Jamestown Foundation, *Monitor* and *Prism*; the State Department; and wire services.

in October 2000 and announced that the United States would increase military aid to bolster the region against civil war in neighboring Afghanistan. A defense cooperation accord was signed in November 2000 providing for U.S. aid for combating weapons of mass destruction, drug trafficking, and terrorism.

Cumulative U.S. humanitarian and technical assistance obligated to Uzbekistan in fiscal years 1992-1999 amounted to $173.84 million. The United States also facilitated the delivery of Department of Defense excess and privately donated commodities worth $86.91 million in FY1992-FY1999. The Administration planned to spend $19.35 million in Uzbekistan in FY2000, and requested $27.25 million for FY2001, mostly for economic and democratic reform programs. Included in these totals, the Administration planned to spend $2.0 million in Foreign Military Financing and International Military Education and Training (IMET) funds in FY2000 and requested $2.25 million for FY2001. Requested spending under the Expanded Threat Reduction Initiative for FY2001 was $5.0 million, including for enhancing export controls and dismantling the Nukus Chemical Research Institute. The U.S. Agency for International Development's *Assistance Strategy for Central Asia, 2001-2005*, states that no aid will be provided for macroeconomic reforms, energy restructuring, elections, or state-controlled institutions until Uzbekistan embraces reform. Instead, aid will focus on primary healthcare, business training, micro-credits, civic education, and water management.

Congressional interest in Uzbekistan is reflected in recent hearings on Central Asia, visits to the region, and legislation. Congressional concerns include energy development, stalled democratization, and human rights problems. Action includes the incorporation of authorizing language termed "The Silk Road Strategy Act" into Foreign Operations Appropriations for FY2000 (P.L. 106-113), directing enhanced policy and aid for conflict amelioration, humanitarian needs, economic development, transport, communications, border control, democracy, and the creation of civil societies in the South Caucasian and Central Asian states. The Security Assistance Act of 2000 (P.L. 106-280; signed into law on October 6, 2000) authorizes $45.5 million over two years to assist Armenia and the GUUAM countries (a group formed in 1997 and named after the initials of the members: Georgia, Ukraine, Uzbekistan, Azerbaijan, and Moldova) to strengthen national control of borders and to promote independence and territorial sovereignty. H.Con.Res.397, passed by the House on November 1, 2000, criticizes Uzbek President Islam Karimov for not permitting opposition parties to register, forcing such parties and leaders underground or into exile, censoring media, conducting show trials of alleged terrorists, using security forces to frame and arrest opponents and religious activists, and holding unfree elections. The resolution calls of Karimov to end torture of political opponents and to register opposition parties, and for U.S. officials to press him and other Central Asian leaders to abide by human rights commitments they undertook through membership in the Organization for Security and Cooperation in Europe.

BASIC FACTS

Area and Population

Land area is 174,486 sq. mi., slightly larger than California. The population is 24.6 million (1999 est., *World Bank*). Administrative subdivisions include the Karakalpak

Republic. A 1991 independence law recognized its theoretical right to secede from Uzbekistan.

Ethnicity

71.4% are Uzbek, 8.3% Russian, 4.7% Tajik, 4.1% Kazak, 2.4% Tatar, 2.1% Karakalpak, and others (1989 census). Uzbeks are the most numerous Central Asian nationality. There are more than 1.2 million Uzbeks residing in Afghanistan, one million in Tajikistan, and a half-million in Kyrgyzstan. Several hundred thousand ethnic Russians have emigrated because of real or perceived discrimination.

Gross Domestic Product

$16.8 billion; per capita GDP is about $700 (1999 *World Bank* est.).

Language and Religion

The official language is Uzbek, a Turkic language. Most Uzbeks belong to the Sunni branch of Islam.

POLITICAL AND ECONOMIC DEVELOPMENTS

Relations with Russia and Other Countries

Uzbekistan seeks working relations with Russia that do not overly compromise its independence. Russia and Uzbekistan signed a Friendship Treaty in 1992 that includes collective security provisions. Uzbekistan, Russia, Armenia, and other Central Asian states signed a collective security pact in 1992, calling for mutual assistance in the case of aggression against the parties. Uzbekistan withdrew from this pact in 1999, citing sovereignty issues, but in 2000 has maintained bilateral security arrangements with Russia and discussions in the CIS. In September 2000, Karimov alleged that the Russian security services were planting rumors about imminent terrorist attacks aimed at panicking Uzbekistan into rejoining the Collective Security Treaty and a Russian-backed military anti-terrorism group. Karimov refused to join a customs union formed by Russia, Belarus, Kyrgyzstan, and Kazakhstan in 1996 (re-launched in 2000 as the Eurasian Economic Union), calling its terms unacceptable to Uzbekistan's independence.

Many in Uzbekistan argue that it should be the "big brother" in relations with the rest of Central Asia. Uzbeks make up over 50% of Central Asians, and, like Russians, are the targets of attacks by nationalist extremists in Tajikistan and elsewhere. Karimov has eschewed such rhetoric but seeks to play a leading regional role. A Central Asian Economic Community (CAEC) composed of Kazakhstan, Uzbekistan, Kyrgyzstan, and Tajikistan has been set back by the fallout of the 1998 Russian financial crisis. Uzbekistan reportedly contributed arms and troops to help rout anti-government forces in Tajikistan in 1992 and its troops were part of

CIS "peacekeeping" forces sent to guard borders in Tajikistan. The Tajik president has accused Uzbekistan of supporting a 1998 uprising in northern Tajikistan, and Uzbekistan has accused Tajikistan of harboring Islamic extremists who aim to overthrow the Uzbek government. In April 2000, all the regional states except Turkmenistan signed an Uzbek-launched anti-terrorism accord pledging mutual aid, with Karimov stating that the region was forced to rely on more of its own efforts to combat terrorism, drug trafficking, and crime. Uzbekistan's relations with Kyrgyzstan and Tajikistan were harmed in late 2000 by its mining of borders.

President Karimov's priority in foreign policy has been to establish good relations with regional powers such as Russia and Turkey, though he has also pursued ties with the United States and other nations. Karimov has stressed the threat Islamic fundamentalism espoused by the Taliban group in Afghanistan poses to Uzbekistan and the region (although contacts with the Taliban in late 2000 led to a pullback of Uzbek troops from the border with Afghanistan). Karimov and other officials have voiced concerns about Iran's economic ties with Turkmenistan and other activities in the region. Iran calls for Karimov to reconcile with many Islamist groups. Relations with Turkey have been mostly positive and it is the biggest investor in Uzbekistan.

Political Leaders

President: Islam Karimov; *Prime Minister*: Otkir Sultonov (Utkur Sultanov); *Chairman of the Oliy Majlis (legislature):* Erkin Khalilov; *Foreign Minister*: Abdulaziz Komilov; *Defense Minister:* Col. Kodir Gulomov.

Biography

Karimov, born in 1938, in 1966 began work in the Uzbek State Planning Committee (Gosplan). In 1983, he became Uzbek Minister of Finance, and then Deputy Chairman of the Uzbek government. In 1989, he became First Secretary of the Uzbek Communist Party. In 1990, the Uzbek Supreme Soviet elected him to the newly created post of President, and he also became a member of the Soviet Communist Party Politburo. In December 1991, he was popularly elected President, winning 86% of the vote against opposition Erk Party candidate Mohammed Solikh. International observers found widespread election fraud by government officials. On March 26, 1995, he won support by 99.6% of 11.25 million voters in a referendum to extend his presidential term until 2000, results the U.S. State Department noted "could not have been valid."

Defense and Security

The Uzbek military is the most advanced in Central Asia. Its major concern, highlighted in a military doctrine approved in February 2000, is mobility to combat terrorism emanating from Tajikistan and Afghanistan. The armed forces consist of 80,000 group troops, an air force, and a national guard (*The Military Balance 1999-2000*). Physicist Kodir Gulomov was appointed defense minister in September 2000, the first such civilian minister in the CIS. A plan was announced to divide the armed forces into a civilian defense ministry and a United Committee of Chiefs of Staff (UCCS), but implementation reportedly has been delayed. The UCCS will have operational control of army, interior ministry, and border guard troops. There are no Russian troops in Uzbekistan, according to the State Department. The officer corps is 85%-90% Uzbek, but most military instructors are Russian, as is equipment. Uzbekistan has built up its own defense capabilities and schools to rely less on Russia, and has expanded ties with NATO countries and others. In joining NATO's Partnership for Peace (PFP) in 1994, Uzbekistan announced that it would seek military training and Tajik-Afghan border security aid. The CAEC's Central Asian Battalion (Centrazbat) has received PFP and U.S. aid.

On February 16, 1999, six bomb blasts in Tashkent's governmental area by various reports killed 16-28 and wounded 100-351. In response, the Uzbek government arrested dozens of suspects, including political dissidents. The motives for the bombing remain murky. Karimov denounced the bombing as an attempt to assassinate him. In April 1999, he alleged that exiled Erk Party leader Mohammad Solikh led the plot, assisted by Afghanistan's Taliban and Uzbek Islamic extremist Tohir Yuldash. A trial of 22 suspects led to six receiving death sentences. Solikh rejected accusations of a role in the bombings, alleging that trial testimony was coerced and scripted. Another secret trial in August 1999 of six suspects (brothers of Solikh or members of his Erk Party) resulted in long sentences. In November 2000, the Uzbekistan sentenced twelve accused terrorists, nine of whom were tried *in absentia*, including Yuldash, Namanganiy, and Solikh, giving Solikh 15.5 years and sentencing the other two to death.

Several hundred Islamic extremists and others who fled repression in Uzbekistan and settled in Tajikistan, and rogue groups from north-central Tajikistan, invaded Kyrgyzstan in July-August 1999. The guerrillas were rumored to be seeking to create an Islamic state in south Kyrgyzstan as a springboard for a jihad in Uzbekistan. By mid-October 1999, the guerrillas had been forced out of Kyrgyzstan. Uzbekistan's assistance included air strikes, border forces, and materiel. Karimov heavily criticized Kyrgyz President Askar Akayev for supposed laxity by not wiping out the guerrillas. Dozens of IMU and other insurgents again invaded Kyrgyzstan and Uzbekistan in early August 2000, and were defeated by October. In September 2000, Akayev acceded to Karimov's demands for access to Kyrgyzstan's water supplies in return for added Uzbek military aid and gas.

The United States has supported Uzbekistan's efforts to combat terrorism, but has stressed that such efforts cannot include human rights abuses. During her April 2000 visit to Uzbekistan, Secretary Albright stated that Uzbek security should not treat "peaceful Muslims as if they were...enemies." In September 2000, the State Department designated the IMU, led by Yuldashev, as a Foreign Terrorist Organization, stating that the IMU actively threatens U.S. interests and attacks American citizens. The "main goal of the IMU is to topple the current government in Uzbekistan," it warned, linking the IMU to bombings and attacks on Uzbekistan in 1999-2000 and to Afghanistan's Taliban and terrorist bin Laden. It asserts that the "United States supports the right of Uzbekistan to defend its sovereignty and territorial integrity from the violent actions of the IMU." U.S. Permanent Representative to the OSCE David Johnson on December 7, 2000, however, stated that the November trial raised "serious questions" about due process, and that violations of the rule of law and human rights were not justified in combating terrorism.

Economy

President Karimov aims to move gradually toward "market socialism" in order to ensure social stability. The economy began to recover in 1996. At the end of 1999, the budget deficit had fallen to 2.7% of GDP, and annual inflation had declined to 26% (compared to 204% in 1995). Some analysts predict a 2% growth in GDP in 2000. The economy is mostly based on agriculture and energy and mineral extraction. It has been the world's third or fourth largest producer of cotton, eighth largest producer of gold, and among the top ten in natural gas production. A restrictive currency conversion system holds back trade and discourages foreign direct investment. State control of prices for agricultural products, mandatory procurement of cotton and wheat, and trade constraints depress production and rural living standards. These problems, along with drought, reduced grain harvests in 2000, forcing Uzbekistan to import grain, and devastating Karakalpak's rice crop. Widespread poverty provides grounds for religious extremism and dissent to grow, according to many observers. Most state-owned apartments and many small enterprises have been privatized. According to the U.S. Department of Energy, Uzbekistan has two billion barrels of proven and possible oil reserves and 109-123 trillion cubic feet of gas reserves. Several U.S. firms are involved in Uzbek energy development. There are severe environmental problems around the Aral Sea and elsewhere. Corruption is rampant, and a black market in cotton may be large.

Political Parties and Groups

By law, no political party whose aim is to "change the existing order" is permitted to register, effectively banning all opposition parties. Five pro-Karimov parties are registered: the People's Democratic Party (PDP), Homeland Progress (Vatan Taraqqiyati), Social-Democratic (Adolot), National Rebirth Democratic (Milli Tiklanish), and Self-Sacrifice (Fidokorlar). In 1991, the UCP renamed itself the PDP at Karimov's urging. Karimov was its head until he resigned in 1996, arguing that he should be above partisanship. PDP claims over 500,000 members. Vatan Taraqqiyati was founded in 1992 by an aide to Karimov. Other pro-Karimov parties were formed in 1995 and led by PDP legislators. In December 1998, Karimov orchestrated the creation of Fidokorlar. He argued that more parties foster democratization and that "if we form a party with a precisely defined ideology," it can become a mass-based party. He chose Fidokorlar to back him in his January 2000 presidential re-election. Karimov launched a crackdown on opposition parties in 1992-1993, causing most party officials to flee the country. Opposition parties include Birlik (Unity) Popular Front Movement, Erk (Freedom), and Islamic Rebirth (IRP). Birlik, founded in 1989, calls for increased emphasis on Uzbek as the national language and freedom religion. Erk, headed by the poet Solikh, was founded in 1990 by intellectuals who broke with Birlik. It was banned in 1993 and its deputies were forced from the legislature. IRP advocates setting up an Islamic republic with equal rights for all citizens. The constitution bans religious parties.

Political Institutions and Policies

According to most analysts, democratization made little headway in Uzbekistan. In 1997, President Karimov admitted that "we do not fully meet many democratic standards today," blaming the "traditionalism" of the people and stating that he aimed to change this way of thinking "gradually and in stages." A new Constitution was adopted by the legislature in 1992 by unanimous vote after two months of public discussion. It provides for a strong president and a weaker, 250-member unicameral legislature, termed the Oliy Majlis or Supreme Assembly.

Elections to the Oliy Majlis were held of December 5, 1999. The five pro-Karimov parties, local councils, and some initiative groups sponsored 1,010 candidates to vie for 250 seats. The CEC announced on December 10, 1999, that 184 seats had been filled and run-offs would be held in 66 districts where no candidate received at least 50% of the vote. The winners included 98 belonging to regional governments, 32 from the PDP, 19 from Fidokorlar, 9 from Adolot, 9 from Vatan Taraqqiyati, 6 from Milli Tiklanish, and 11 from citizens' groups. The OSCE sent only a limited mission and would not observe balloting, concluding that the race would not be competitive. It reported after the race that deficient laws, interference by local officials with nominations and electoral commissions, and the lack of independent media had prevented a free and fair vote. The State Department expressed "its regret" that Uzbekistan "has chosen to ignore [OSCE] commitments." Two candidates were registered to run in the January 9, 2000 presidential race, Karimov and Abdulkhafiz Jalolov. Jalolov was nominated by his PDP, which Karimov formerly headed, to give the appearance of a contested race. All other registered parties and councils vied to support Karimov. He won 91.9% of 12.1 million votes cast. The State Department announced that the race "offered Uzbekistan's voters no true choice," mentioning that the government had refused to register opposition candidates and that Jalolov had endorsed Karimov during the campaign. Some critics argued that the race marked groups competing for Karimov's favor and spoils.

Human Rights and Freedoms

According to the U.S. State Department's *Country Reports on Human Rights Practices for 1999*, Uzbekistan's poor human rights record worsened in 1999. Citizens cannot exercise their right to change their government peacefully because the government "severely represses opposition groups and individuals and applies strict limits on freedom of expression." Only approved public meetings and demonstrations may be held. Police and security forces allegedly use murder, torture, harassment, illegal searches, property confiscations, and arbitrary arrest and detention to stifle dissent. Beating of detainees is routine. No opposition newspapers are allowed; the last was banned in 1993. Radio Free Europe and Voice of America are not allowed to broadcast within Uzbekistan. Thirty to forty independent television companies have operated, though they practice self-censorship. The State Department's *Report of International Religious Freedom for 2000* states that the Uzbek government's respect for religious freedom improved with regard to minority religions, including Christians, but that repression intensified with respect to the rights of unauthorized Muslim groups.

Chapter 2

TURKMENISTAN: CURRENT DEVELOPMENTS AND U.S. INTERESTS[2]

James P. Nichol

SUMMARY

Turkmenistan, under the authoritarian leadership of Saparmurad Niyazov, has scarcely reformed its Soviet-era political institutions or revitalized its largely traditional economy. U.S. policy has called for building diversified pipeline routes to export Turkmenistan's sizable natural gas and oil resources and opposed moves by Russia and Iran to gain control over these resources.

U.S. POLICY

The U.S. agenda has stressed energy and human rights issues. According to Ambassador-at-Large Stephen Sestanovich, U.S. interests in Turkmenistan include bolstering its potential as a source of prosperity and stability in the Central Asian region and as a source of oil and natural gas for Turkish and other Western markets. Development of these energy sources will increase the world diversity of supplies, of U.S. interest, and provide an opportunity for U.S. trade and investment. There has been scant progress in democratization and the creation of free markets in Turkmenistan, so U.S. aid has focused recently on security assistance to enhance export controls and to train law enforcement and customs personnel and border guards. Such aid helps Turkmenistan to combat narcotics trafficking and the proliferation of weapons of mass destruction and encourages Turkmen participation in U.S. training programs and NATO's Partnership for Peace (PFP). Plans for FY2001 include upgrades to facilitate U.S. Air Force landings at an airfield; air assault, infantry, and maritime officer training; and

[2] Sources include Foreign Broadcast Information Service, *Daily Report: Central Eurasia*; RFE/RL *Newsline*; Jamestown Foundation, *Monitor* and *Prism*; *Central Asia Monitor*; *Central Asia Survey*; *Eurasia Insight*; *Turkestan Newsletter*; State Department; World Bank; and Reuters wire service reports.

training to foster stable civil-military relations (State Department, *Congressional Presentation of Foreign Operations*, FY2000 and FY2001). U.S. policy has opposed Iranian and Russian moves to gain control over Turkmenistan's oil and gas industry and has endorsed building a trans-Caucasus gas pipeline to Turkey, with a trans-Caspian link to Turkmenistan, as part of the "Eurasian Transport Corridor" initiative. The Administration supports a negotiated solution to Caspian Sea delineation that divides seabed resources, permits their timely development, and allows unrestricted transport. Administration concerns about human rights abuses in Turkmenistan were relayed during President Niyazov's visit to the United States in 1993, when President Clinton reportedly chose not to meet with him. In contrast, Turkmenistan's potential as a major oil and gas exporter was acknowledged during Niyazov's April 1998 U.S. visit, when he met with both President Clinton and Vice President Gore. He signed accords with U.S. firms on energy exploration and production, and brushed aside Administration concerns about democratization by asserting that there was no organized domestic opposition to his rule.

Growing Congressional interest in the region was highlighted by several hearings that have been held in 1997-1999 on the Caspian Sea region and other legislative actions. Among recent legislation, the conferees on Omnibus Appropriations for FY1999 (Conf.Rept. 105-825; P.L. 105-277) recommended that up to $10 million be made available to promote energy development in Turkmenistan. They stated that they "believe that the development of energy resources in the Caspian Sea region is important for the economic development of the countries involved, as well as regional stability," endorsed "alternatives to a pipeline through Iran," and supported "an east-west energy corridor to assist in developing the region's energy resources." Authorizing language termed "The Silk Road Strategy Act" was included in Foreign Operations Appropriations for FY2000 (P.L. 106-113) calling for enhanced policy and aid to support conflict amelioration, humanitarian needs, economic development, transport and communications, border controls, democracy, and the creation of civil societies in the South Caucasian and Central Asian states.

Cumulative U.S. aid obligated to Turkmenistan in FY1992-1999 was $170.36 million, most involving food aid and training and exchanges. The United States also facilitated the delivery of Department of Defense excess and privately donated commodities worth $34.28 million in FY1992-FY1999. Estimated U.S. spending for FY2000 was $6.28 million (down from $11/26 for FY1999), and the Administration requested $8.0 million for FY2001, including $1.025 million for Foreign Military Financing and International Military Education and Training. In FY2000, the United States provided Turkmenistan with a coastal patrol vessel under the Excess Defense Articles grant program.

BASIC FACTS

Area and Population

Land area is 190,359 sq. mi.; slightly larger than California. The Kara Kum desert covers about 80% of land area. Population was 4.8 million in 1999 (*World Bank* est.).

Ethnicity

3.45 million (77%) are Turkmen, 300 thousand Russian (6.7%), 400 thousand Uzbek (9.2%), and 320 thousand (7.1%) others (1995 Turkmen census). About 150,000 ethnic Turkmen reside elsewhere in the former Soviet Union, and three million or more in Iran and Afghanistan. The Tekke clan in central Turkmenistan is the largest of the six main clans, followed by the Ersary in the south and Yomud in the west. President Niyazov, though a Tekke by birth, claims his upbringing in an orphanage has raised him above clan loyalty, though many ministries are headed by Tekkes. He has been careful to appoint regional leaders from dominant clans.

Gross Domestic Product

$3.3 billion; per capita GDP is about $690 (*World Bank* est. for 1999).

Language and Religion

Turkmen speak a Turkic language, and most are Sunni Muslim.

POLITICAL AND ECONOMIC DEVELOPMENTS

Relations with Russia and Other Countries

Turkmenistan supports some of Russia's policies in the region while endeavoring, where possible, to resist, contravene, or reduce Russian influence. Russian military and border troops assisted Turkmenistan until it built up its own forces, and Russia's influence has been used to counter Uzbek policies in the region. In 1992, the two states signed a Friendship and Cooperation Treaty containing security provisions. Russia objects to Turkmen efforts to reduce dependence on existing natural gas export routes that transit Russia. President Niyazov has resisted proposals by Kazakhstan and Russia to strengthen the Commonwealth of Independent States (CIS) and has refused to sign several CIS agreements viewed as violating Turkmen sovereignty. Instead, Niyazov has stressed the establishment of bilateral ties with CIS states. Relations with Uzbekistan have been volatile, with both states vying for regional influence and arguing over water sharing. Uzbekistan has criticized Turkmenistan's ties with Iran and Afghanistan's Taliban as threatening the region's stability. In September 2000, Uzbek President Islam Karimov visited Turkmenistan, marking improved relations, and the two presidents signed a border demarcation accord. Turkmenistan and Azerbaijan dispute ownership over Caspian Sea oil fields.

Turkmenistan's "neutral" foreign policy is enshrined in its constitution. Niyazov has declared that Turkmenistan's "open door" or "permanent neutrality" policy precludes joining political or military alliances and entails good relations with the East and the West, though priority will be placed on relations with Central Asia and other Islamic states. Turkmenistan joined the Non-Aligned Movement in 1995, and the United Nations General Assembly in 1995 recognized Turkmenistan's status as a neutral state. Turkmenistan has pursued close ties with both Iran and Turkey. In addition to growing trade ties with Iran, Turkmenistan is also interested in cultural ties with the approximately one million Turkmen residing in Iran. In November 2000, a Turkmen official reportedly indicated support for Iran's call for the Caspian Sea littoral states to divide disputed waters as well as the sea bottom among themselves, and for demilitarizing the sea. Turkmenistan has mediated between Afghanistan's fundamentalist Taliban group and its northern alliance leaders, and seeks good relations with the Taliban. Turkey is the largest foreign investor in Turkmenistan and has far surpassed Russia in trade turnover with Turkmenistan.

Political Leaders

President and Chairman of the Cabinet of Ministers: Saparmurad Niyazov; *Chairman of the Supreme Council (legislature)*: Sakhat Muradov; *Foreign Minister*: Batyr Berdiyev; *Minister of Defense*: Batyr Sardzhayev.

Biography

Niyazov, born in 1940, became the first secretary of the Turkmen Communist Party (TCP) in 1985. In 1990, Niyazov received 98.3% of the popular vote in an uncontested election to the new post of president. He won another uncontested presidential election in 1992 with 99.95% of the vote. In a referendum in January 1994, he received the support of 99.99% of the vote for extending his term until 2002. Niyazov is president, supreme commander of the armed forces, first secretary of the Democratic Party of Turkmenistan (DPT, formerly the TCP), head of the People's Council, and chairman of the Cabinet of Ministers and the National Security Council. He has created the "cult of personality" by awarding himself medals and titles, including the title of "Turkmenbashi," leader of all Turkmen. The national oath includes the phrase "[if] I betray...Turkmenbashi, may my breath stop."

Defenses

Turkmen armed forces have numbered 17,000-19,000, including ground, air, and air defense forces (*The Military Balance* 2000). Turkmenistan has replaced its higher officer corps with ethnic Turkmen and has replaced almost all lower echelon officers from Russia. Turkmen are receiving officer's training in Russia, Ukraine, and Turkey. Budget support for the military is tight, with the forces expected to grow their own food. In 1993, Russia and Turkmenistan agreed that Russian border guards would work with Turkmen border guards under Turkmen command at borders with Iran and Afghanistan. In 1999, Turkmenistan canceled this agreement, and Russia's 1,000 border troops in Turkmenistan left in late 1999 (some "special border troops" reportedly remained into 2000). During Niyazov's May 1995 visit to Moscow, he and then-President Boris Yeltsin signed agreements on air defense, military transport, Russian use of Turkmen military facilities, and others they typified as creating a "strategic partnership." However, actual cooperation has been minimal. New Russian President Vladimir Putin visited Turkmenistan in May 2000 to inaugurate economic and military cooperation commissions. In early 1995, Turkmenistan became the first Central Asian state to join NATO's Partnership for Peace (PFP). Turkmen officers have participated in or observed several PFP exercises.

Economy

Turkmenistan's GDP increased by 16% in 1999, boosted by harvests of wheat and cotton, as well as increased oil and gas production. A severe 32.8% drop in agricultural production in 1996 was reversed in 1997-1998. Niyazov reported in late 2000 that GDP had increased nearly 17% during the year, led by gains in oil and gas production, but said the 2000 cotton harvest was harmed by drought. Turkmenistan is among the world's top ten in cotton production, and agriculture accounts for about 40% of employment. According to the World Bank, Turkmenistan's underlying fiscal position has weakened over the years as public sector deficits have ballooned (including subsidies for consumer goods and industry and agriculture). Deficits are largely financed by foreign borrowing. High consumer inflation rates eased from nearly 1,000% in 1995-1996 to low single digits in 2000. Poverty is widespread, though perhaps not as extreme as elsewhere in Central Asia, because subsidies for some necessities provide relief. Infant mortality and unemployment are relatively high. Major drug trafficking from Afghanistan through Turkmenistan has exacerbated corruption. Privatization efforts launched in 1994 have resulted in private ownership of most small retail firms, and private ownership and leasing of agricultural land (resale is forbidden), but the economy remains heavily state controlled. Niyazov in late 1999 announced that many economic goals of a 1992 "transition" plan had been fulfilled, and launched an eleven-year development plan. He announced in late 2000 that the economic goals of the plan were mostly on target.

The new country has abundant resources that could bring in ample export earnings, ranging from oil, gas, electricity, coal, aluminum, and cotton to wool, grapes, and carpets. The U.S. Department of Energy reports estimates of 1.4 billion barrels of proven reserves and 98-155 trillion cubic feet of natural gas in Turkmenistan. In 1993, Russia's Gazprom natural gas firm has halted Turkmen gas exports to Western markets through its pipelines, permitting exports only to debt-ridden NIS customers. In March 1997, it cut off these exports because of transit fee arrears and other problems. In late 1998, Turkmenistan and Ukraine acceded to Gazprom's pricing demands for gas shipments to Ukraine. This arrangement ended due to payment arrears, but in late 1999, Turkmenistan agreed to export 20 billion cubic meters of its gas at concessionary prices to Russia in 2000 under an accord with Gazprom (since raised to 30 bcm). In late 2000, Turkmenistan agreed to export 30 bcm of gas to Russia and 35 bcm to Ukraine at concessionary rates, but also pressed past debtors such as Armenia and Kazakhstan for repayment. Seeking alternate routes, Turkmenistan in December 1997 opened a 125-mile gas pipeline to connect with the Iranian pipeline system. A 1998 framework agreement (and a 1999 delivery agreement) between Turkey and Turkmenistan envisages Turkmen gas flows to Turkey when a pipeline either traversing Iran or a trans-Caspian route through Azerbaijan and Georgia is built. In November 1999, Turkmenistan, Azerbaijan, Georgia, and Turkey signed a framework accord on a trans-Caspian gas pipeline (with an eventual capacity of sixteen billion meters per year). Attending the signing, President Clinton hailed it as "advanc[ing] the prosperity and security of [lands on the ancient Silk Road] critical to the future of the entire world." Contention between Azerbaijan and Turkmenistan over shipment quotas for this planned pipeline, and other problems, have stymied plans for Turkmen participation. As per a 1996 Turkey-Iran gas purchase agreement, Iran has largely finished building a section of an Iran-Turkey gas pipeline (with eventual link proposed to Turkmenistan). Turkmenistan ships some oil to northern Iranian ports, and in return Iran ships some of its oil to Western customers.

Political Parties and Groups

President Niyazov rejects what he calls the "chaos and permissiveness" of multiparty democracy, favoring the collective "togetherness" of one-party rule. The DPT, like the TCP before it, is the only party allowed to operate. It is closely controlled by Niyazov. The DPT proclaims that it stands for the rule of law, a mixed economy, and a multiparty system, but it operates like the old Communist Party through cells in the workplace and elsewhere. The DPT reports that it has 60,000 members. Seeking to bring together most major cultural, religious, and public groups as a wider political bloc, in early 1994, Niyazov created a National Revival Movement, which he heads. Unregistered parties are tiny and have been severely repressed. Many of their leaders have been forced into exile or arrested Most significant it the "Agzybirlik" (Unity) popular front. Banned in 1990, it mostly consists of Turkmen intellectuals and backs democratization and ties to Turkey. Co-chair Nurberdi Nurmamedov was convicted of attempted murder in early 2000, in a trial the U.S. State Department said lacked open and due process. Opposition figure Avdy Kuliyev, former foreign minister, is in exile. Physician Pirkuli Tangrikuliyev announced that he wanted to create an opposition party and would run in the 1999 Mejlis election but he was quickly convicted of corruption.

Political Institutions and Policies

Democratization in Turkmenistan has proceeded more slowly than in other ex-Soviet republics. In May 1992, Turkmenistan became the first Central Asian republic to enact a post-independence constitution. It sets up a "secular democracy" embracing a presidential system of rule, granting Niyazov wide powers as head of state and government, though it formally upholds the balance of powers between executive, legislative, and judicial branches. Niyazov issues edicts that have the force of law and appoints and removes judges and local officials. The constitution includes an impressive list of individual rights (though not freedom of the press), but cautions that the exercise of rights must not violate public order or damage national security.

The new constitution created a People's Council (Khalk Maslakhaty) with mixed executive and legislative powers, consisting of the president, ministers, the fifty legislators of the Supreme Council (Mejlis), sixty "people's representatives," and others. The people's representatives were elected by district in a virtually uncontested vote in December 1992. The Khalk Maslakhaty serves as a forum and rubber stamp for the president's policy initiatives. Resurrecting pre-Soviet customs, a Council of Elders, handpicked by Niyazov, was also created to advise the president and choose presidential candidates. Oppositionists complained that both these bodies were designed to stifle dissent. A new Mejlis of 50 members was elected in December 1994. The candidates were all nominated by Niyazov, ran unopposed, and most were members of his DPT. The Mejlis routinely supports presidential decrees and has little legislative initiative. The court system retains its basic Soviet-era structure and functions. The President appoints all judges for 5-year terms without legislative consent, except for the Chairman of the Supreme Court, and removes them by decree.

The lack of democratization in Turkmenistan was accentuated during the April 11, 1998 election of sixty unpaid "people's representatives" to the Khalk Maslakhaty. Turnout was reported at 99.5%, though some of the candidates ran unchallenged and no real campaigning or political party contestation occurred. Elections to the Turkmen 50-seat legislature (Mejlis)were held on December 12, 1999. Niyazov rejected a role for parties, stating that partisanship could lead to clan rivalries. Instead, he directed that nominating groups choose "professional" candidates, and they dutifully selected two candidates per constituency to run. Prior to the race, Niyazov stepped up his repression of political and religious dissidents. The OSCE refused to send monitors, citing the government's control over the electoral process. Changes to the Constitution were introduced in late December 1999 during a joint meeting of the Mejlis, the quasi-legislative Khalk Maslakhaty, and Niyazov's National Revival Movement, to include naming Niyazov president for life. The State Department termed the life term as signaling Turkmenistan's disregard for its OSCE commitments and "a further step backward on the path toward democracy." Niyazov has repeatedly announced that a Turkmen moral guide, the *Rukhname*, will soon be completed.

Human Rights and Freedoms

According to most observers, Turkmenistan's human rights record is extremely poor. The U.S. State Department's *Country Reports on Human Rights Practices for 1999* states that the government severely restricts political and civil liberties. Arbitrary arrest, detention, unfair trials, and interference with citizens' privacy and correspondence are reported. Regime opponents are arrested on false charges and committed to psychiatric hospitals, peaceful demonstrations are forcibly dispersed, and security forces beat suspects, according to the State Department. The government severely restricts freedom of speech and completely controls and censors the media, forbidding the expression of criticism of the government. In signing the Helsinki Final Act in 1992, Niyazov stated that human rights are defined and limited by Turkmen national interests, namely, law and order and political stability. He denies that there have been political prisoners in Turkmenistan during his rule. According to the State Department's *Annual Report on International Religious Freedom for 2000*, Turkmenistan allows only some Russian Orthodox and Sunni Muslim congregations to register, limits religious expression and education, and represses minority faiths, though a slight easing of harassment against minority religious groups occurred during 2000.

Chapter 3

TAJIKISTAN

Kenneth Katzman

SUMMARY

Tajikistan remains embroiled in a civil war between former communists on one side and democratic and Islamic fundamentalist groups on the other. The conflict has already generated about 120,000 refugees, about 60,000 of whom have fled to neighboring Afghanistan. The civil war also involves outside powers, with Iran and Afghanistan said to be aiding the Islamic fundamentalists, and Russia and reportedly Uzbekistan intervening militarily to bolster the old guard communist forces. The United States is concerned about the refugee crisis, civilian deaths, the possibility of spillover into a wider regional war, and the opportunity for increased Iranian influence in Central Asia.

BACKGROUND

Area and Population

Land area is 55,809 sq. mi., which is slightly smaller than the state of Iowa, and 0.6 percent of the former Soviet Union. As of a 1989 census, the population was 5.1 million, of which 62.3 percent are ethnic Tajiks; 23.5 percent Uzbek; 7.4 percent Russian; 1.4 percent Tatar; and 1.3 percent Kirghiz. According to the Conference on Soviet Jewry, there are about 6,000 Jews in Tajikistan. About 80 percent of the population of Tajikistan are Muslims, and of those, the overwhelming majority are Sunni rather than Shiite Muslims which dominate Iran.

History

Tajiks trace their origins to Persian settlers in the sixth century B.C. and speak a language closely related to Farsi, the chief language of Iran. The other Central Asian states are predominantly of Turkic rather than Persian descent. The Tajiks also have been predominantly sedentary rather than nomadic, which largely characterizes the peoples in other Central Asian states. What is now Tajikistan has been subjected to frequent invasions by the Arabs in the seventh century, the Mongols in the thirteenth, the Uzbeks in the fifteenth, and the Russians in the nineteenth, among others.

The Bolsheviks established control of northern Tajikistan in 1918, and the rest of the country after the conquest of the khanate of Bukhara in 1921. In the 1920s, Soviet leader Joseph Stalin divided Central Asia into ethnically based republics to better control them. In 1924, a Tajik soviet republic was set up within a new Uzbek soviet republic and in 1929, a separate Tajik republic was established. However, the historic centers of Tajik culture, Samarkand and Bukhara, were included in Uzbekistan, not Tajikistan. Stalin collectivized agriculture despite strong local resistance and purged the Tajik leadership. After Stalin's death, Tajiks were restored to the republic's leadership, albeit heavily supervised by Moscow.

Ethnic and Political Tensions

Greater freedom in the era of former Soviet leader Mikhail Gorbachev led to greater Tajik national assertiveness. On August 24, 1990, Tajikistan declared its sovereignty, following similar moves by other republics. Then Tajik Communist Party (TCP) chief Kakhar Makhkamov's support for the failed August 1991 coup in Moscow led to his forced resignation. Under pressure from the democratic and Islamic opposition, the Tajik legislature declared the republic's independence on September 9, 1991 and suspended TCP activities. This prompted a backlash from former Communist deputies who deposed Acting President Kadreddin Aslonov, declared a state of emergency, reconstituted the TCP in parliament, and elected Rakhmon Nabiyev as President. (Nabiyev had headed the TCP for about two decades before Gorbachev removed him in 1985.) Nabiyev stood for and won a popular election on November 24, 1991, beating cinematographer Davlat Khudonazarov by 57 percent to 30 percent.

Ethnic, regional and political differences in Tajikistan have turned a power struggle into a major civil war, with foreign party involvement. The opposition is composed of nationalist groups such as the Democratic Party, founded in response to government repression; the Rastokhiz (Rebirth) Popular Front, founded in September 1989 by members of the Writers' Union and cultural intelligentsia; and Islamic groups (primarily the Islamic Renaissance Party, IRP). They attributed Nabiyev's victory to fraud. His election further polarized the government, supported by the traditional elite from the Khojent region of northern Tajikistan and the southern Kulyab region, and the opposition, which has strong support in eastern Tajikistan and in the Kurgan Tyube region of southern Tajikistan. One analyst adds that the former communists also have the backing of Tajikistan's ethnic Uzbeks. The IRP, which was legalized in Tajikistan on October 22, 1991, has traditionally drawn its strength from the many unofficial (as opposed to state-sponsored) Islamic clerics that have operated in Tajikistan. However, the party gained important support when Tajikistan's official Islamic leader, the Qazi (Islamic judge) Akbar Turandzhonzoda, aligned himself with the IRP and called for Nabiyev to relinquish power.

In April and May 1992, opposition demonstrators led by the IRP demanded Nabiyev's resignation and the election of a new legislature. After gun battles in which the opposition seized most of the capital, Nabiyev agreed to form a coalition government. However, the compromise angered Nabiyev's hardline supporters and failed to satisfy the more militant elements of the opposition. On September 7, 1992, six days after storming the presidential palace and seizing top officials, the opposition captured Nabiyev as he tried to escape to his stronghold in Khojent and forced him to resign. After Nabiyev's resignation, the parliament selected its chairman, Akbarsho Iskandarov, as acting President and Abdulmalik Abdullodzhanov, a businessman from Khojent and close relative of former Communist Party boss Makhkamov, was elected interim Prime Minister. The nationalist and Islamic opposition received key posts in the new government; a top IRP leader Davlat Usmon, for example, became Deputy Prime Minister.

Supporters of the former Communists subsequently regrouped under former parliament chairman Safarli Kenjaev (who had been deposed in the earlier compromise between Nabiyev and the opposition) and pushed into the capital Dushanbe in October 1992. This forced a special session of parliament in Khojent, at which Iskandarov was replaced by executive chairman of the Kulyab region, Imamali Rakhmanov, a Nabiyev supporter. Abdullodzhanov was retained as Prime Minister. A parliamentary system was adopted and Rakhmanov became Chairman of Parliament and Head of State; the posts of President and Vice President were abolished. Following the installation of the new government in Dushanbe, warlords from the pro-Communist Kulyab region, led by ex-convict Sangak Safarov, launched an offensive against retreating opposition forces, reportedly leaving 3,000-5,000 dead and forcing the Qazi, Turandzhonzoda, to flee. The Kulyabis and their allies from Khojent are currently pressing this offensive into the Islamic strongholds of Garm in central Tajikistan and the southeastern Gorno-Badakhshan region.

Foreign Policy and Defense

Some analysts fear that the involvement of outside powers in Tajikistan's internal strife threatens to provoke a wider, regional war. During 1992, Russia sent progressively more forces into Tajikistan, largely at the request of Nabiyev and the urging of other Central Asian leaders, to keep order and protect already committed forces and ethnic Russians. On September 3, 1992, the presidents of Russia and the other Central Asian states of Uzbekistan, Kyrgyzstan, and Kazakhstan declared that they would each send a battalion of border troops to Tajikistan to prevent the infiltration of Islamic guerrillas and weapons into Tajikistan. However, Russian troops did impede somewhat the pro-Nabiyev insurgency in October 1992. Nonetheless, reports persist that the Russian troops, primarily the 201st Motorized Rifle Division deployed in Dushanbe itself, subsequently sided with the former Communists in overturning the brief opposition regime. On February 4, 1992, Russia's Defense Minister visited Tajikistan and agreed to help build a new Tajik army, reportedly offering a central role in that army to Safarov's Kulyab-dominated militia force. (Analysts estimate the eventual size of the Tajik army to be about 20,000 soldiers.) There are reports that Russia intervened on the side of the old guard at the behest of Uzbekistan, which reportedly itself intervened on behalf of the former Communists with helicopter gunships and aircraft. Some analysts warn that the Uzbek intervention could be a part of a strategy on the part of Uzbek leaders to build a "Greater Uzbekistan" -- political and military domination of the region. Uzbek President Islam Karimov has also tried to prevent spillover of the Tajik civil war into Uzbekistan by closing the border with Tajikistan and launching a major crackdown against dissent in Uzbekistan.

Most observers agree that some light weapons, as well as other support, are flowing from Afghanistan to the Islamic and democratic opposition, but the is no consensus on which Afghan factions are the most heavily involved in Tajikistan. Reports say a primary source is the radical Islamic fundamentalist Gulbuddin Hikmatyar. However, Hikmatyar is a Pashtun and has no natural affinity with any of the factions in Tajikistan. Others believe the Tajik forces loyal to Afghan President Burhanuddin Rabbani are helping their ethnic brethren across the border. (There are a greater number of Tajiks in Afghanistan than in Tajikistan.) Meanwhile, a powerful Afghan militia leader, General Dostam (an Uzbek), is said to be supporting Tajikistan's old guard, favored by Uzbekistan. Iran's role is even less clear. In February 1992, Iran, stressing economic cooperation, brought Tajikistan (and the other new Muslim states) into the Economic Cooperation Organization (ECO), which Iran, Turkey and Pakistan formed in 1985. Subsequently, there have been persistent reports that Iran has been establishing ties to IRP leaders in Tajikistan, with which Iran shares the Persian language, and that it helped the opposition take power in September 1992. However, Iran publicly denies that it is involved in Tajikistan and has offered to mediate in the civil war.

Tajikistan became a member of the United Nations in March 1992 and of the World Bank and the International Monetary Fund (IMF) in April 1992. It is also a member of the European Bank for Reconstruction and Development. Although membership in these institutions makes Tajikistan eligible for development loans, each loan must be approved on a case by case basis. No loans have yet been made to Tajikistan. Tajikistan was also admitted to the Conference on Security and Cooperation in Europe (CSCE) and the North Atlantic Cooperation Council in 1992, partly out of a desire of the United States and its allies to counter Iranian influence. Although it is a member of the Commonwealth of Independent States (CIS), in January 1993 Tajikistan and the other Central Asian states agreed to create a common market and to take other steps to integrate themselves into what they call the "United States of Central Asia."

Human Rights and Freedoms

According to the U.S. Government's worldwide human rights report for 1992, the civil war in Tajikistan has resulted in the torture, beating, and rape of civilians presumed to be sympathetic to the opposing side. The report adds that the abuses of the Soviet system, such as arbitrary detention without arrest, are still evident. It noted a continuation of press freedoms that began after the 1991 declaration of independence, however. Moreover, according to the report, the successive governments of Tajikistan have been willing to discuss human rights issues with representatives of such international organizations as CSCE and the International Committee of the Red Cross. The civil war has created some limitations on Tajik citizens' freedom of movement, there are reports that Tajik and CIS border guard forces have been trying to prevent Tajik refugees from crossing into neighboring Afghanistan. The fighting, particularly that in the southern Kurgan Tyube region, has created 350,000 refugees, of which the State Department says 100,000 have crossed into Afghanistan. Hundreds reportedly were drowned or were shot to death in the process of crossing the Amu Darya river into that country. The conflict has also cost an estimate 20,000-40,000 lives thus far.

Economy

Tajikistan is the least developed and poorest of the former Soviet republics. Its Gross National Product (GNP) is only 0.75 percent of the total for the former Soviet Union (1991 estimate). It has the greatest percentage of rural population, the lowest per capita income, the lowest education level, and the highest infant mortality rate of the former republics. Livestock herding is widespread in this mountainous country, and only a very small portion of the land is arable. However, the republic possesses rich mineral deposits as well as sizable deposits of oil and natural gas. For example, Tajikistan has 14 percent of the world's uranium reserves. However, fifty years of Soviet central planning have left Tajikistan's natural resources vastly underdeveloped and reliant almost exclusively on a cotton monoculture. Moreover, a massive exodus of technologically skilled Russians from Central Asia has exacerbated economic difficulties and added to the many frustrated unemployed and unskilled rural youths. The Tajik Government has followed Russia's lead in liberalizing the prices of goods and services.

U.S. POLICY

U.S. policy has faced a dilemma in Tajikistan. While some believed the United States should hold Tajikistan to strict criteria of democratization and human rights, others believed that doing so might pave the way for Islamic fundamentalists in Tajikistan to gain power, opening the door to substantial Iranian influence. It appears that the United States has tried to work with the former Communists -- and encourage them to accept democratic principles -- rather than see them replaced by an Islamic fundamentalist opposition. However, the United States has promoted democratization bilaterally and by supporting Tajikistan's inclusion in the CSCE. The United States also has publicly expressed concern about the civil war and supported a peaceful settlement that preserves Tajikistan's territorial integrity and independence.

The United States recognized the independence of Tajikistan on December 25, 1991. In February, 1992, three months after Nabiyev's election, former Secretary of State James Baker visited Tajikistan and said the United States was satisfied with Tajikistan's pledge to adhere to U.S. conditions for recognition, including respect for human rights, democracy, free markets, and arms control. The United States opened an embassy in Dushanbe in March 1992. In June 1992, former President Bush issued Presidential Determination 92-31, waiving trade restrictions on Tajikistan, imposed by Section 402(c)(2)(a) of the Trade Act of 1974. Bush told Congress that doing so would promote the objectives of that Act and that he had Tajikistan's assurances with respect to the emigration practices required by Section 402 of that Act. Critics of the U.S. gestures believed that the United States was not applying its criteria for recognition strictly -- that it was opting for stability before democratic principle. Some, including Senator Bill Bradley, believe that Baker's failure to meet with the opposition during his trip undercut its arguments that leadership by former Communists would lead to international isolation. Some observers believe U.S. concerns about Islamic fundamentalism also led former President Bush to congratulate President Rakhmanov after he was chosen to head the pro-communist successor to the Islamic/democratic opposition regime. On November 20, 1992, in response to the escalating civil war, the United States evacuated its embassy in Dushanbe. On February 20, 1993, the evacuation status was lifted and a limited number of U.S. diplomats are scheduled to return to the Embassy in March.

The United States also has begun providing aid to Tajikistan. It delivered food and medical supplies under the Project Hope relief program for the former Soviet Union in early 1992, and made Tajikistan eligible for a share of unallocated agricultural credit guarantees and for several technical assistance programs. Many of the programs will be continued in FY1993 under the Freedom Support Act (P.L. 102-511, signed October 24, 1992). The Overseas Private Investment Corporation (OPIC) has signed a bilateral agreement with Tajikistan to facilitate U.S. investment there, although the level of U.S. investor interest there is low given the unstable political situation. On January 19, 1993, President Bush issued a Presidential Determination, contributing $5 million in emergency refugee assistance to Tajik refugees in response to a U.N. appeal for $20 million. However, the U.S. desire to aid Tajikistan was dampened somewhat by the Commerce Department, which issued a ruling on May 29, 1992, that Tajikistan (and other former Soviet republics) were selling uranium at unfairly low prices. (In April 1992, Tajikistan successfully petitioned to cancel the Commerce Department probe of it uranium export practices.) The Commerce Department imposed a punitive tariff on Tajik uranium imports into the United States. Congress, which often takes an active role in anti-dumping cases, took little interest in this case, largely because the U.S. uranium industry has declined and now employs only a few thousand people. In October 1992, Tajikistan signed an agreement with the United States to half the dumping of uranium on the U.S. market.

Chapter 4

TAJIKISTAN: CURRENT DEVELOPMENTS AND U.S. INTERESTS

James P. Nichol

SUMMARY

With the peaceful settlement of its 1992-2000 civil war, Tajikistan has begun to address urgent economic development and social needs. The key U.S. concern is that Tajikistan remain stable in this transition period. Possible threats to stability of U.S. concern include renewed civil conflict, new challenges to Tajikistan's independence posed by policies of Russia and Iran, the growth of Islamic fundamentalism hostile to reforms, and continued human suffering.

U.S. POLICY

The United States has faced a number of dilemmas in its policy toward Tajikistan. It has cautiously supported the role of Commonwealth of Independent States (CIS) "peacekeepers" and Russia's mediation of the Tajik civil war, as well as Iran's mediation efforts, though remaining concerned about possible threats to Tajikistan's sovereignty and independence. It has supported a peace process that provides a role for Islamic and other opposition groups willing to abide by democratic procedures, while remaining concerned about the threat of Islamic fundamentalism to Tajikistan and the region.

According to Ambassador-at-Large to the New Independent States (NIS) Stephen Sestanovich, U.S. interests in Tajikistan focus on its "critical strategic" proximity to Iran and Afghanistan and the danger instability poses to economic and democratic reforms, non-proliferation, arms control, and border security. Instability also fosters "opportunities for interference by outside powers" and international crime, narcotics trafficking, and terrorism. Goals for FY2001, he averred, include bolstering the peace process, national reconciliation, and reforms, and addressing urgent humanitarian needs (*Congressional Presentation for Foreign Operations, FY2000 and FY2001*). Drought in 2000 led late in the year to threatened famine for up to one-half the population, according to U.S. Ambassador to Tajikistan Robert Finn, leading the United States and international organizations to announce new food aid. In addition to famine, he stated, Tajikistan confronts growing threats from Islamic extremism, drug trafficking, water shortages, and refugee influxes from Afghanistan. Tajikistan is a "conduit for fundamentalism" to enter Central Asia from Afghanistan, such as terrorists belonging to the Islamic Movement of Uzbekistan. Drug trafficking from Afghanistan also represents "an extremely serious problem," he warned.

State Department officials served as observers at the U.N.-sponsored inter-Tajik peace talks, an example of the Administration's diplomatic efforts to head off or ease ethnic and civil tensions in the NIS. The United States also supported the presence of U.N. military observers in Tajikistan during the conflict. The United States has been the major humanitarian and developmental aid donor to facilitate implementation of the Tajik peace accord and for resettlement of displaced persons. Over the period FY1992-FY1999, the United States has obligated $250.34 million in aid to Tajikistan, mainly for food and other humanitarian needs. The Administration has requested $12.0 million in FY2001 for Tajikistan (in FY2000, estimated spending was $10.01 million; in FY1999, actual spending was $13.05 million). A larger share of aid is planned for economic rebuilding and grass-roots democracy-building. U.S. programs in Tajikistan have been complicated by the closure of the U.S. Embassy in September 1998 because of the heightened threat of terrorist attacks against U.S. personnel worldwide. Many U.S. personnel have moved to Kazakhstan, but some began traveling back and forth to Dushanbe during 2000. A new site will be identified where a secure chancery can be built. Ambassador Sestanovich warned in March 1999 that the lack of a U.S. diplomatic presence could allow Iran to increase its influence.

Congressional concerns about Tajikistan have included hearings, visits, and legislation. Recent action includes the incorporation of authorizing language termed "The Silk Road Strategy Act" into Foreign Operations Appropriations for FY2000 (P.L. 106-113), directing enhanced policy and aid to support conflict amelioration, humanitarian needs, economic development, transport and communications, border controls, democracy, and the creation of civil societies in the South Caucasian and Central Asian states. H.Con.Res. 397, passed by the House on November 1,2000, criticizes irregularities in recent elections in Tajikistan and urges it to pursue democratization as the means to overcome the legacy of civil war. The resolution calls of U.S. Officials to press Central Asian leaders to abide by human rights commitments they undertook through membership in the Organization for Security and Cooperation in Europe.

BASIC FACTS

Area and Population

Land area is 55,800 sq. mi., slightly smaller than Wisconsin. Population is 6.2 million (1999 est., *World Bank*). The Gorno Badakhshan Autonomous Region has called for greater autonomy, which is opposed by the Tajik government.

Ethnicity

62.3% of the population is Tajik, 23.5% Uzbek, and 7.6% Russian (1989 Soviet census). Since that time, up to 75% or more ethnic Russians have emigrated. Clan and regional identities are significant among most Tajiks, and include the Khojenti, Kulyabi, Garmi, and Pamiri groups. More than a million Tajiks reside in Uzbekistan and 4 million in Afghanistan.

Gross Domestic Product

$1.1 billion; per capita GDP is about $180 (1999 est., *World Bank*).

Language and Religion

The official language is Tajik, closely related to Farsi, the chief language in Iran. Most Tajiks belong to the Sunni branch of Islam, though about 3% of the population, mainly Pamiris, belong to the Ismaeli branch, originally a dissident branch of Shiism.

POLITICAL AND ECONOMIC DEVELOPMENTS

Relations with Russia and Other Countries

President Emomali Rakhmanov has proclaimed Tajikistan's willingness to establish amicable relations with all countries, and has supported stronger ties with regional and other states sharing Tajikistan' language, history, or culture. He has emphasized cooperation with China and India, and has called for increased economic ties with the United States, Europe, and Japan. Iran helped mediate the civil war and is a guarantor of the peace settlement. Tajikistan's economic straits have restrained its ability to open legations abroad, but it is active in the U.S. and the CIS.

The top priorities of Tajik foreign policy, Rakhmanov stated in October 1999, are close ties with Russia and other former Soviet republics. Critics of Russia's large security role in Tajikistan argue that it jeopardizes Tajikistan's independence, while still failing to safeguard it from drug trafficking, terrorism and other trans-border criminal activity. In 1999, Tajikistan gained membership in the CIS customs union (composed of Belarus, Russia, Kazakhstan, and Kyrgyzstan; renamed the Eurasian Economic Community in 2000) and in 1998 gained membership in a customs unit formed by Kazakhstan, Kyrgyzstan, and Uzbekistan, though these remain moribund. Tajikistan's relations with Uzbekistan have been tense. Tajikistan has accused Uzbekistan of harboring Tajik separatist Mahmud Khudoyberdiyev, and Uzbekistan has accused Tajikistan of harboring Uzbek terrorist Juma Namangani and others intent on overthrowing the Uzbek government. In 2000, Uzbekistan increased border controls with Tajikistan, including introduction of a visa regime and mining of some border areas, constraining regional travel and trade. In late 2000, Kazakhstan temporarily blocked rail transit from Tajikistan, alleging that drugs, refugees, and diseases were entering the country. A victory by the Islamic fundamentalist Taliban group in Afghanistan might present

Tajikistan with regimes in both the north (Uzbekistan) and south (Afghanistan) that seek to gain undue influence, according to some observers.

Political Leaders

President: Emomali Rakhmanov; *Prime Minister*: Oqil Oqilov; *Speaker of the National Assembly (upper legislative chamber)*: Mohammad Sayed Ubaydulloyev; *Speaker of the Assembly of Representatives (lower legislative chamber)*: Saydullo Khayrulloyev; *Foreign Minister*: Talbak Nazarov; *Defense Minister*: Col. Gen. Sherali Khayrulloyev. Rakhmanov, a Tajik belonging to the Kulyabi clan, was born in 1952 and studied economics at Dushanbe's Lenin State University. In 1988, he became a state farm director in Kulyab region. He quickly rose to power, boosted by his links to the paramilitary leader and ex-convict Sangak Safarov and his Communist Party ties. He became chair of the Kulyab regional government in late 1992, and weeks later was elected chair of the Supreme Soviet and proclaimed head of state. In 1994, he was elected president in a two-man race deemed unfair by international observers.

Defenses

According to *The Military Balance 1999-2000*, the Tajik armed forces consist of 7,000-9,000 ground and air defense troops. The armed forces are underfunded and riven by regional clan loyalties that compromise their responsibilities. Rakhmanov has often criticized crime and corruption in the military and has cracked down on illegal actions, but some reports have linked him to such activities. In 1999-2000, some 2,000 UTO fighters were incorporated into the Tajik armed forces. Reorganization, to include downsizing, is stymied by lack of funds for retraining those mustered out. Many Tajik officers and technicians receive training at Russian military schools, and the Tajik military is reliant on a Russian officer corps. The Russian Border Troops (about 10,000) is mainly composed of ethnic Tajiks, and the Tajik Interior Ministry fields about 1,200 border guards under Russian commanders. Russia's 201st Motorized Rifle Division consists of about 6,200 Russian contract and Tajik troops. To formalize their military presence in Tajikistan after the peace settlement, in April 1999, Russia and Tajikistan signed alliance and military basing accords.

Economy

In late 1997, Tajikistan's economic decline appeared to reverse as the peace accord took hold. GDP grew about 3.7% in 1999, according to the World Bank. However, crop shortfalls caused by drought, and a major earthquake, harmed the economy in 2000. The grain harvest was 236,000 tons in 2000, down from 356,000 tons in 1999. Inflation in consumer prices slowed from over 500% in 1996 to 2.7% by the end of 1998, but economic problems contributed to a 31% increase in 1999 and a larger increase in 2000. Rakhmanov announced a new currency, the somoni, in October 2000, causing panic buying. By mid-1999, most small enterprises had been privatized, but most major firms remain in state hands. Tajikistan's major export industry is the aluminum smelter in Tursunzade, one of the world's largest, although it is currently producing below capacity. Cotton and silk production and sheep herding are the main livelihoods. Until 2000, Tajikistan was a major supplier of water to the rest of Central Asia. Economic reforms face the challenges of the lowest educational level and the highest infant mortality and poverty rates of the former Soviet republics. According to U.N. estimates, at least 80% of the population lives in poverty. Crime and corruption, mainly drug-related, also threaten economic reforms. Despite these challenges, Tajikistan has considerable development potential, according to the World Bank. U.S. trade and investment ties with Tajikistan have been modest because of civil conflict.

The Tajik Civil War

State Department officials served as observers at the U.N.-sponsored inter-Tajik peace talks, an example of the Administration's diplomatic efforts to ease ethnic and civil tensions in the NIS. The United States has been the major humanitarian and developmental aid donor to alleviate the effects of the Tajik civil war. The United States supported the presence of U.N. observers in Tajikistan, and urged Russian-CIS "peacekeeping" forces to cooperate fully with them and to abide by international law.

Tajikistan was among the Central Asian republics least prepared and inclined toward independence when the Soviet Union broke up. In September 1992, a loose coalition of nationalist, Islamic, and democratic parties and movements and largely composed of members of Pamiri and Garmi regional elites based in east and central Tajikistan -- who had long been excluded from political power -- tried to take over. Kulyabi and Khojenti regional elites, assisted by Uzbekistan and Russia, launched a successful counteroffensive that by the end of 1992 has resulted in 20,000-40,000 casualties and up to 800,000 refugees or displaced persons, about 80,000 of whom fled to Afghanistan. In 1993, the CIS authorized "peacekeeping" in Tajikistan. These forces consisted of Russia's 201st Rifle Division, based in Tajikistan, and token Kazakh, Kyrgyz, and Uzbek troops. After Tajik government and opposition emissaries agreed to a cease-fire in September 1994, the U.N. Security Council formally established the several dozen-member UNMOT in December 1994 with a mandate to monitor the cease-fire, later expanded to investigate cease-fire violations, monitor the demobilization of UTO fighters, assist ex-combatants to integrate into society, and offer electoral advice. In December 1996, the two sides agreed to set up a National Reconciliation Commission (NRC), an executive body composed equally of government and opposition emissaries.

On June 27, 1997, Rakhmanov and UTO leader Seyed Abdullo Nuri signed the *comprehensive peace agreement*, under which Rakhmanov remained president but 30% of ministerial posts were allocated to the opposition and Nuri headed the NRC. Benchmarks of the peace process were largely met, including the return of refugees, demilitarization of rebel forces, legalization of rebel parties, and the holding of elections. On March 26, 2000, Tajikistan disbanded its NRC, and UNMOT pulled out in May 2000. The CIS declared its peacekeeping role fulfilled in September 2000, but Russian troops remain based in Tajikistan. After forces led by former UTO commander Mullah Abdullo Rakhimov (that had refused to disarm and were linked to Namangani's forces) surrendered in September 2000, Rakhmanov stated that most armed anti-regime groups had been eliminated. Stability in Tajikistan remains fragile. An unsuccessful insurrection in the Leninabad region of northern Tajikistan launched by Khudoyberdiyev in November 1998 highlights concerns by some observers about secessionist tendencies in Leninabad region and about ethnic tensions between ethnic Tajiks and Uzbeks in Tajikistan.

Political Parties and Groups

Six parties were registered to participate in the party list part of the February 2000 legislative election. These included the ruling People's Democratic (PDP), Communist (TCP), Socialist, Democratic ("Almaty platform"), Islamic Renaissance (IRP), and Justice "Adolathol." In late 1994, Rakhmanov orchestrated the creation of the PDP, and in 1998 became its head. The TCP is headed by former Rakhmanov client Shodi Shabdolov. The TCP fell into Rakhmanov's disfavor in 1998. The Democratic Party split in 1994, with one group forming the "Tehran platform" (registered in 1998; de-registered in late 1999). The remaining wing ("Almaty platform") was registered in December 1999. The UTO's main parties are the Democratic Party (Almaty platform) and the Islamic Rebirth Party (headed by Nuri, and registered in September 1999). The IRP has traditionally drawn its strength from many unofficial (as opposed to state-sponsored) Islamic clerics. The social democratic Party of Justice was registered in 1996 and it formed a New Opposition bloc with several small parties to run in the 2000 legislative contest.

Political Institutions and Policies

According to a new constitution approved by referendum in November 1994, the Oliy Majlis (legislature) enacts laws, interprets the constitution, determines basic directions of domestic and foreign policy, sets dates for referenda and elections, and approves key ministerial and other appointments. The legislature also approves the state budget determines tax policy, ratifies treaties, and approves a state of war or emergency as decreed by the president. The constitution also calls for creation of a presidium to "organize work," to be elected by the legislators and the total number of deputies, and a presidential veto may be overridden by the same margin. The main Tajik opposition groups boycotted the November 1994 presidential election and constitutional referendum because they had no say in drawing up the draft constitution and would not be allowed to field their own candidates. The Tajik legislature in mid-1999 rubber-stamped constitutional changes proposed by Rakhmanov calling for a seven year presidential term, a two-house Supreme Assembly (legislature), and the legalization of religious parties. A popular referendum approved the changes in September, and the legislature scheduled a presidential election for November 6, 1999. Tajik opposition candidates alleged that government harassment prevented them from gathering required signatures to register. The Central Electoral Commission (CEC), controlled by Rakhmanov, then pronounced him the only candidate. This prompted the resignation of opposition members of the NRC and calls for an electoral boycott. To provide the gloss of a multi-candidate race, the CEC "registered" IRP nominee Davlat Usmon, though he refused to run. Going ahead with the election, the CEC reported that 98% of 2.85 million Tajiks turned out and 96.9% voted for Rakhmanov. The OSCE refused to monitor the election. Seeking to avert renewed war, Nuri agreed to respect the outcome of the election and rejoin the NRC in return for pledges by Rakhmanov to allow fair legislative elections scheduled for early 2000.

A legislative electoral law was approved with input from the UTO in December 1999 calling for an upper legislative chamber, the National Assembly (representing regional interests), to consist of 33 members, and a lower chamber, the Assembly of Representatives, to consist of 63 members. Elections to the lower chamber were set for February 27,2000 (and a run-off on March 12). In all, 191 candidates contested 41 single mandate seats and 107 candidates on six party lists competed for 22 seats. Turnout was reported by the CEC at 93.36% of 2.87 million voters. In the party list voting, the ruling PDP won fifteen seats, the TCP won five seats, and the IRP won two seats. Most winners of single mandate seats were PDP members. Over 107 U.N. and OSCE observers monitored the race. They stated that voters "were presented with a genuine and broad range of alternatives," but concluded that the electoral process must be improved "to meet the minimum democratic standards for equal, fair, free, secret, transparent, and accountable elections." They raised questions about freedom of the media, the independence of electoral commissions, the questionable de-registration of some candidates, apparently inflated turnout figures, and the transparency of vote tabulation. Thirty-three upper legislative chamber seats were filled on March 23, 2000, by indirect voting by local council assemblies and the appointment of eight members by Rakhmanov. Most seats were filled by PDP members.

Human Rights and Freedoms

According to State Department's *Country Reports on Human Rights Practices for 1999,* Tajikistan during most of the 1990s was an authoritarian state, where the government limited the right of citizens peacefully to change their government. Tajik government security forces in 1999 were responsible for some killing and beatings of detainees, and also engaged in threats, extortion, looting, and other abuse of civilians. Prison conditions were life threatening, and the judicial system was subject to political pressure. Opposition forces were responsible for serious abuses of civilians in 1999, including killing, kidnapping, threats, and extortion. According to the State Department's *2000 Annual Report on International Religious Freedom*, the vast majority of Tajiks consider themselves Muslims and are not anti-Islamic, but "fear" Islamic fundamentalism. The government has restricted visas for Muslim missionaries and arrested dozens of members of the banned Hizb e-Tahrir fundamentalist party.

Chapter 5

TAJIK CIVIL WAR: RECENT DEVELOPMENTS AND U.S. POLICY CONCERNS*

James P. Nichol

SUMMARY

Civil conflict in Tajikistan intensified in December, with Tajik opposition forces taking the strategic town of Garm in central Tajikistan and threatening other areas near the capital of Dushanbe. The U.N. Security Council, meeting December 13, agreed to extend the mandate of the U.N.'s observer mission in Tajikistan to mid-March 1997, after which it will reexamine the U.N. role there. Congress has supported urgent humanitarian aid and U.S. and multilateral diplomacy to end the conflict.

BACKGROUND

Tajikistan (population about 6 million; slightly smaller than Iowa) was among the Central Asian republics least inclined toward independence when the Soviet Union broke up at the end of 1991. Its permanence as a state is threatened by regional and ethnic divisions, as well as geographical isolation of many mountainous areas from central rule. Its communist-dominated elite, largely composed of members of the Khojenti and Kulyabi regional clans, have tried to rebuild traditional ties with Russia. In September 1992, opposition forces, a loose coalition of nationalist, Islamic, and democratic parties and movements largely composed of members of Pamiri and Garmi regional clans -- who had long been excluded from political power -- tried to overturn a coalition of government and seize power. Kulyabi

* Sources include Foreign Broadcast Information Service, *Daily Report*; *Central Eurasia*, by wire service; Open Media Research Institute, *Daily Report*; Jamestown Foundation, *Monitor Daily Report* and *Prism*; *Central Asia Monitor*; the CENASIA Listserver; State Department, embassy, and United Nations documents and interviews; Reuters, AP, AFP, and Interfax wire service reports; and others mentioned below.

and Khojenti elites resisted these efforts, and by December 1992 had routed the oppositionists from the capital and launched a concerted countrywide offensive.

Sending Commonwealth of Independent States (CIS) "peacekeeping" forces to Tajikistan was endorsed at the CIS summit of leaders in January 1993 to protect what Yeltsin has termed "CIS borders." The actual number of CIS and border troops in Tajikistan is less than 15,000, and these forces include many ethnic Tajik draftees. At a U.N.-sponsored meeting in Tehran, Tajik government and opposition emissaries agreed on September 17, 1994, to a cease-fire, to begin when U.N. observers were in place along the Tajik-Afghan border. They also formed a Joint commission to monitor the cease-fire. The U.N. Security Council approved sending a contingent of temporary U.N. military observers.

In October 1994, the sides agreed to extend the cease-fire (the first of repeated extensions). Because of this progress, the U.N. Security Council formally established a U.N. Mission of Observers in Tajikistan (UNMOT) on December 16, 1994, to monitor the cease-fire. Total personnel of 96 in December 1996 included 44 military observers from Austria, Bangladesh, Bulgaria, Denmark, Jordan, Poland, Switzerland, Ukraine, and Uruguay. Boutros Ghali has reported that the CIS "peacekeepers" generally cooperate with UNMOT. The U.N. mandate has been extended several times. During fighting in June 1996, when the Security Council was considering extending the mandate, U.S. Ambassador Madeleine Albright noted that "we are dismayed by the seeming inability of two sides thus far to agree even on confidence-building measures such as prisoner exchanges," and she "strongly endorsed" a review of UNMOT's mandate in December, should prospects for peace not improve.

RECENT DEVELOPMENTS

The town of Tavil-Dara in central Tajikistan has been the scene of yearly fighting. In mid-1996, the city changed hands several times during intense fighting. Despite this, the two sides reconvened stalled peace talks in Ashgabat, Turkmenistan on July 8-21, attended by Gerd Merrem, the U.N. Secretary-General's resident special envoy and head of the UNMOT Mission. They agreed on a reinstated and enhanced cease-fire on the Tajik-Afghan border and throughout Tajikistan, and a prisoner exchange. Ongoing conflict in Tavil-Dara, however, prevented implementation of the agreements. The fighting reportedly resulted in over 16,000 displaced persons and hundreds of casualties. On September 17, 1996, local opposition commanders and the Tajik government agreed to a cease-fire brokered by UNMOT and the Joint Commission limited to part of the Karategin Valley in central Tajikistan, an arrangement that recognized opposition gains. The opposition agreed to keep the road open to Kyrgyzstan and to the token reinstatement of some local government authority, while the government pledged to remove most of its checkpoints to allow freedom of movement to oppositionists. The Karategin Valley cease-fire led to decreased fighting for several weeks. United Tajik Opposition (UTO) chair Sayid Abdullah Nuri did not fully endorse the cease-fire, and would not sanction its extension to the nearby area around Tavil-Dara, limiting its usefulness.

The Attack on Garm

In late October, the Karategin Valley cease-fire appeared to fray with oppositionist occupation of some villages within the area covered by the agreement. In November, oppositionist activities increased including their bloodless occupation of the strategically significant district capital of Komsomolabad (south of Garm; cutting off the main roads to central and eastern Tajikistan). Fighting was renewed around the ravaged town of Tavil-Dara. Then, on December 1, 1996, the opposition launched a surprise attack and took Garm, which is strategically situated on the Dushanbe-to-Kyrgyzstan road. Observers note that an opposition cutoff of the road isolates remaining Tajik government outposts in central Tajikistan, threatening the loss of these positions. Along with cease-fire violations, UNMOT reports "repeated instances of the gross use of force" against observers by government troops. Heightening calls among some in the U.N. that the UNMOT mandate not be renewed. In his December 5, 1996 report to the Security Council, Boutros Ghali noted that intensified fighting raised doubts about the sincerity and intentions of the Tajik parties, but stressed that talks were imminent, and advised continuing the UNMOT's mandate.

The New Cease-fire

During late 1996, the two sides discussed convening a high-level inter-Tajik summit in Moscow. Prior to the Moscow meeting, Rakhmanov and Nuri met "informally" in northern Afghanistan on December 10-11 under U.N. auspices, and agreed on a temporary cease-fire to begin on December 12 to last until the summit in Moscow was convened on December 19. Both sides called for UNMOT to help observe the cease-fire, and pledged to work toward agreement on a political settlement at the Moscow meeting, or at follow-on talks. They reportedly agreed to disengage and demilitarize some towns in central Tajikistan, allow free movement on the east-west highway, jointly operate a customs post at the Tajik-Kyrgyz border, and exchange prisoners. In many respects, the interim cease-fire is similar to the September cease-fire, allowing joint government-opposition influence in some areas under contention. The two sides also initialed a draft agreement on a political settlement, which calls for setting up a reconciliation council. Its makeup and functions were discussed at the December 19 summit. On December 23, the two sides signed an agreement calling for a general amnesty, a prisoner exchange, and the return of refugees. Most significantly, they agreed to set up a reconciliation council, headed by the opposition, that will participate in executive branch activities, long opposed by Rakhmanov, and review proposed Tajik constitutional changes.

Meeting on December 13, the U.N. Security Council condemned ongoing fighting in Tajikistan, but agreed to extend UNMOT's mandate for three months. It requested that by mid-January 1997, the Secretary General submit a report containing his recommendations on UNMOT's future. New violence against UNMOT observers heightens questions about the utility of their presence.

IMPLICATIONS FOR TAJIKISTAN AND REGIONAL INTERESTS

Tajik government control over its territory appears increasingly tenuous, particularly over the relatively inaccessible Gorno Badakhshan Autonomous Region in eastern Tajikistan, where most Pamiris live, and central Tajikistan, where most Garmis live. Russia, Uzbekistan, the United States, and others have urged the Tajik government to become more representative of Tajik interest. Kulyabis, led by Rakhmanov, have increasingly excluded Khojentis from political and economic power. Khojentis have responded with several armed uprisings and demonstrations, resulting in limited concessions by Rakhmanov. A mainly Khojenti political group led by former prime minister Abdumalik Abdullajanov has called for representation in the peace talks, a demand backed by Nuri but opposed by Rakhmanov. Both sides use the cease-fires as opportunities to regroup for future battles and to petition world opinion, according to critics. They use UNMOT's presence to publicize the other side's cease-fire violations, and neither has complete control over their forces (including the government's control over allied paramilitaries). Some among the opposition coalition oppose cease-fire and peace talks, now that Tajik government forces appear weak. UTO first deputy chair Qadi Akbar Turajonzadah, head of the Islamic Revival Party, has opposed aspects of the December cease-fire, while UTO chief of staff of armed formations Davlat Usmon and Nuri support it. Russia's military loss in Chechnya has provided a psychological boost to insurgencies in Tajikistan and elsewhere in the CIS.

The civil conflict in Tajikistan has contributed to up to 60,000 casualties and nearly one million displaced person s (one out of six of the population), of whom over 250,000 fled the country. Up to 30,000 or more refugees remain in four camps in Afghanistan. The U.N. High Commissioner for Refugees (UNHCR) special mission for Tajikistan, the International Organization for Migration (IOM), and the International Committee of the Red Cross (ICRC) have sponsored refugee camps in northern Afghanistan and repatriation and humanitarian aid efforts. (Arab nongovernmental organizations and the Iranian Red Crescent also give aid, but do not cooperate with UNHCR and other international organizations.) A UTO ban on repatriation has left some refugees in Afghanistan against their will. The World Bank in August 1994 estimated that the conflict had resulted in $7 billion in economic damage. In November 1996, the U.N. issued an urgent appeal for $22 million in humanitarian aid for Tajikistan for the next six months, noting that some regions of Tajikistan face an "acute humanitarian crisis" during the winter.

Tajikistan is located at a crossroads of major world civilizations -- Russia, Turkey, Iran, India-Pakistan, and China -- and has been influenced by each. Russia, China, and India share an interest in restraining Islamic fundamentalism, while Iran and Pakistan vie to reinforce Tajikistan's Islamic identity. Russia and Tajikistan's fellow Central Asian neighbors -- Kazakhstan, Kyrgyzstan, and Uzbekistan -- have been concerned about drug and gun running across the borders as well as Islamic fundamentalism, and have mostly supported Tajikistan's secular regime. Russia has been concerned to safeguard the 70,000 ethnic Russians still residing in Tajikistan, and Uzbekistan to safeguard the 1.5 million ethnic Uzbeks residing there. Discrimination against ethnic Russians in Tajikistan has increased and fuels a continuing exodus. Uzbekistan has played a central role in Tajik affairs, contributing to the overthrow of the coalition government in 1992. Even some pro-government Tajiks have raised concerns about Uzbek military deployments in Tajikistan and increased dependence on Uzbekistan, viewing Uzbekistan as seeking to establish hegemony over Tajikistan (some ethnic Uzbeks in Tajikistan welcome Uzbekistan's aid). Some Uzbeks have raised concerns that the heightened Russian presence in Tajikistan might jeopardize their own sovereignty or their hegemonial plans. While regarding Russia's presence as useful at first, they increasingly call for a peace settlement involving creation of a Tajik coalition government that would permit a reduction in the Russian presence. Some in Russia regard their troops in Tajikistan as a remaining imperial foothold in Central Asia and as leverage against a regionally assertive Uzbekistan and truculent Turkmenistan.

Iran, classified by the United States as a terrorist state, seeks influence in Tajikistan by serving as a headquarters for some Tajik oppositionists. The fall of Kabul to the pro-Pakistani Taliban, however, has encouraged Iran to put pressure on the Tajik opposition to reach a political settlement with the Tajik government. In this, Iran shares Russia's desire to resolve this conflict so that attention can be devoted to curbing Taliban's gains, according to some observers. Iran also hosts inter-Tajik peace talks and supports Russian "peacekeeping" as a means of combating increased Turkish and Turkic Central Asian influence in Persian-speaking Tajikistan. Various groups in Afghanistan also have interest in Tajikistan.

U.S. POLICY CONCERNS

U.S. State Department officials have observed the U.N.-sponsored inter-Tajik peace talks, part of the Administration's offer to assist in diplomacy to address ethnic and civil tensions in the New Independent States (NIS). The United States also supported the sending of U.N. observers to Tajikistan, and urged CIS "peacekeeping" forces to cooperate fully with U.N. peace efforts and abide by international law. Ambassador at Large to the New Independent States James Collins, in discussing U.S. policy toward Central Asia in a speech in October 1996, stressed that the United States "continues to support the efforts of the U.N. to find an equitable, negotiated settlement [in Tajikistan] ensuring a broad-based government essential to a lasting solution." While recognizing Russian interests in Tajikistan, the United States also stresses that Russia should not encroach on Tajikistan's independence or block U.S. interests there. In its FY1995 annual report on U.S. assistance to the NIS (the latest), the Administration stated that Russian forces in Tajikistan were present at the invitation of its government and that Moscow supported OSCE and U.N. involvement in settling the conflict.

The United States is the major humanitarian and developmental aid donor to alleviate the impact of the civil war in Tajikistan. Cumulative U.S. aid obligations to Tajikistan were $146 million as of June 30, 1996, with Tajikistan ranking ninth out of twelve in U.S. aid to the NIS. The bulk of U.S. assistance has been for urgent humanitarian needs. The FY1997 AID request calls for aid of $5 million for Tajikistan to reduce human suffering, and for medical and family planning aid. The Administration hoped that abatement of conflict would allow it to shift to project to develop infrastructure, but recent intensified fighting has heightened urgent humanitarian needs. Besides bilateral aid, the United States has contributed over $8 million to UNHCR, IOM, and ICRC for refugee repatriation and urgent human needs in Tajikistan.

Congressional Action

Concerns over Russia's motives in Tajikistan and other NIS were reflected in provision in the FY1994 through FY1997 Foreign Operations Appropriations Acts prohibiting aid to any NIS that violates the territorial integrity or national sovereignty of other NIS (a Presidential waiver is permitted). In first introducing this condition in 1993, Senator Mitch McConnell and cosponsor Sen. Patrick Leahy stressed that Russian military actions in Georgia, Moldova, and *Tajikistan* were of particular concern. Concern with conditions in Tajikistan led the House in October 1994 to urge the president to maintain humanitarian support for refugees and displaced persons and encourage democratization, respect for human rights, and a peace settlement in Tajikistan (H.Con.Res.302; Co-sponsors Gilman and Andrews). In late 1994, Representative Robert Andrews urged AID to step up aid to Tajikistan. Ongoing concerns were reflected in hearings on Tajikistan and Central Asia held by the Europe Subcommittee of the House Foreign Relations Committee in 1992 and 1994, and by the Commission on Security and Cooperation in Europe in 1993.

Concerns about Tajikistan's future and possible U.S. responses were reflected in Section 528 of the FY1994-95 Foreign Relations Authorization Act (P.L. 103-236) requesting a Presidential report to Congress assessing Russia's objectives toward the NIS. Senator William Cohen noted that a report would impel further Administration analysis of Russian motives and provide findings for congressional consideration. A classified version of this report was submitted to Congress. In 1995, the Senate approved an amendment sponsored by Senator Cohen to the FY1996 Foreign Operations Appropriations Act calling for the Administration to "declassify [the report], to the maximum extent possible," and to add information about Russian border troop deployments and Russian efforts to integrate the security, defense, and intelligence forces of the NIS, among other topics. Senator Cohen voiced concerns that "Russian troops are heavily involved in the civil war in Tajikistan and patrol the border," among other Russian interventions. Conferees deleted this requirement (H.Rept.104-295, October 26, 1995), but called on the Administration to submit a declassified or substantially declassified version of the report, along with the added information. In late 1996, the State Department indicated to Congress that it was still considering how to revamp the project.

Chapter 6

KAZAKHSTAN: A COUNTRY STUDY*

Glenn E. Curtis (Editor)

HISTORICAL BACKGROUND

By far the largest of the Central Asian republics of the former Soviet Union, independent Kazakhstan is the world's ninth-largest nation in geographic area. The population density of Kazakhstan is among the lowest in the world, partly because the country includes large areas of inhospitable terrain. Kazakhstan is located deep within the Asian continent, with coastline only on the landlocked Caspian Sea. The proximity of unstable countries such as Afghanistan, Tajikistan, and Azerbaijan to the west and south further isolates Kazakhstan.

Within the centrally controlled structure of the Soviet system, Kazakhstan played a vital industrial and agricultural role; the vast coal deposits discovered in Kazakhstani territory in the twentieth century promised to replace the depleted fuel reserves in the European territories of the union. The vast distances between the European industrial centers and coal fields in Kazakhstan presented a formidable problem that was only partially solved by Soviet efforts to industrialize Central Asia. That endeavor left the newly independent Republic of Kazakhstan a mixed legacy: a population that includes nearly as many Russians as Kazaks; the presence of a dominating class of Russian technocrats, who are necessary to economic progress but ethnically unassimilated; and a well-developed energy industry, based mainly on coal and oil, whose efficiency is inhibited by major infrastructural deficiencies.

Kazakhstan has followed the same general political pattern as the other four Central Asian states. After declaring independence from the Soviet political structure completely dominated by Moscow and the Communist Party of the Soviet Union (CPSU) until 1991, Kazakhstan retained the basic governmental structure and, in fact, most of the same leadership that had occupied the top levels of power in 1990. Nursultan Nazarbayev, first secretary of the Communist Party of Kazakhstan (CPK) beginning in 1989, was elected president of the republic in 1991 and remained in undisputed power five years later. Nazarbayev took several effective steps to ensure his position. The constitution of 1993 made

* Excerpted from the Library of Congress Country Studies Website at: http://lcweb2.loc.gov/frd/cs/cshome.html.

the prime minister and the Council of Ministers responsible solely to the president, and in 1995 a new constitution reinforced that relationship. Furthermore, opposition parties were severely limited by legal restrictions on their activities. Within that rigid framework, Nazarbayev gained substantial popularity by limiting the economic shock of separation from the security of the Soviet Union and by maintaining ethnic harmony, despite some discontent among Kazak nationalists and the huge Russian minority.

In the mid-1990s, Russia remained the most important sponsor of Kazakhstan in economic and national security matters, but in such matters Nazarbayev also backed the strengthening of the multinational structures of the Commonwealth of Independent States (CIS--see Glossary), the loose confederation that succeeded the Soviet Union. As sensitive ethnic, national security, and economic issues cooled relations with Russia in the 1990s, Nazarbayev cultivated relations with China, the other Central Asian nations, and the West. Nevertheless, Kazakhstan remains principally dependent on Russia.

Kazakhstan entered the 1990s with vast natural resources, an underdeveloped industrial infrastructure, a stable but rigid political structure, a small and ethnically divided population, and a commercially disadvantageous geographic position. In the mid-1990s, the balance of those qualities remained quite uncertain.

Historical Setting

Until the arrival of Russians in the eighteenth century, the history of Kazakhstan was determined by the movements, conflicts, and alliances of Turkic and Mongol tribes. The nomadic tribal society of what came to be the Kazak people then suffered increasingly frequent incursions by the Russian Empire, ultimately being included in that empire and the Soviet Union that followed it.

Early Tribal Movements

Humans have inhabited present-day Kazakhstan since the earliest Stone Age, generally pursuing the nomadic pastoralism for which the region's climate and terrain are best suited. The earliest well-documented state in the region was the Turkic Kaganate, which came into existence in the sixth century A.D. The Qarluqs, a confederation of Turkic tribes, established a state in what is now eastern Kazakhstan in 766. In the eighth and ninth centuries, portions of southern Kazakhstan were conquered by Arabs, who also introduced Islam. The Oghuz Turks controlled western Kazakhstan from the ninth through the eleventh centuries; the Kimak and Kipchak peoples, also of Turkic origin, controlled the east at roughly the same time. The large central desert of Kazakhstan is still called Dashti-Kipchak, or the Kipchak Steppe.

In the late ninth century, the Qarluq state was destroyed by invaders who established the large Qarakhanid state, which occupied a region known as Transoxania, the area north and east of the Oxus River (the present-day Syrdariya), extending into what is now China. Beginning in the early eleventh century, the Qarakhanids fought constantly among themselves and with the Seljuk Turks to the south. In the course of these conflicts, parts of present-day Kazakhstan shifted back and forth between the combatants. The Qarakhanids, who accepted Islam and the authority of the Arab Abbasid caliphs of Baghdad during their dominant period, were conquered in the 1130s by the Karakitai, a Turkic confederation from northern China. In the mid-twelfth century, an independent state of Khorazm (also seen as Khorezm or Khwarazm) along the Oxus River broke away from the weakening Karakitai, but the bulk of the Karakitai state lasted until the invasion of Chinggis (Genghis) Khan in 1219-21.

After the Mongol capture of the Karakitai state, Kazakhstan fell under the control of a succession of rulers of the Mongolian Golden Horde, the western branch of the Mongol Empire. (The horde, or *zhuz*, is the precursor of the present-day clan, which is still an important element of Kazak society--see Population and Society.) By the early fifteenth century, the ruling structure had split into several large groups known as khanates, including the Nogai Horde and the Uzbek Khanate.

Forming the Modern Nation

The present-day Kazaks became a recognizable group in the mid-fifteenth century, when clan leaders broke away from Abul Khayr, leader of the Uzbeks, to seek their own territory in the lands of Semirech'ye, between the Chu and Talas rivers in present-day southeastern Kazakhstan. The first Kazak leader was Khan Kasym (r. 1511-23), who united the Kazak tribes into one people. In the sixteenth century, when the Nogai Horde and Siberian khanates broke up, clans from each jurisdiction joined the Kazaks. The Kazaks subsequently separated into three new hordes: the Great Horde, which controlled Semirech'ye and southern Kazakhstan; the Middle Horde, which occupied north-central Kazakhstan; and the Lesser Horde, which occupied western Kazakhstan.

Russian traders and soldiers began to appear on the northwestern edge of Kazak territory in the seventeenth century, when Cossacks established the forts that later became the cities of Oral (Ural'sk) and Atyrau (Gur'yev). Russians were able to seize Kazak territory because the khanates were preoccupied by Kalmyk invaders of Mongol origin, who in the late sixteenth century had begun to move into Kazak territory from the east. Forced westward in what they call their Great Retreat, the Kazaks were increasingly caught between the Kalmyks and the Russians. In 1730 Abul Khayr, one of the khans of the Lesser Horde, sought Russian assistance. Although Abul Khayr's intent had been to form a temporary alliance against the stronger Kalmyks, the Russians gained permanent control of the Lesser Horde as a result of his decision. The Russians conquered the Middle Horde by 1798, but the Great Horde managed to remain independent until the 1820s, when the expanding Quqon (Kokand) Khanate to the south forced the Great Horde khans to choose Russian protection, which seemed to them the lesser of two evils.

The Kazaks began to resist Russian control almost as soon as it became complete. The first mass uprising was led by Khan Kene (Kenisary Kasimov) of the Middle Horde, whose followers fought the Russians between 1836 and 1847. Khan Kene is now considered a Kazak national hero.

Russian Control

In 1863 Russia elaborated a new imperial policy, announced in the Gorchakov Circular, asserting the right to annex "troublesome" areas on the empire's borders. This policy led immediately to the Russian conquest of the rest of Central Asia and the creation of two administrative districts, the Guberniya (Governorate General) of Turkestan and the Steppe District. Most of present-day Kazakhstan was in the Steppe District, and parts of present-day southern Kazakhstan were in the Governorate General.

In the early nineteenth century, the construction of Russian forts began to have a destructive effect on the Kazak traditional economy by limiting the once-vast territory over which the nomadic tribes could drive their herds and flocks. The final disruption of nomadism began in the 1890s, when many Russian settlers were introduced into the fertile lands of northern and eastern Kazakhstan. Between 1906 and 1912, more than a half-million Russian farms were started as part of the reforms of Russian minister of the interior Petr Stolypin, shattering what remained of the traditional Kazak way of life.

Starving and displaced, many Kazaks joined in the general Central Asian resistance to conscription into the Russian imperial army, which the tsar ordered in July 1916 as part of the effort against Germany in World War I. In late 1916, Russian forces brutally suppressed the widespread armed resistance to the taking of land and conscription of Central Asians. Thousands of Kazaks were killed, and thousands of others fled to China and Mongolia.

In the Soviet Union

In 1917 a group of secular nationalists called the Alash Orda (Horde of Alash), named for a legendary founder of the Kazak people, attempted to set up an independent national government. This state lasted less than two years (1918-20) before surrendering to the Bolshevik authorities, who then sought to preserve Russian control under a new political system. The Kyrgyz Autonomous Soviet Socialist Republic was set up in 1920 and was renamed the Kazak Autonomous Soviet Socialist Republic in 1925 when the Kazaks were differentiated officially from the Kyrgyz. (The Russian Empire recognized the ethnic difference between the two groups; it called them both "Kyrgyz" to avoid confusion between the terms "Kazak" and "Cossack.")

In 1925 the autonomous republic's original capital, Orenburg, was reincorporated into Russian territory. Almaty (called Alma-Ata during the Soviet period), a provincial city in the far southeast, became the new capital. In 1936 the territory was made a full Soviet republic. From 1929 to 1934, during the period when Soviet leader Joseph V. Stalin was trying to collectivize agriculture, Kazakhstan endured repeated famines because peasants had slaughtered their livestock in protest against Soviet agricultural policy. In that period, at least 1.5 million Kazaks and 80 percent of the republic's livestock died. Thousands more Kazaks tried to escape to China, although most starved in the attempt.

Many European Soviet citizens and much of Russia's industry were relocated to Kazakhstan during World War II, when Nazi armies threatened to capture all the European industrial centers of the Soviet Union. Groups of Crimean Tatars, Germans, and Muslims from the North Caucasus region were deported to Kazakhstan during the war because it was feared that they would collaborate with the enemy. Many more non-Kazaks arrived in the years 1953-65, during the so-called Virgin Lands campaign of Soviet premier Nikita S. Khrushchev (in office 1956-64). Under that program, huge tracts of Kazak grazing land were put to the plow for the cultivation of wheat and other cereal grains. Still more settlers came in the late 1960s and 1970s, when the government paid handsome bonuses to workers participating in a program to relocate Soviet industry close to the extensive coal, gas, and oil deposits of Central Asia. One consequence of the decimation of the nomadic Kazak population and the in-migration of non-Kazaks was that by the 1970s Kazakhstan was the only Soviet republic in which the eponymous nationality was a minority in its own republic (see Ethnic Groups).

Reform and Nationalist Conflict

The 1980s brought glimmers of political independence, as well as conflict, as the central government's hold progressively weakened. In this period, Kazakhstan was ruled by a succession of three Communist Party officials; the third of those men, Nursultan Nazarbayev, continued as president of the Republic of Kazakhstan when independence was proclaimed in 1991.

In December 1986, Soviet premier Mikhail S. Gorbachev (in office 1985-91) forced the resignation of Dinmukhamed Kunayev, an ethnic Kazak who had led the republic as first secretary of the CPK from 1959 to 1962, and again starting in 1964. During 1985, Kunayev had been under official attack for cronyism, mismanagement, and malfeasance; thus, his departure was not a surprise. However, his replacement, Gennadiy Kolbin, an ethnic Russian with no previous ties to Kazakhstan, was unexpected. Kolbin was a typical administrator of the early Gorbachev era--enthusiastic about economic and administrative reforms but hardly mindful of their consequences or viability.

The announcement of Kolbin's appointment provoked spontaneous street demonstrations by Kazaks, to which Soviet authorities responded with force. Demonstrators, many of them students, rioted. Two days of disorder followed, and at least 200 people died or were summarily executed soon after. Some accounts estimate casualties at more than 1,000.

Kunayev had been ousted largely because the economy was failing. Although Kazakhstan had the third-largest gross domestic product (GDP--see Glossary) in the Soviet Union, trailing only Russia and Ukraine, by 1987 labor productivity had decreased 12 percent, and per capita income had fallen by 24 percent of the national norm. By that time, Kazakhstan was underproducing steel at an annual rate of more than a million tons. Agricultural output also was dropping precipitously.

While Kolbin was promoting a series of unrealistic, Moscow-directed campaigns of social reform, expressions of Kazak nationalism were prompting Gorbachev to address some of the non-Russians' complaints about cultural self-determination. One consequence was a new tolerance of bilingualism in the non-Russian regions. Kolbin made a strong commitment to promoting the local language and in 1987 suggested that Kazak become the republic's official language. However, none of his initiatives went beyond empty public-relations ploys. In fact, the campaign in favor of bilingualism was transformed into a campaign to improve the teaching of Russian.

While attempting to conciliate the Kazak population with promises, Kolbin also conducted a wholesale purge of pro-Kunayev members of the CPK, replacing hundreds of republic-level and local officials. Although officially "nationality-blind," Kolbin's policies seemed to be directed mostly against Kazaks. The downfall of Kolbin, however, was the continued deterioration of the republic's economy during his tenure. Agricultural output had fallen so low by 1989 that Kolbin proposed to fulfill meat quotas by slaughtering the millions of wild ducks that migrate through Kazakhstan. The republic's industrial sector had begun to recover slightly in 1989, but credit for this progress was given largely to Nursultan Nazarbayev, an ethnic Kazak who had become chairman of Kazakhstan's Council of Ministers in 1984.

As nationalist protests became more violent across the Soviet Union in 1989, Gorbachev began calling for the creation of popularly elected legislatures and for the loosening of central political controls to make such elections possible. These measures made it increasingly plain in Kazakhstan that Kolbin and his associates soon would be replaced by a new generation of Kazak leaders.

Rather than reinvigorate the Soviet people to meet national tasks, Gorbachev's encouragement of voluntary local organi-zations only stimulated the formation of informal political groups, many of which had overtly nationalist agendas. For the Kazaks, such agendas were presented forcefully on national television at the first Congress of People's Deputies, which was convened in Moscow in June 1989. By that time, Kolbin was already scheduled for rotation back to Moscow, but his departure probably was hastened by riots in June 1989 in Novyy Uzen, an impoverished western Kazakhstan town that produced natural gas. That rioting lasted nearly a week and claimed at least four lives.

The Rise of Nazarbayev

In June 1989, Kolbin was replaced by Nazarbayev, a politician trained as a metallurgist and engineer. Nazarbayev had become involved in party work in 1979, when he became a protégé of reform members of the CPSU. Having taken a major role in the attacks on Kunayev, Nazarbayev may have expected to replace him in 1986. When he was passed over, Nazarbayev submitted to Kolbin's authority and used his party position to support Gorbachev's new line, attributing economic stagnation in the Soviet republics to past subordination of local interests to the mandates of Moscow.

Soon proving himself a skilled negotiator, Nazarbayev bridged the gap between the republic's Kazaks and Russians at a time of increasing nationalism while also managing to remain personally loyal to the Gorbachev reform program. Nazarbayev's firm support of the major Gorbachev positions in turn helped him gain national and, after 1990, even international visibility. Many reports indicate that Gorbachev was planning to name Nazarbayev as his deputy in the new union planned to succeed the Soviet Union.

Even as he supported Gorbachev during the last two years of the Soviet Union, Nazarbayev fought Moscow to increase his republic's income from the resources it had long been supplying to the center. Although his appointment as party first secretary had originated in Moscow, Nazarbayev realized that for his administration to succeed under the new conditions of that time, he had to cultivate a popular mandate within the republic. This difficult task meant finding a way to make Kazakhstan more Kazak without alienating the republic's large and economically significant Russian and European populations. Following the example of other Soviet republics, Nazarbayev sponsored legislation that made Kazak the official language and permitted examination of the negative role of collectivization and other Soviet policies on the republic's history. Nazarbayev also permitted a widened role for religion, which encouraged a resurgence of Islam. In late 1989, although he did not have the legal power to do so, Nazarbayev created an independent religious administration for Kazakhstan, severing relations with the Muslim Board of Central Asia, the Soviet-approved oversight body in Tashkent.

In March 1990, elections were held for a new legislature in the republic's first multiple-candidate contests since 1925. The winners represented overwhelmingly the republic's existing elite, who were loyal to Nazarbayev and to the Communist Party apparatus. The legislature also was disproportionately ethnic Kazak: 54.2 percent to the Russians' 28.8 percent.

Sovereignty and Independence

In June 1990, Moscow declared formally the sovereignty of the central government over Kazakhstan, forcing Kazakhstan to elaborate its own statement of sovereignty. This exchange greatly exacerbated tensions between the republic's two largest ethnic groups, who at that point were numerically about equal. Beginning in mid-August 1990, Kazak and Russian nationalists began to demonstrate frequently around Kazakhstan's parliament building, attempting to influence the final statement of sovereignty being developed within. The statement was adopted in October 1990.

In keeping with practices in other republics at that time, the parliament had named Nazarbayev its chairman, and then, soon afterward, it had converted the chairmanship to the presidency of the republic. In contrast to the presidents of the other republics, especially those in the independence-minded Baltic states, Nazarbayev remained strongly committed to the perpetuation of the Soviet Union throughout the spring and summer of 1991. He took this position largely because he considered the republics too interdependent economically to survive separation. At the same time, however, Nazarbayev fought hard to secure republic control of Kazakhstan's enormous mineral wealth and industrial potential. This objective became particularly important after 1990, when it was learned that Gorbachev had negotiated an agreement with Chevron, a United States oil company, to develop Kazakhstan's Tengiz oil fields. Gorbachev did not consult Nazarbayev until talks were nearly complete. At Nazarbayev's insistence, Moscow surrendered control of the republic's mineral resources in June 1991. Gorbachev's authority crumbled rapidly throughout 1991. Nazarbayev, however, continued to support him, persistently urging other republic leaders to sign the revised Union Treaty, which Gorbachev had put forward in a last attempt to hold the Soviet Union together.

Because of the coup attempted by Moscow hard-liners against the Gorbachev government in August 1991, the Union Treaty never was signed. Ambivalent about the removal of Gorbachev, Nazarbayev did not condemn the coup attempt until its second day. However, once the incompetence of the plotters became clear, Nazarbayev threw his weight solidly behind Gorbachev and continuation of some form of union, largely because of his conviction that independence would be economic suicide.

At the same time, however, Nazarbayev pragmatically began preparing his republic for much greater freedom, if not for actual independence. He appointed professional economists and managers to high posts, and he began to seek the advice of foreign development and business experts. The outlawing of the CPK, which followed the attempted coup, also permitted Nazarbayev to take virtually complete control of the republic's economy, more than 90 percent of which had been under the partial or complete direction of the central Soviet government until late 1991. Nazarbayev solidified his position by winning an uncontested election for president in December 1991.

A week after the election, Nazarbayev became the president of an independent state when the leaders of Russia, Ukraine, and Belarus signed documents dissolving the Soviet Union. Nazarbayev quickly convened a meeting of the leaders of the five Central Asian states, thus effectively raising the specter of a "Turkic" confederation of former republics as a counterweight to the "Slavic" states (Russia, Ukraine, and Belarus) in whatever federation might succeed the Soviet Union. This move persuaded the three Slavic presidents to include Kazakhstan among the signatories to a recast document of dissolution. Thus, the capital of Kazakhstan lent its name to the Alma-Ata Declaration, in which eleven of the fifteen Soviet republics announced the expansion of the thirteen-day-old CIS. On December 16, 1991, just five days before that declaration, Kazakhstan had become the last of the republics to proclaim its independence.

PHYSICAL ENVIRONMENT

With an area of about 2,717,300 square kilometers, Kazakhstan is more than twice the combined size of the other four Central Asian states. The country borders Turkmenistan, Uzbekistan, and Kyrgyzstan to the south; Russia to the north; Russia and the Caspian Sea to the west; and China's Xinjiang Uygur Autonomous Region to the east.

Topography and Drainage

There is considerable topographical variation within Kazakhstan. The highest elevation, Khan Tengri Mountain, on the Kyrgyz border in the Tian Shan range, is 6,995 meters; the lowest point, at Karagiye, in the Caspian Depression in the west, is 132 meters below sea level. Only 12.4 percent of Kazakhstan is mountainous, with most of the mountains located in the Altay and Tian Shan ranges of the east and northeast, although the Ural Mountains extend southward from Russia into the northern part of west-central Kazakhstan. Many of the peaks of the Altay and Tian Shan ranges are snow covered year-round, and their run-off is the source for most of Kazakhstan's rivers and streams.

Except for the Tobol, Ishim, and Irtysh rivers (the Kazak names for which are, respectively, Tobyl, Esil, and Ertis), portions of which flow through Kazakhstan, all of Kazakhstan's rivers and streams are part of landlocked systems. They either flow into isolated bodies of water such as the Caspian Sea or simply disappear into the steppes and deserts of central and southern Kazakhstan. Many rivers, streams, and lakes are seasonal, evaporating in summer. The three largest bodies of water are Lake Balkhash, a partially fresh, partially saline lake in the east, near Almaty, and the Caspian and Aral seas, both of which lie partially within Kazakhstan.

Some 9.4 percent of Kazakhstan's land is mixed prairie and forest or treeless prairie, primarily in the north or in the basin of the Ural River in the west. More than three-quarters of the country, including the entire west and most of the south, is either semidesert (33.2 percent) or desert (44 percent). The terrain in these regions is bare, eroded, broken uplands, with sand dunes in the Qizilqum (red sand; in the Russian form, Kyzylkum) and Moyunqum (in the Russian form, Moin Kum) deserts, which occupy south-central Kazakhstan. Most of the country lies at between 200 and 300 meters above sea level, but Kazakhstan's Caspian shore includes some of the lowest elevations on Earth.

Climate

Because Kazakhstan is so far from the oceans, the climate is sharply continental and very dry. Precipitation in the mountains of the east averages as much as 600 millimeters per year, mostly in the form of snow, but most of the republic receives only 100 to 200 millimeters per year. Precipitation totals less than 100 millimeters in the south-central regions around Qyzylorda. A lack of precipitation makes Kazakhstan a sunny republic; the north averages

120 clear days a year, and the south averages 260. The lack of moderating bodies of water also means that temperatures can vary widely. Average winter temperatures are -3°C in the north and 18°C in the south; summer temperatures average 19°C in the north and 28°-30°C in the south. Within locations differences are extreme, and temperature can change very suddenly. The winter air temperature can fall to -50°C, and in summer the ground temperature can reach as high as 70°C.

Environmental Problems

The environment of Kazakhstan has been badly damaged by human activity. Most of the water in Kazakhstan is polluted by industrial effluents, pesticide and fertilizer residue, and, in some places, radioactivity. The most visible damage has been to the Aral Sea, which as recently as the 1970s was larger than any of the Great Lakes of North America save Lake Superior. The sea began to shrink rapidly when sharply increased irrigation and other demands on the only significant tributaries, the Syrdariya and the Amu Darya (the latter reaching the Aral from neighboring Uzbekistan), all but eliminated inflow. By 1993 the Aral Sea had lost an estimated 60 percent of its volume, in the process breaking into three unconnected segments. Increasing salinity and reduced habitat have killed the Aral Sea's fish, hence destroying its once-active fishing industry, and the receding shoreline has left the former port of Aral'sk more than sixty kilometers from the water's edge. The depletion of this large body of water has increased temperature variations in the region, which in turn have had an impact on agriculture. A much greater agricultural impact, however, has come from the salt- and pesticide-laden soil that the wind is known to carry as far away as the Himalaya Mountains and the Pacific Ocean. Deposition of this heavily saline soil on nearby fields effectively sterilizes them. Evidence suggests that salts, pesticides, and residues of chemical fertilizers are also adversely affecting human life around the former Aral Sea; infant mortality in the region approaches 10 percent, compared with the 1991 national rate of 2.7 percent.

By contrast, the water level of the Caspian Sea has been rising steadily since 1978 for reasons that scientists have not been able to explain fully. At the northern end of the sea, more than a million hectares of land in Atyrau Province have been flooded. Experts estimate that if current rates of increase persist, the coastal city of Atyrau, eighty-eight other population centers, and many of Kazakhstan's Caspian oil fields could be submerged by 2020.

Wind erosion has also had an impact in the northern and central parts of the republic because of the introduction of wide-scale dryland wheat farming. In the 1950s and 1960s, much soil was lost when vast tracts of Kazakhstan's prairies were plowed under as part of Khrushchev's Virgin Lands agricultural project. By the mid-1990s, an estimated 60 percent of the republic's pastureland was in various stages of desertification.

Industrial pollution is a bigger concern in Kazakhstan's manufacturing cities, where aging factories pump huge quantities of unfiltered pollutants into the air and groundwater. The capital, Almaty, is particularly threatened, in part because of the postindependence boom in private automobile ownership.

The gravest environmental threat to Kazakhstan comes from radiation, especially in the Semey (Semipalatinsk) region of the northeast, where the Soviet Union tested almost 500 nuclear weapons, 116 of them above ground. Often, such tests were conducted without evacuating or even alerting the local population. Although nuclear testing was halted in 1990, radiation poisoning, birth defects, severe anemia, and leukemia are very common in the area (see Health Conditions).

With some conspicuous exceptions, lip service has been the primary official response to Kazakhstan's ecological problems. In February 1989, opposition to Soviet nuclear testing and its ill effects in Kazakhstan led to the creation of one of the republic's largest and most influential grass-roots movements, Nevada-Semipalatinsk, which was founded by Kazak poet and public figure Olzhas Suleymenov. In the first week of the movement's existence, Nevada-Semipalatinsk gathered more than 2 million signatures from Kazakhstanis of all ethnic groups on a petition to Gorbachev demanding the end of nuclear testing in Kazakhstan. After a year of demonstrations and protests, the test ban took effect in 1990. It remained in force in 1996, although in 1995 at least one unexploded device reportedly was still in position near Semey.

Once its major ecological objective was achieved, Nevada-Semipalatinsk made various attempts to broaden into a more general political movement; it has not pursued a broad ecological or "green" agenda. A very small green party, Tagibat, made common cause with the political opposition in the parliament of 1994.

The government has established a Ministry of Ecology and Bioresources, with a separate administration for radioecology, but the ministry's programs are underfunded and given low priority. In 1994 only 23 percent of budgeted funds were actually allotted to environmental programs. Many official meetings and conferences are held (more than 300 have been devoted to the problem of the Aral Sea alone), but few practical programs have gone into operation. In 1994 the World Bank (see Glossary), the International Monetary Fund (IMF--see Glossary), and the United States Environmental Protection Agency agreed to give Kazakhstan US$62 million to help the country overcome ecological problems.

POPULATION AND SOCIETY

Total population was estimated in 1994 at 17,268,000, making Kazakhstan the fourth most populous former Soviet republic. As of 1990, 57 percent of the country's residents lived in cities. Because much of the land is too dry to be more than marginally habitable, overall population density is a very low 6.2 persons per square kilometer. Large portions of the republic, especially in the south and west, have a population density of less than one person per square kilometer. In 1989 some 1.4 million Kazaks lived outside Kazakhstan, nearly all in the Russian and Uzbek republics. At that time, an estimated 1 million Kazaks lived in China, and a sizeable but uncounted Kazak population resided in Mongolia.

Demographic Factors

The birth rate, which is declining slowly, was estimated at 19.4 births per 1,000 population in 1994 (see table 1). The death rate, which has been climbing slowly, was estimated at 7.9 per 1,000 population--leaving a rate of natural increase of 1.1 percent, by far the lowest among the five Central Asian republics. In 1995 the total fertility rate--2.4 births per woman, a drop from the 1990 figure of 2.8--also was far below the rates for the other Central Asian republics. In the first six months of 1994, some 1.8 percent fewer babies were born than in the same period the previous year. In the same months, the number of deaths rose by 2.5 percent compared with those in the same period in 1993. In some provinces, death rates are much higher than the average, however. Shygys Qazaqstan (East Kazakhstan) Province has a death rate of 12.9 per thousand; Soltustik Qazaqstan (North Kazakhstan) Province, eleven per 1,000; and Almaty Province, 11.3 deaths per 1,000. The cause of nearly half of these deaths is cardiovascular disease.

Table 1. Central Asia: Demographic Indicators, 1989-93

Indicator	Kazakhstan	Kyrgyzstan	Tajikistan	Turkmenistan	Uzbekistan
Live births	316,369	128,352	186,504	124,992	711,000
Birth rate	18.7	28.6	32.5	34.9	33.3
Deaths	156,253	32,163	49,326	27,609	139,900
Death rate6	9.2	7.2	8.6	7.7	6.5
Life expectancy, male	63.8	64.6	66.8	61.8	66.0
Life expectancy, female	73.0	72.7	71.7	68.4	72.1
Marriages	146,161	40,818	53,946	34,890	235,900
Marriage rate*	8.6	9.1	0.9	9.8	11.0
Divorces	45,516	8,043	5,293	4,940	29,953
Divorce rate*	2.7	1.8	0.9	1.4	1.5

Source: Based on information from United Nations, Department for Economic and Social Information and Policy Analysis, *Demographic Yearbook 1994*, New York, 1996, 140-43.
Note: * Per 1,000 population.

Because of declining life expectancy and decreases in the size of the Russian population, which is demographically older and has a low birth rate, the republic's residents are a relatively young group; in 1991 there were only 149 pensioners per 1,000 population, as opposed to 212 per 1,000 in the former Soviet Union as a whole (see table 2). The republic is experiencing a pronounced outflow of citizens, primarily non-Kazaks moving to other former Soviet republics. Although figures conflict, it seems likely that as many as 750,000 non-Kazaks left the republic between independence and the end of 1995. Official figures indicate that in the first half of 1994 some 220,400 people left, compared with 149,800 in the same period of 1993. In 1992 and 1993, the number of Russian emigrants was estimated at 100,000 to 300,000. Such out-migration is not uniform. Some regions, such as Qaraghandy, have lost as much as 10 percent of their total population, resulting in shortages of technicians and skilled specialists in that heavily industrial area.

To some extent, the outflow has been offset by in-migration, which has been of two types. Kazakhstan's government has actively encouraged the return of Kazaks from elsewhere in the former Soviet Union and from China and Mongolia. Unlike other ethnic groups, ethnic Kazaks are granted automatic citizenship. More than 60,000 Kazaks emigrated from Mongolia in 1991-94, their settlement--or resettlement--eased by government assistance. Most were moved to the northern provinces, where the majority of Kazakhstan's Russian population lives. Because these "Mongol Kazaks" generally do not know Russian and continue to pursue traditional nomadic lifestyles, the impact of their resettlement has been disproportionate to their actual numbers.

Table 2. Central Asia: Population Distribution, 1989-92 (in thousands)

Population Group	Kazakhstan	Kyrgyzstan	Tajikistan	Turkmenistan*	Uzbekistan*
Urban male	4,577	800	813	783	3,937
Urban female	5,029	881	842	808	4,104
Urban total	9,606	1,681	1,655	1,591	8,041
Urban percentage	57.6	37.9	32.5	43.9	40.6
Rural male	3,539	1,383	1,717	952	5,847
Rural female	3,576	1,388	1,720	980	5,922
Rural total	7,115	2,771	3,437	1,932	11,769
Total male	8,116	2,183	2,530	1,735	9,784
Total female	8,605	2,269	2,562	1,788	10,026
14 and younger	5,248	1,673	2,187	n.a.	8,083
15 to 39	6,851	1,794	1,996	1,453	8,029
50 to 64	3,623	756	717	510	2,894
65 and older	999	228	192	132	804

Source: Based on information from United Nations, Department for Economic and Social Information and Policy Analysis, *Demographic Yearbook 1994*, New York, 1996, 240-45.
Note: * All figures 1989.

The other major source of in-migration has been non-Kazaks arriving from other parts of Central Asia to avoid inhospitable conditions; most of these people also have settled in northern Kazakhstan. Although officially forbidden and actively discouraged, this in-migration has continued. In a further attempt to control in-migration, President Nazarbayev decreed that no more than 5,000 families would be permitted to take up residence in the republic in 1996.

Ethnic Groups

Kazakhstan is the only former Soviet republic where the indigenous ethnic group is not a majority of the population. In 1994 eight of the country's eleven provinces had Slavic (Russian and Ukrainian) population majorities. Only the three southernmost provinces were populated principally by Kazaks and other Turkic groups; the capital city, Almaty, had a European (German and Russian) majority. Overall, in 1994 the population was about 44 percent Kazak, 36 percent Russian, 5 percent Ukrainian, and 4 percent German. Tatars and Uzbeks each represented about 2 percent of the population; Azerbaijanis, Uygurs, and Belarusians each represented 1 percent; and the remaining 4 percent included approximately ninety other nationalities (see table 3).

Kazakhstan's ethnic composition is the driving force behind much of the country's political and cultural life. In most ways, the republic's two major ethnic groups, the Kazaks and the "Russian-speakers" (Russians, Ukrainians, Germans, and Belarusians), may as well live in different countries. To the Russians, most of whom live in northern Kazakhstan within a day's drive of Russia proper, Kazakhstan is an extension of the Siberian frontier and a product of Russian and Soviet development. To most Kazaks, these Russians are usurpers. Of Kazakhstan's current Russian residents, 38 percent were born outside the republic, while most of the rest are second-generation Kazakhstani citizens.

Table 3. Central Asia: Ethnic Composition, Selected Years, 1989-94 (in percentages)

Country and Ethnic Group	1989	1991	1993	1994
Kazakhstan				
Kazak	39.7	41.9	43.2	44.3
Russian	37.8	37.0	36.5	35.8
Ukrainian	5.4	5.2	5.2	5.1
German	5.8	4.7	4.1	3.6
Uzbek	2.0	2.1	2.2	2.2
Tatar	2.0	2.0	2.0	2.0
Kyrgyzstan				
Kyrgyz	52.4	n.a.	56.5	n.a.
Russian	21.5	n.a.	18.8	n.a.
Uzbek	12.9	n.a.	12.9	n.a.
Ukrainian	2.5	n.a.	2.1	n.a.
German	2.4	n.a.	1.0	n.a.
Tajikistan				
Tajik	62.3	63.8	n.a.	n.a.
Uzbek	23.5	24.0	n.a.	n.a.
Russian	7.6	6.5	n.a.	n.a.
Tatar	1.4	1.4	n.a.	n.a.
Turkmenistan				
Turkmen	72.0	n.a.	73.3	n.a.
Russian	9.8	n.a.	9.5	n.a.
Uzbek	9.0	n.a.	9.0	n.a.
Kazak	2.0	n.a.	2.5	n.a.
Uzbekistan				
Uzbek	71.4	73.0	n.a.	n.a.
Russian	8.3	7.7	n.a.	n.a.
Tajik	4.7	4.8	n.a.	n.a.
Kazak	4.1	n.a.	n.a.	n.a.
Tatar	2.4	2.3	n.a.	n.a.

Source: Based on information from *The Europa World Year Book 1994*, 2, London, 1994, 1679; *The Europa World Year Book 1995*, 2, London, 1995, 1679, 1735, 1823, 2950, 3070, 3363; United States, Central Intelligence Agency, *The World Factbook 1994*, Washington, 1994, 210, 222, 385, 403, 420; and *1995 Britannica Book of the Year*, Chicago, 1995, 726, 746.

The Nazarbayev government has announced plans to move the capital from Almaty in the far southeast to Aqmola in the north-central region by 1998. That change would cause a shift of the Kazak population northward and accelerate the absorption of the Russian-dominated northern provinces into the Kazakhstani state. Over the longer term, the role of Russians in the society of Kazakhstan also is determined by a demographic factor--the average age of the Russian population is higher, and its birth rate much lower.

The Role of Women

Like its 1993 predecessor, the constitution of 1995 defends women's rights implicitly, if not entirely explicitly. The document guarantees citizens the right to work and forbids discrimination based on geographic origin, gender, race, nationality, religious or political belief, and language.

In practice, social opinion tends to associate women in the workplace with the abuses of the Soviet past. The early 1990s saw the loss of more than 100,000 day-care spaces, and public opinion strongly favors returning primary responsibility for the rearing and educating of children to mothers. In April 1995, President Nazarbayev said that one of the republic's goals must be to create an economy in which a mother can work at home, raising her children. This general opinion has been reflected in governmental appointments and private enterprise; almost no women occupy senior positions in the country, either in government or in business.

The declining birth rate is another issue with the potential to become politicized because it affects the demographic "race" between Kazaks and Russians. With demographic statistics in mind, Kazak nationalist parties have attempted to ban abortions and birth control for Kazak women; they have also made efforts to reduce the number of Kazak women who have children outside marriage. In 1988, the last year for which there are figures, 11.24 percent of the births in the republic were to unmarried women. Such births were slightly more common in cities (12.72 percent) than in rural areas (9.67 percent), suggesting that such births may be more common among Russians than among Kazaks.

Women's health issues have not been addressed effectively in Kazakhstan. Maternal mortality rates average 80 per 10,000 births for the entire country, but they are believed to be much higher in rural areas. Of the 4.2 million women of childbearing age, an estimated 15 percent have borne seven or more children. Nevertheless, in 1992 the number of abortions exceeded the number of births, although the high percentage of early-stage abortions performed in private clinics complicates data gathering. According to one expert estimate, the average per woman is five abortions. Rising abortion rates are attributable, at least in part, to the high price or unavailability of contraceptive devices, which became much less accessible after 1991. In 1992 an estimated 15 percent of women were using some form of contraception.

Clans

One aspect of Kazak traditional culture, clan membership, is acquiring importance in the postindependence environment. Historically the Kazaks identified themselves as belonging to one of three groups of clans and tribes, called *zhuz*, or hordes, each of which had traditional territories. Because the Lesser Horde controlled western Kazakhstan and the Middle Horde migrated across what today is northern and eastern Kazakhstan, those groups came under Russian control first, when colonial policies were relatively benign. The traditional nobles of these hordes managed to retain many of their privileges and to educate their sons in Russian schools. These sons became the first Kazak nationalists, and in turn their sons were destroyed by Stalin, who tried to eradicate the Kazak intelligentsia during his purges of the 1930s.

The Large, or Great, Horde was dominant in the south, and hence did not fall under Russian control until colonialism was much harsher. Substantially fewer Great Horde Kazaks became involved in politics before the revolution, but those who did became socialists rather than nationalists. For that reason, the Great Horde members came to dominate once the Bolsheviks took power, especially after Kazakhstan's capital was moved from the Lesser Horde town of Orenburg (now in Russia) to a Great Horde wintering spot, Almaty. Kunayev and Nazarbayev are said to have roots in clans of the Great Horde.

With the collapse of the CPK and its patronage networks, and in the absence of any other functional equivalent, clan and *zhuz* membership has come to play an increasingly important role in the economic and political life of the republic at both the national and the province level. The power of clan politics has been visible in the dispute over moving the national capital to Aqmola, which would bolster the prestige of the Middle Horde, on whose lands Aqmola is located. In general, members of the Lesser and Middle hordes are more Russified and, hence, more inclined to cooperate with Russian industrial and commercial interests than are the members of the Great Horde. Akezhan Kazhegeldin, prime minister in 1996, was a Middle Horder, as was the opposition leader Olzhas Suleymenov. Although mindful of Russia's strength, the Great Horders have less to lose to Russian separatism than do the Lesser and Middle horders, whose lands would be lost should the Russian-dominated provinces of northern Kazakhstan become separated from the republic.

RELIGION

By tradition the Kazaks are Sunni Muslims of the Hanafi school, and the Russians are Russian Orthodox. In 1994, some 47 percent of the population was Muslim, 44 percent was Russian Orthodox, and 2 percent was Protestant, mainly Baptist. Some Jews, Catholics, and Pentacostalists also live in Kazakhstan; a Roman Catholic diocese was established in 1991. As elsewhere in the newly independent Central Asian states, the subject of Islam's role in everyday life, and especially in politics, is a delicate one in Kazakhstan.

Islam in the Past

As part of the Central Asian population and the Turkic world, Kazaks are conscious of the role Islam plays in their identity, and there is strong public pressure to increase the role that faith plays in society. At the same time, the roots of Islam in many segments of Kazak society are not as deep as they are in neighboring countries. Many of the Kazak nomads, for instance, did not become Muslims until the eighteenth or even the nineteenth century, and urban Russified Kazaks, who by some counts constitute as much as 40 percent of the indigenous population, profess discomfort with some aspects of the religion even as they recognize it as part of their national heritage.

Soviet authorities attempted to encourage a controlled form of Islam as a unifying force in the Central Asian societies while at the same time stifling the expression of religious beliefs. Since independence, religious activity has increased significantly. Construction of mosques and religious schools has accelerated in the 1990s, with financial help from Saudi Arabia, Turkey, and Egypt. Already in 1991, some 170 mosques were operating, more than half of them newly built; at that time, an estimated 230 Muslim communities were active in Kazakhstan

Islam and the State

In 1990 Nazarbayev, then party first secretary, created a state basis for Islam by removing Kazakhstan from the authority of the Muslim Board of Central Asia, the Soviet-approved and politically oriented religious administration for all of Central Asia. Instead, Nazarbayev created a separate muftiate, or religious authority, for Kazak Muslims. However, Nazarbayev's choice of Ratbek hadji Nysanbayev to be the first Kazak mufti proved an unpopular one. Accusing him of financial irregularities, religious mispractice, and collaboration with the Soviet and Kazakhstani state security apparatus, a group of believers from the nationalist Alash political party attempted unsuccessfully to replace the mufti in December 1991.

With an eye toward the Islamic governments of nearby Iran and Afghanistan, the writers of the 1993 constitution specifically forbade religious political parties. The 1995 constitution forbids organizations that seek to stimulate racial, political, or religious discord, and imposes strict governmental control on foreign religious organizations. As did its predecessor, the 1995 constitution stipulates that Kazakhstan is a secular state; thus, Kazakhstan is the only Central Asian state whose constitution does not assign a special status to Islam. This position was based on the Nazarbayev government's foreign policy as much as on domestic considerations. Aware of the potential for investment from the Muslim countries of the Middle East, Nazarbayev visited Iran, Turkey, and Saudia Arabia; at the same time, however, he preferred to cast Kazakhstan as a bridge between the Muslim East and the Christian West. For example, he initially accepted only observer status in the Economic Cooperation Organization (ECO), all of whose member nations are predominantly Muslim. The president's first trip to the Muslim holy city of Mecca, which did not occur until 1994, was part of an itinerary that also included a visit to Pope John Paul II in the Vatican.

By the mid-1990s, Nazarbayev had begun occasionally to refer to Allah in his speeches, but he had not permitted any of the Islamic festivals to become public holidays, as they had elsewhere in Central Asia. However, certain pre-Islamic holidays such as the spring festival Navruz and the summer festival Kymyzuryndyk were reintroduced in 1995.

NATIONAL IDENTITY

As in the other Central Asian republics, the preservation of indigenous cultural traditions and the local language was a difficult problem during the Soviet era. The years since 1991 have provided opportunities for greater cultural expression, but striking a balance between the Kazak and Russian languages has posed a political dilemma for Kazakhstan's policy makers.

Language

The two official languages in Kazakhstan are Russian and Kazak. Kazak is part of the Nogai-Kipchak subgroup of northeastern Turkic languages, heavily influenced by both Tatar and Mongol. Kazak was first written only in the 1860s, using Arabic script. In 1929 Latin script was introduced. In 1940 Stalin decided to unify the written materials of the Central Asian republics with those of the Slavic rulers by introducing a modified form of Cyrillic. In

1992 the return of a Latin-based alphabet came under discussion, but the enormous costs involved appear to have stopped further consideration of the idea.

Kazak first became a state language in the late Soviet period, when few of the republic's Russians gave serious thought to the possibility that they might need Kazak to retain their employment, to serve in the armed forces, or to have their children enter a Kazakhstani university. At that point, fewer than 5 percent of Russians could speak Kazak, although the majority of Kazaks could speak Russian. However, with the separation between Russia and Kazakhstan that followed independence, Russian nationalist sentiment and objections to alleged discrimination in official language policies have increased, especially in the north, as Russians have felt the threat of Kazak becoming the sole legal state language. Meanwhile, Kazaks have strongly defended the preeminence of their tongue, although mastery of the language is far from universal even among Kazaks. According to some estimates, as much as 40 percent of the Kazak population is not fluent in Kazak. The standard language of business, for example, is Russian.

Even those who are fluent find Kazak a difficult language to work with in science, business, and some administrative settings because it remained largely a "kitchen" language in Soviet times, never developing a modern technical vocabulary. Nor has there been extensive translation of technical or popular literature into Kazak. Thus, for most Kazaks Russian remains the primary "world language." In fact, President Nazarbayev defended making Kazak the sole official language on the grounds that decades of Russification had endangered the survival of Kazak as a language. The practical primacy of Russian is reflected in the schools. Despite efforts to increase the number of schools where Kazak is the primary language of instruction, Russian appeared to continue its domination in the mid-1990s. In 1990 about twice as many schools taught in Russian as in Kazak. Although institutions of higher learning now show a strong selection bias in favor of Kazak students, Russian remains the language of instruction in most subjects.

The issue of languages is one of the most politicized and contentious in Kazakhstan. The volatility of the language issue has been augmented by Russia's controversial proposals, beginning in 1993, that Kazakhstan's Russians be granted dual citizenship. Although Nazarbayev rejected such a policy, the language controversy prompted him to postpone deadlines for implementation of laws making Kazak the sole official language. Thus, it is unlikely that most adult non-Kazaks will have to learn Kazak. Nevertheless, demographic trends make it probable that the next generation will have to learn Kazak, a prospect that generates considerable discomfort in the non-Kazak population. The 1995 constitution does not provide for dual citizenship, but it does alleviate Russian concerns by declaring Russian an official language. That status means that Russian would continue as the primary language of communication for many ethnic Kazaks, and it will remain acceptable for use in schools (a major concern of Russian citizens) and official documents.

Culture

Before the Russian conquest, the Kazaks had a well-articulated culture based on their nomadic pastoral economy. Although Islam was introduced to most of the Kazaks in the seventeenth and eighteenth centuries, the religion was not fully assimilated until much later. As a result, it coexisted with earlier elements of shamanistic and animistic beliefs. Traditional

Kazak belief held that separate spirits inhabited and animated the earth, sky, water, and fire, as well as domestic animals. To this day, particularly honored guests in rural settings are treated to a feast of freshly killed lamb. Such guests are sometimes asked to bless the lamb and to ask its spirit for permission to partake of its flesh. Besides lamb, many other traditional foods retain symbolic value in Kazak culture.

Because animal husbandry was central to the Kazaks' traditional lifestyle, most of their nomadic practices and customs relate in some way to livestock. Traditional curses and blessings invoked disease or fecundity among animals, and good manners required that a person ask first about the health of a man's livestock when greeting him and only afterward inquire about the human aspects of his life.

The traditional Kazak dwelling is the yurt, a tent consisting of a flexible framework of willow wood covered with varying thicknesses of felt. The open top permits smoke from the central hearth to escape; temperature and draft can be controlled by a flap that increases or decreases the size of the opening. A properly constructed yurt can be cooled in summer and warmed in winter, and it can be disassembled or set up in less than an hour. The interior of the yurt has ritual significance; the right side generally is reserved for men and the left for women.

Although yurts are less used for their original purpose than they once were, they remain a potent symbol of "Kazakness." During demonstrations against Nazarbayev in the spring of 1992, demonstrators and hunger strikers erected yurts in front of the government building in Almaty. Yurts are also frequently used as a decorative motif in restaurants and other public buildings.

Because of the Kazaks' nomadic lifestyle and their lack of a written language until the mid-nineteenth century, their literary tradition relies upon oral histories. These histories were memorized and recited by the *akyn*, the elder responsible for remembering the legends and histories, and by *jyrau*, lyric poets who traveled with the high-placed khans. Most of the legends concern the activities of a *batir*, or hero-warrior. Among the tales that have survived are *Koblandy-batir* (fifteenth or sixteenth century), *Er Sain* (sixteenth century), and *Er Targyn* (sixteenth century), all of which concern the struggle against the Kalmyks; *Kozy Korpesh* and *Bain sulu*, both epics; and the love lyric *Kiz-Jibek*. Usually these tales were recited in a song-like chant, frequently to the accompaniment of such traditional instruments as drums and the *dombra*, a mandolin-like string instrument. President Nazarbayev has appeared on television broadcasts in the republic, playing the *dombra* and singing.

The Russian conquest wreaked havoc on Kazak traditional culture by making impossible the nomadic pastoralism upon which the culture was based. However, many individual elements survived the loss of the lifestyle as a whole. Many practices that lost their original meanings are assuming value as symbols of post-Soviet national identity.

For the most part, preindependence cultural life in Kazakhstan was indistinguishable from that elsewhere in the Soviet Union. It featured the same plays, films, music, books, paintings, museums, and other cultural appurtenances common in every other corner of the Soviet empire. That Russified cultural establishment nevertheless produced many of the most important figures of the early stages of Kazak nationalist self-assertion, including novelist Anuar Alimzhanov, who became president of the last Soviet Congress of People's Deputies, and poets Mukhtar Shakhanov and Olzhas Suleymenov, who were copresidents of the political party Popular Congress of Kazakhstan (see Structure of Government; Political

Organizations). Shakhanov also chaired the commission that investigated the events surrounding the riots of December 1986.

An even more powerful figure than Shakhanov, Suleymenov in 1975 became a pan-Central Asian hero by publishing a book, *Az i Ia*, examining the *Lay of Igor's Campaign*, a medieval tale vital to the Russian national culture, from the perspective of the Turkic Pechenegs whom Igor defeated. Soviet authorities subjected the book to a blistering attack. Later Suleymenov used his prestige to give authority to the Nevada-Semipalatinsk antinuclear movement, which performed the very real service of ending nuclear testing in Kazakhstan. He and Shakhanov originally organized their People's Congress Party as a pro-Nazarbayev movement, but Suleymenov eventually steered the party into an opposition role. In the short-lived parliament of 1994-95, Suleymenov was leader of the Respublika opposition coalition, and he was frequently mentioned as a possible presidential candidate.

The collapse of the Soviet system with which so many of the Kazak cultural figures were identified left most of them in awkward positions. Even more damaging has been the total collapse of public interest in most forms of higher culture. Most of the books that Kazakhstanis buy are about business, astrology, or sex; the movies they see are nearly all American, Chinese, or Turkish adventure and action films; most concerts feature rock music, not infrequently accompanied by erotic dancing; and television provides a diet of old Soviet films and dubbed Mexican soap operas. Kazakhstan's cultural elite is suffering the same decline affecting the elites of all the former Soviet republics. Thus, cultural norms are determined predominantly by Kazakhstan's increasing access to global mass culture.

EDUCATION

The constitution of 1995 specifies that education through secondary school is mandatory and free, and that citizens have the further right to compete for free education in the republic's institutions of higher learning. Private, paid education is permitted but remains subject to state control and supervision.

In 1994 Kazakhstan had 8,575 elementary and secondary schools (grades one through twelve) attended by approximately 3.2 million students, and 244 specialized secondary schools with about 222,000 students. In 1992 about 51 percent of eligible children were attending some 8,500 preschools in Kazakhstan. In 1994 some 272,100 students were enrolled in the republic's sixty-one institutes of higher learning. Fifty-four percent of the students were Kazak, and 31 percent were Russian.

The educational situation since independence is somewhat difficult to judge because of incomplete information. The republic has attempted to overhaul both the structure of its education system and much of its substance, but the questions of what should be taught and in what manner continue to loom large. A particularly sensitive and unresolved issue is what the language of instruction should be, given the almost equal distribution of the population between ethnic Kazaks and ethnic Russians. In 1994 most instruction still was in Russian because Kazak-language textbooks and Kazak teachers were in short supply. Enrollment was estimated to be 92 percent of the total age-group in both primary and secondary grades, but only 8 percent in the postsecondary age-group.

Serious shortages in funding and resources have hindered efforts to revamp the education system inherited from the Soviet Union. Even in 1990, more than half the republic's schools were operating on two and even three shifts per day; since then, hundreds of schools, especially preschools, have been converted to offices or stores. Elementary- and secondary-school teachers remain badly underpaid; in 1993 more than 30,000 teachers (or about one-seventh of the 1990 teaching staff) left education, many of them to seek more lucrative employment.

Despite the obstacles, efforts have been made to upgrade the education system, especially at the highest level. Kazakhstani citizens still can enroll in what once were the premier Soviet universities, all of which are now in foreign countries, in particular Russia and Ukraine. In the mid-1990s, however, such opportunities have become rare and much more expensive. This situation has forced the upgrading of existing universities in Kazakhstan, as well as the creation of at least one new private university, Al-Farabi University, formerly the S.M. Kirov State University, in Almaty. The largest institution of higher learning in Kazakhstan, Al-Farabi had 1,530 teachers and about 14,000 students in 1994. A second university, Qaraghandy State University, had about 8,300 students in 1994. In addition, technical secondary schools in five cities--Aqmola, Atyrau, Pavlodar, Petropavl (formerly Petropavlovsk), and Taldyqorghan (formerly Taldy-Kurgan)--have been reclassified as universities, increasing regional access to higher education. Altogether, in 1994 Kazakhstan had thirty-two specialized institutes of higher learning, offering programs in agriculture, business and economics, medicine, music, theater, foreign languages, and a variety of engineering and technical fields. In the area of technical education, the republic has taken aggressive advantage of offers from foreign states to educate young Kazaks. In 1994 about 3,000 young people were studying in various foreign countries, including the United States.

One trend that particularly worries republic administrators is the pronounced "Kazakification" of higher education, as the republic's Russians either send their children to schools across the Russian border or find it impossible to enroll them in local institutions. Kazakhstan's law forbids ethnic quotas, but there is evidence of prejudicial admittance patterns. The class that entered university in 1991, for example, was 73.1 percent Kazak and only 13.1 percent Russian.

HEALTH

The early years of independence have had a disastrous effect on public health. In the 1980s, Kazakhstan had an extensively developed public health system that delivered at least basic care without charge even to very remote communities. By 1993, however, Kazakhstan rated below average or lower among the former Soviet republics in medical system, sanitation, medical industry, medical research and development, and pharmaceutical supply.

Health System

In 1994 the health system had twenty-nine doctors per 1,000 people and 86.7 other medical personnel per 1,000. There were 1,805 hospitals in the republic, with seventy-six beds per 1,000 people. There were 3,129 general health clinics and 1,826 gynecological and pediatric clinics. Conditions and services at these facilities varied widely; it was not uncommon, for example, for rural clinics and hospitals to be without running water.

The constitution of 1995 perpetuates the Soviet-era guarantee of free basic health care, but financing has been a consistent problem. In 1992 funding allotted to public health care was less than 1.6 percent of GDP, a level characterized by the World Bank as that of an underdeveloped nation.

Because doctors and other medical personnel receive very low pay, many medical professionals have moved to other republics--a large percentage of Kazakhstan's doctors are Russian or other non-Kazak nationalities--or have gone into other professions. Nonpayment even of existing low wages is a common occurrence, as are strikes by doctors and nurses.

In the 1980s, Kazakhstan had about 2,100 pharmaceutical-manufacturing facilities; drugs were also available from other Soviet republics or from East European trading partners within the framework of the Council for Mutual Economic Assistance (Comecon). Since independence most such supply connections have been terminated, and many domestic pharmaceutical plants have closed, making some types of drugs virtually unavailable. As a result, vaccination of infants and children, which reached between 85 and 93 percent of the relevant age-groups in 1990, decreased sharply in the early 1990s. Kazakhstan ran out of measles and tuberculosis vaccine in late 1991, and the World Health Organization (WHO) estimated that more than 20 percent of children were not receiving basic vaccinations in 1992.

To some extent, the provision of drugs has been taken over by a government-owned company, Farmatsiya, which purchases about 95 percent of the medical equipment and supplies for the government. There have been persistent complaints that Farmatsiya pays far too much for foreign equipment and medicines in return for nonmedical considerations.

Private medical practice is permitted in general medicine and in some specialized fields; private surgical practice is forbidden, as is private treatment of cancer, tuberculosis, venereal disease, pregnancy, and infectious diseases. Some types of private practice have been introduced directly into the state clinics, creating a confusing situation in which identical procedures are performed by the same personnel, some for state fees and others for higher private fees. A substantial unofficial market has developed in the distribution of hospital supplies; patients often are expected to pay for the bandages, anesthesia, and other materials and services required for the "free" treatment received at medical facilities. Kazakhstan has no system of medical insurance.

In the mid-1990s, the largest growth area in medicine was in services not requiring large capital outlays by the practitioner. This area, which includes acupuncturists, fertility consultants, substance-abuse therapists, physical therapists, and dentists, is only lightly regulated, and the incidence of charlatanism is high.

Kazakhstan has negotiated some international agreements to improve health care. In 1992 an association of scientific organizations specializing in contagious diseases established its headquarters in Almaty. The group, which includes doctors and technicians from Kyrgyzstan, Tajikistan, Turkmenistan, and Uzbekistan, conducts joint research with scientists in China, Mongolia, and Vietnam. A 1995 medical cooperation agreement between the Kazakhstani and Iranian ministries of health called for exchanges of medical students and experts, joint research projects, exchanges of information on the latest medical advances (with an emphasis on contagious diseases), and mutual natural-disaster assistance.

Health Conditions

The deterioration of the public health system has hit Kazakhstan's population hard. Rates of infant mortality and overall mortality have risen in the 1990s as the fertility rate has decreased, contributing to the first drop in the republic's population since World War II. Infant mortality was twenty-seven per 1,000 live births in 1991, the lowest rate among the five Central Asian republics but higher than that for any non-Central Asian republic. A lack of medicines and facilities, together with a general deterioration in physical environment and living standards, has promoted outbreaks of several potentially epidemic diseases, including diphtheria (its incidence increased from thirty-five cases in 1993 to 312 in the first ten months of 1994), poliomyelitis (two cases in 1994), viral hepatitis, and cholera (of which outbreaks occurred in 1992 and 1993). The incidence of tuberculosis has grown substantially, with as many as 11,000 new cases and 2,000 deaths reported annually (see table 4). According to a 1995 report of the Contagious Disease Association in Almaty, a bubonic plague-carrying rat population was moving from the Balkhash region, where the plague is endemic, southward toward Almaty, whose municipal government had taken no measures to control rats.

Table 4. Central Asia: Incidence of Selected Diseases and Mortality, 1989-91

	Kazakhstan	Kyrgyzstan	Tajikistan	Turkmenistan	Uzbekistan
Viral hepatitis	465.6	710.8	918.3	735.1	1,074.5
Cancer	289.9	219.0	163.1	203.0	169.2
Tuberculosis*	65.8	53.3	44.4	63.6	46.1
Maternal mortality	53.1	42.7	38.9	55.2	42.8
Infant mortality	27.1	29.6	40.0	46.6	35.8

Source: Based on information from Christopher M. Davis, "Health Care Crisis: The Former Soviet Union," *RFE/RL Research Report* [Munich], 2, No. 40, October 8, 1993, 36.
Note: * All figures 1992 except life expectancy (1991).

The first death in Kazakhstan attributed to acquired immune deficiency syndrome (AIDS) was reported in July 1993. At that time, nineteen carriers of the human immunodeficiency virus (HIV) reportedly were registered in Kazakhstan. Of that number, three were identified as homosexuals, two were preschool children, and nine were foreign citizens, who were deported. In mid-1995, the WHO reported that twenty-seven people had been diagnosed with AIDS or as HIV-positive between 1993 and 1995. The Kazakhstan AIDS Prevention and Control Dispensary was established in Almaty in 1991, with twenty-two branch offices and diagnostic laboratories elsewhere in the republic. However, in the early 1990s diagnosis and treatment relied on foreign funds and equipment because domestic health funds were barely sufficient to maintain clinic buildings. Fewer than 500 requests for screening were received in 1993. In mid-1995, the government set up the Coordinating Council for Combating AIDS under the direct administration of the prime minister.

The shortage of health care has put children at particular risk. Approximately 15 percent of newborns in 1994 were unhealthy, most often suffering from bronchiopulmonary and cardiovascular problems. Measles, diphtheria, brucellosis, and other childhood diseases became more prevalent during the early 1990s.

Extensive pollution and degradation of large segments of the natural environment have increased the strain on public health. Both the air and water of many of the large cities are badly polluted. Three regions have been identified as having particularly hazardous environments. Öskemen (formerly Ust-Kamenogorsk) in the far northeast has been rated the third most polluted city in the former Soviet Union, with ten times the maximum permitted levels of lead in the air and high concentrations of beryllium, thallium, mercury, cadmium, antimony, and arsenic in the municipal water supply. Just west of Öskemen, in Semey, a major site of Soviet nuclear testing from 1949 to 1991, radiation has contaminated the air and soil. Experts believe that the tests, which were conducted in the atmosphere until 1963, contaminated the environment of the entire country of Kazakhstan. In one village, Kaynar, near the main proving ground, 140 of 3,400 children were found to have been disabled since birth; in a random sample of another 600 of the town's children, all were found to be suffering ill health of one form or another. Radiation is believed the cause of such statistics. The third major area of environmental degradation is the Aral Sea Basin along the southwestern border, where agricultural runoff and untreated sewage have caused advanced pollution of groundwater (see Environmental Problems).

Water contamination is a serious environmental health hazard in Kazakhstan because of poor management of drinking water and insufficient sewage treatment. About 30 percent of rural communities obtain water from shallow wells; the water is vulnerable to contamination by materials leached from the surface. As late as 1985, only 37 percent of homes had sewerage systems and running water, and even schools and hospitals had primitive sanitary systems that caused frequent outbreaks of intestinal illness.

The diet and lifestyle of many citizens, especially in the cities, contribute further to poor health. The average diet is high in meat and salt and low in vegetables and fruits. The hyperinflation of 1992-93 cut deeply into family budgets, limiting both the variety and quantity of food most ordinary people consume. Smoking is almost universal, especially among men, and alcoholism is common. Other forms of substance abuse such as the use of hemp, morphia products, and glue are common, especially among young people.

Occupational hazards constitute another major health problem. Especially during the economic hardships of the early 1990s, public health authorities refrained from measures such as closing polluting factories or restricting the use of fertilizers, pesticides, and irrigation water out of a fear of accelerating the general decline in production. Because of the dangers posed by exposure to toxic smoke and fumes, lead and phosphate plants limit workers to ten years of employment. With little restriction on how they are operated, factories in Kazakhstan note high rates of morbidity, absenteeism, and permanent disability among their employees.

Social Welfare

The Soviet system of social welfare, which remained in place in Kazakhstan in the early 1990s, presupposed a very high level of public services. The 1993 constitution maintained most of the assumptions of the Soviet era without providing a clear mechanism for paying for "guaranteed" workers' benefits such as free education, medical care, pensions, and vacations. The constitution ratified in 1995 somewhat reduces the list and scale of guaranteed protections, but remaining guarantees include a minimum wage, pensions for the retired and the disabled, social benefits for orphans and for people who are elderly or infirm, legal assistance, housing, and what is called "social defense against unemployment."

In practice, social benefits have proven difficult to supply because of financial considerations and the lack of a firm organizational structure for service provision. For example, in the Soviet period housing was supplied by the state or by employers. In 1990 housing began to be privatized, a process almost completed by the mid-1990s. The result has been a healthy resale market for existing housing. In 1995 apartment costs in Almaty could exceed 15,000 tenge (for value of the tenge, see Glossary) per square meter, but there had been no corresponding boom in new housing construction, in part because privatization of the land on which such housing would stand remained a sensitive and unresolved issue. As a result, the republic's housing crisis, already acute in the Soviet period, has grown far worse. In the mid-1990s the housing shortage was especially serious in Almaty, where tens of thousands were on waiting lists. In 1995 housing construction decreased by about 25 percent.

Perhaps the biggest problems have emerged in the areas of pensions, aid to large families and other social assistance, and unemployment compensation. An independent pension fund was created in 1991 on the basis of a social insurance tax on enterprises (37 percent of wages in 1992) and contributions by employees (1 percent of wages in 1992). The national budget nominally covers remaining deficits in the pension fund. Pensions initially were set at 60 percent of average pay, with minimal pensions available even to elderly citizens such as housewives who never had drawn a salary. However, the high inflation of 1991-93 badly eroded existing pensions; the state has continually adjusted pensions upward in a futile struggle to keep pace (see Prices, Wages, and Currency). In addition, the administration of pensions has been reconfigured several times, leading to lengthy delays in the payment even of the small sums pensioners are owed. Such delays have prompted numerous public demonstrations. Although the value of pensions has shrunk dramatically in real terms, by 1992 government expenditures on them were 4.7 percent of the GDP. In March 1995, the government had to divert 632 million tenge from the national budget to cover pension arrears.

Similar problems have occurred in other categories of allowances to citizens, especially lump-sum payments to newborns; child allowances to large families (those with four or more children) and abandoned children; assistance to single mothers; and assistance to the children of soldiers. In 1992 payments in these categories reached 5 percent of Kazakhstan's GDP. Slow payment and the lag between inflation and cost-of-living adjustments have had a particularly severe effect on Kazakhstan's poorer families, for some of whom government subsidies provide as much as one-quarter of total income. In 1994 about 2.1 million citizens received retirement pensions, and about 800,000 received other types of pension.

Unemployment is perhaps the most difficult category of social problem because it is a phenomenon that officially did not exist until 1991 and still carries a considerable social stigma. As of January 1, 1995, some 85,700 people officially were registered as unemployed, about 55 percent of them in rural areas. However, this figure is commonly assumed to be too low because many workers still are nominally employed, even though their salaries have been reduced or stopped altogether under a variety of cutback conditions. In January 1995, some 230 enterprises, with a normal work force of about 51,000 employees, were standing idle; by April 1995, the number had grown to 376 enterprises with more than 90,000 employees.

THE ECONOMY

Although Kazakhstan has the potential to be a wealthy nation, since independence it has suffered consistent and precipitous economic decline. Reporting problems and incompatibility of data make precise measurement of the republic's economic shrinkage difficult, but it is generally accepted that, by the mid-1990s, GDP had dropped to about half of what it was in 1990 (see table 5). Despite the presence of rich deposits of natural resources, the republic's industrial sector was developed in the Soviet period only in specific areas such as metal processing, chemicals, textiles, and food processing. The semiarid condition of much of Kazakhstan's territory does not preclude the export of wheat, meat, and some vegetables.

Table 5. Central Asia: Percentage Change in Major Economic Indicators, 1992-93 and 1993-94

	GDP		Industrial Output		Agricultural Output	
Country	**1992-93**	**1993-94**	**1992-93**	**1993-94**	**1992-93**	**1993-94**
Kazakhstan	-12	-26	-17	-28	-3	-23
Kyrgyzstan	-13	-25	-24	-25	-8	-17
Tajikistan	-21	-12	-20	-31	-4	-26
Turkmenistan	8	-24	6	-24	9	-2
Uzbekistan	-3	-4	-4	1	0	13

Source: Based on information from United States, Central Intelligence Agency, *Handbook of International Economic Statistics 1995*, Washington, 1995, 52.

Natural Resources

Soviet geologists once boasted that Kazakhstan was capable of exporting the entire Periodic Table of Elements. During the Soviet period, Kazakhstan supplied about 7 percent of the union's gold, or about twenty-four tons per year. Since independence, the republic has attracted large foreign partners to develop existing or new mines. President Nazarbayev announced intentions to increase annual gold production to fifty or sixty tons by 1995 or 1996.

In 1989 the mines of Kazakhstan yielded 23.8 million tons of iron ore and 151,900 tons of manganese. The republic also possesses deposits of uranium, chrome, titanium, nickel, wolfram, silver, molybdenum, bauxite, and copper. Major phosphate mines feed fertilizer plants in the southern city of Zhambyl. Three major coal fields--Torghay, Qaraghandy, and Ekibastuz--produced 140 million tons of hard coal in 1991, but by 1994 Kazakhstan's national total had dropped to 104 million tons.

In the mid-1990s, all minerals in Kazakhstan belonged to the republic. Authority for decisions concerning their development was delegated to the prime minister, provided that these decisions were consistent with laws on natural resource development. The fundamental law "On Natural Resources and the Development of Mineral Resources" was passed in May 1992, but its treatment of foreign development of minerals is limited to two brief paragraphs stipulating that foreign development be conducted in accordance with international and national law.

Agriculture

In the early 1990s, agriculture was the second largest sector of the economy, contributing about 36 percent of GDP and employing about 18 percent of the workforce in 1993. The climate and soil of most of Kazakhstan are best suited to the light grazing by which the nomadic Kazaks had traditionally supported themselves, following herds of sheep, cattle, camels, and horses about the open steppe. Despite such natural advantages, Soviet policy encouraged cultivation, especially in the northern parts of the republic. The major transformation occurred under premier Khrushchev during the Virgin Lands program of the late 1950s and early 1960s. Its objectives were to reduce Soviet grain imports to Central Asia and settle the remaining nomadic herdsmen of Kazakhstan and Kyrgyzstan. Under that program, 60 percent of Kazakhstan's pastureland went under cultivation. An estimated 30 percent of that land was not suitable for cultivation, however, and Khrushchev was ousted in 1964 after a series of crop failures in Kazakhstan. In 1992 the total area under cultivation was 36.5 million hectares, of which 2.3 million hectares were irrigated. Much of this land is dedicated to large-scale wheat farming, which requires intensive capitalization and does not lend itself to privatization. Even with the emphasis on grain production, about 84 percent of the republic's agricultural land, or about 187 million hectares, remains devoted to pasturage, mainly of cattle and sheep. Continuation of the Soviet system of intensive livestock management, dependent on fodder more than on natural grazing, has left much grazing land unused and has distorted cultivation in favor of fodder production.

The primary agricultural regions are the north-central and southern parts of the republic. Grain production is especially important in the north-central region, and cotton and rice predominate in the south (see table 6). Kazakhstan also is a major producer of meat and milk.

Table 6. Kazakhstan: Production of Principal Agricultural Crops, 1992-94 (in thousands of tons)

Crop	1992	1993	1994
Wheat	18,285	11,585	9,052
Barley	8,511	7,149	5,497
Potatoes	2,570	2,295	1,950
Oats	727	802	822
Tomatoes	380	320	300
Rice	467	403	283
Rye	524	835	264
Watermelons	250	202	250
Corn	370	355	233
Sugar beets	1,276	925	169
Millet	447	233	130

Source: Based on information from *The Europa World Year Book 1996*, 2, London, 1996, 1811.

In 1993 only about 1.5 percent of agricultural land was in private hands. Although some privatization had occurred, the bulk of Kazakhstan's agriculture remained organized in 7,000 to 8,000 state and collective farms that averaged 35,000 to 40,000 hectares each. Many of those farms had moved into a transitional stage of joint-stock ownership, private collectives, or farming associations (see Post-Soviet Economic Developments). The state also has maintained control of agricultural inputs and equipment, as well as some processing and marketing policies and operations. In the wake of price liberalization, the mandated state share of agricultural sales has decreased annually from the 1991 level of 70 percent.

Until the early 1990s, western Kazakhstan was an important fishing area, but sharply increased salination has made the Aral Sea sterile. Fishing output dropped from 105,300 tons in 1960 to 89,600 tons in 1989. The current figure is probably close to zero, judging by the decision of Soviet central planners in 1990 to fly Arctic fish to Kazakhstan for processing as a means of maintaining local employment in that operation.

Industry

Kazakhstan inherited a decaying but still powerful manufacturing and processing capacity from the centrally managed Soviet system. In that system, among Kazakhstan's designated products for the general all-union market were phosphate fertilizer, rolled metal, radio cables, aircraft wires, train bearings, tractors, and bulldozers. Kazakhstan also had a well-developed network of factories producing military goods that supplied about 11 percent of the total military production of the Soviet Union. In some areas of military production, Kazakhstan had a virtual monopoly. In the post-Soviet era, much of the defense industry has stopped or slowed production; some plants now produce nonmilitary electronic equipment and machines.

Most of the republic's manufacturing, refining, and metallurgy plants are concentrated in the north and northeast, in Semey, Aqmola, Petropavl, and Aqtöbe. In south-central Kazakhstan, the most important industrial centers are Shymkent (chemicals, light industry, metallurgy, and food processing), Almaty (light industry, machine building, and food processing), and Zhambyl (chemicals, machine building, and food processing).

Structure of Industry

The energy sector is the most productive component of Kazakhstan's industrial structure, accounting for about 42 percent of total output. Metallurgy generates about one-quarter of industrial output, divided equally between the processing of ferrous and nonferrous metals (see table 7). Engineering and metalworking account for 6.2 percent of industrial output, chemicals and petrochemicals for 3.6 percent, and construction materials for 2.7 percent. Kazakhstan's entire light industry sector accounts for only 4.8 percent of industrial output. In the Soviet era, the republic had more than fifty military-industrial enterprises, employing as many as 75,000 workers. Because Baykonur, one of the world's two largest spaceports, was located in Kazakhstan, as were 1,350 nuclear warheads, the prosperity of this sector was assured during the Soviet period. Military-related enterprises produced or processed beryllium, nuclear reactor fuel, uranium ore, heavy machine guns, antiship missiles, torpedoes, chemical and biological weapons, support equipment for intercontinental ballistic missiles, tactical missile launcher equipment, artillery, and armored vehicles.

Table 7. Kazakhstan: Production of Principal Industrial Products, 1991-93 (in thousands of tons unless otherwise indicated)

Product	1991	1992	1993
Coke	3,711	3,404	3,300
Cotton yarn	40	37	39
Crude steel	6,754	6,337	n.a.
Electric power (in millions of kilowatt-hours)	87,379	86,128	79,174
Fabric (in thousands of square meters)	325,461	248,708	n.a.
Footwear (in thousands of pairs)	36,464	35,410	n.a.
Margarine	71	48	n.a.
Pig iron	5,226	4,952	4,666
Rubber tires (in thousands)	2,633	3,029	2,899
Sulfuric acid	3,151	2,815	2,349

Source: Based on information from *The Europa World Year Book 1996*, 2, London, 1996, 1811.

Production Levels

In general, Kazakhstan's industry suffered a disastrous year in 1994, when overall output dropped 28.5 percent. The metallurgy and energy industries were the main contributors to the 1994 decline, although by percentage light industry (down 56 percent) and engineering and metalworking (down 43 percent) suffered the sharpest reductions. However, in the last few months of 1994 and the first half of 1995, production decreased more slowly. Although monthly production continued to decline compared with 1994, the rate of decline between 1994 and 1995 was about half the rate shown between 1993 and 1994. By mid-1995, the chemical, oil-refining, natural gas, timber, ferrous metallurgy, and oil extraction industries were showing higher outputs than they had for the same periods of 1994. Reduced consumer purchasing power exacerbated declines in most processing and consumer goods industries, however; overall light industry output was 61.2 percent lower in the first five months of 1995 than in the same period of 1994. In the first five months of 1995, the republic's industries produced goods valued at 253.1 billion tenge, or about US$4 billion--a drop of 16.5 percent from the five-month output value for 1994.

Kazakhstan has remained highly dependent on Russia as a customer for its manufactured products; this dependence has been the main cause of the shrinkage in the industrial base, as Russia has reduced its demand for most of Kazakhstan's export products in the early and mid-1990s (see International Financial Relations). Although more than 80 percent of Kazakhstan's industrial production is still intended for sale in Russia, trade with Russia in 1995 was only about 20 percent of what it was in 1991. In January 1995, some 230 enterprises, with about 51,000 employees, were idle; by April the figures had grown to 376 enterprises and more than 90,000 employees. Also alarming is the growing debt load of the enterprises, which continue to support their unprofitable operations by unregulated borrowing among themselves. By March 1994, total agricultural and industrial indebtedness had reached 230.6 billion tenge. One consequence of falling production and growing indebtedness is that the republic's enterprises are increasingly unprofitable. As of March 1995, the government categorized 2,483 enterprises, or about one-third of the republic's total, as unprofitable. As of early 1996, however, very few had been forced into formal bankruptcy.

Energy

Kazakhstan is well endowed with energy resources, including abundant reserves of coal, oil, and natural gas, which made the republic one of the top energy-producing regions of the Soviet Union. In 1993 Kazakhstan was the second largest oil producer, third largest coal producer, and sixth largest natural gas producer among the former Soviet republics. Industry in Kazakhstan is dominated by the energy sector; in 1994 electric power generation accounted for 19 percent of GDP, and fuel extraction and processing accounted for nearly 23 percent. Thus, the national economy is strongly affected by changes in levels of fuel extraction and energy production.

Oil

Kazakhstan's oil reserves have been estimated at as much as 2,100 million tons, most of which is in relatively new fields that have not yet been exploited. In addition, new offshore discoveries in the north Caspian more than replaced the annual drawdown of known reserves in the early 1990s. In 1993 Chevron Oil made an initial investment in a joint venture, Tengizchevroil, to exploit the Tengiz oil fields at the northern end of the Caspian Sea in what was envisioned as the leading project among foreign oil investments. Recoverable reserves at Tengiz are estimated at 25 billion barrels, or about twice the amount in the Alaskan North Slope, although Tengiz oil is extremely high in sulfur. The French firm Elf-Aquitaine has leased about 19,000 square kilometers of land in the Emba region northeast of the Caspian, where there are known to be large quantities of sulfur-free oil and natural gas. Other oil deposits, with paraffin, asphalt, or tar (all harder to process), have been found in the Caspian Sea near Novyy Uzen and Buzachiy.

Oil production, which increased by an average of 3 percent per year through 1991, reached a peak production of 26.6 million tons that year before output began to decline in 1992. The most productive region in the early 1990s was the Mangyshlak Peninsula on the east shore of the Caspian Sea. In the early 1990s, Mangyshlak yielded more than 50 percent of the republic's oil output before experiencing a decline of 11 percent in 1992. Kazakhstan also is known to be rich in deposits of heavy oil, which currently are not commercially viable but which are potentially valuable.

The republic planned to increase its oil exports from the 7.8 million tons of 1992 (15 percent of total exports) to as much as 37 million tons in 1996 (50 percent of total exports), for which anticipated revenue was about US$2.9 billion. By 1993, however, domestic and CIS industry conditions made such goals unrealistic. The most important obstacles to increased oil production and export involve Russia. In 1994 Russian refineries in western Siberia, upon which Kazakhstan's oil industry continues to rely heavily for processing, cut their operations drastically because paying customers could not be found; this cut resulted in the plants' lower demand for crude oil from Kazakhstani suppliers. Thus, in the first nine months of 1994, Kazakhstan's oil sales fell to 4.5 million tons from 8 million tons in the same period of 1993, and production for the year fell 11.7 percent. Because of the oil-exchange agreement with Russia, the cutback in Russian refinery production also reduced domestic refinery production nearly 25 percent in 1994.

The second obstacle to greater production and export of oil is pipeline access through Russia to Western customers, which Russia has curtailed because of capacity limits and political maneuvering. The lack of pipeline facilities caused Chevron to announce substantial capital investment cutbacks in the Tengiz oil fields for 1995. In the mid-1990s, the pipeline that connects Kazakhstani oil fields with the Russian Black Sea port Novorossiysk provided the sole access to the oil of the Tengiz fields for Chevron and its Western customers (see Transportation and Telecommunications). The uncertainties of relying on the existing Russian line or on a second line passing through the war-torn Caucasus region led to discussions of new pipeline projects passing through Iran or even eastward across China to the Pacific Ocean. In September 1995, a new agreement with Turkey laid plans for pipelines crossing Georgia to ports in Georgia and Turkey, providing a new outlet possibility for Kazakhstan's Tengiz oil. Also, in October 1995 Kazakhstan joined in a new consortium with Russian and United States companies to build a pipeline to the Black Sea. Chevron and Mobil Oil of the United States, British Gas, Agip of Italy, and Russia's LUKoil enterprise were to fund the entire pipeline project in return for a 50 percent share in the pipeline. The governments of Kazakhstan and Russia were to receive the other 50 percent. However, pipeline construction was delayed amid further international negotiation over alternative routes.

In the first quarter of 1995, major accidents and power shortages at drilling sites reduced production by about 10 percent compared with output in the first quarter of 1994. Refinery output in that period was even lower; only about half the first quarter's oil was refined, and the Pavlodar refinery closed entirely because it received no crude oil from Russia.

Natural Gas

Kazakhstan has enormous reserves of natural gas, most notably the giant Karachaganak field in the northwest near the Russian border, under codevelopment by a consortium of Agip of Italy, British Gas, and the Russian Natural Gas Company (Gazprom). In 1992 natural gas production was 8.5 million cubic meters, half of which came from Karachaganak. By 1994, however, production was only 4.1 million cubic meters because Russian consumption had dropped drastically in the early 1990s. A 1995 deal with Gazprom gave that organization part ownership of Karachaganak in exchange for a guaranteed purchase of natural gas from Kazakhstan. Foreign investment projects at Tengiz and Karachaganak were expected to triple domestic gas output and enhance gas processing capabilities in the later 1990s. The usefulness of increased output depends on new pipeline agreements--still in the formative stage in 1996--with Russia and other countries in the region.

Coal

In 1994 coal production decreased 6.7 percent to 104.4 million tons, after a production peak of 140 million tons was reached in 1991. About thirty major coalfields exist, most of them within 400 kilometers of Qaraghandy in north-central Kazakhstan. This region offers some of the most accessible and cheaply extracted coal in the CIS; however, most of Kazakhstan's coal is high in ash. The largest open-pit mines are located in the Ekibastuz Basin northeast of Qaraghandy. According to estimates, presently exploited mines contain 100 years of coal reserves at today's rate of consumption. Coal is a key input for industry; in the early 1990s, more than 75 percent of coal consumption in Kazakhstan went to thermoelectric stations for power generation, and another 14 percent went to the steel industry. In the early 1990s, Kazakhstan exported about 40 percent of its coal to CIS customers, mainly Russia.

The coal industry has been plagued by poor management and strikes that shut down major underground operations at Qaraghandy and surface operations at Ekibastuz in 1994 and 1995. The large metallurgical works of Qaraghandy, built under the Soviet concept of the territorial-industrial complex combining heavy industry with on-site fuel reserves, has been forced to curtail production when strikes are called.

Current Fuel Supply and Consumption

Despite its fuel endowments, Kazakhstan remains a net importer of energy, partly because of falling production in the early 1990s and partly because of remaining barter agreements from the Soviet era. Undeveloped east-to-west transportation infrastructure has prevented efficient supply of domestic fuels to industries, which are energy intensive. As a consequence, Kazakhstan still must import oil, natural gas, lubricating oil, gasoline, and diesel fuel from Russia, which in the postindependence years has taken advantage of its neighbor's vulnerability to economic pressure. In the mid-1990s, the oil exchange system between Kazakhstan and Russia meant that declining demand in Russia reduced availability of those Russian products to Kazakhstan. In 1994 Russia sent only 40 percent of the crude oil and 48 percent of the refined products prescribed in the bilateral agreement for that year. Gas imports showed a similar drop.

The national electric power system is divided into three grids. The northern grid, which serves a large part of heavy industry, is connected to the adjacent Siberian grid in Russia, and the southern grid is connected to the Central Asian System. Kazakhstan depends on Russia for electricity and fuel. Although the Siberian generating stations that supply the northern grid are located in Russia, they are fired largely by coal exported from Kazakhstan. Some electric power also is received from Kyrgyzstan's hydroelectric stations to the south in exchange for coal.

In 1991 Kazakhstan consumed 101.6 billion kilowatt-hours of electricity (84.7 percent of which was produced domestically), making it a relatively heavy energy consumer among nations of its economic stature. About 85 percent of domestic generation occurs in coal-fired thermoelectric plants. A few thermoelectric plants use natural gas or oil; the remaining 15 percent of energy comes from those plants and from hydroelectric stations. The main sources of coal-generated electricity are the fields of Ekibastuz, Maykubin, Torghay, and Borlin. There are three large hydroelectric stations, at Bukhtarmin, Öskemen, and Kapchagay. The republic's one nuclear power station is located near the city of Aqtau.

Work Force

In 1992 some 16 percent of Kazakhstan's work force was employed in manufacturing 24 percent in agriculture and forestry, 9 percent in construction, 9 percent in transportation and communications, and 32 percent in trade and services (see table 8). An estimated 28.3 percent of the work force had at least a secondary education at the time of independence. Russians generally were employed in higher-paying sectors such as industry, transportation, and science, and Kazaks predominated in lower-paying areas such as health care, culture, art, and education. Overall, about two-thirds of workers and about 80 percent of industrial workers were non-Kazaks. In state enterprises, which provided 95 percent of employment before independence, one-half of the work force was female in 1990. The high participation rate of women contributed to an overall participation rate of 79 percent of working-age citizens in some form of employment.

Table 8. Kazakhstan: Structure of Employment, 1990-92 (in thousands of workers)

Sector	1990	1991	1992
Agriculture, forestry, and fishing	1,686	1,715	1,762
Mining and quarrying	235	251	257
Manufacturing	1,247	1,218	1,160
Construction	833	690	681
Trade, restaurants, and hotels	470	461	437
Transport and communications	704	700	665
Community, social, and personal services	1,867	1,901	1,906
Utilities	66	73	83
Other activities	690	736	662
TOTAL	7,798	7,745	7,613

Source: Based on information from *The Europa World Year Book, 1995*, 2, London, 1995, 1736.

In 1990 the working population of the republic peaked at around 6.7 million people, in a command economy where the legal requirement of full employment of both men and women meant substantial underemployment not revealed by official statistics. By the end of 1994, the number of employed people had declined about 8.9 percent, to about 6.1 million. This drop was caused in part by the privatization of Kazakhstan's economy (by 1993 about 7 percent of Kazakhstanis were working outside the state sector), but it also reflected growing unemployment and underemployment. In January 1995, there were 85,700 officially registered unemployed people in the republic, up from 4,000 in 1992. That figure does not include an unknown but significant number of workers whose names remained on official payroll lists while they were on forced leave, reduced hours, and delayed wage-payment schedules.

Post-Soviet Economic Developments

Until 1990, when the whole central planning system collapsed, Kazakhstan was part of the Soviet command economy. Even at the time of the 1991 coup that led to independence, 43 percent of the republic's industrial capacity was under Moscow's direct control, 48 percent was under joint republic and union control, and only 8 percent was strictly under republic control.

Although economic production declined dramatically in the early 1990s, some indicators showed a slower rate of decline by early 1995. In 1994 GDP declined 25.4 percent compared with 1993, including drops of 28.5 percent in industry and 21.2 percent in agriculture. In January and February 1995, additional GDP declines of 18.8 percent and 15.8 percent occurred (against the same months in 1994); however, March 1995 showed an increase of 4 percent (against 1994), fueled mainly by an increase in industrial production. Agricultural production, however, continued to drop in early 1995; 1994 first-quarter production was 79 percent of the same period in 1993, and the first quarter of 1995 almost duplicated that decline.

Much of Kazakhstan's economic future depends upon its ambitious three-stage privatization program, which began in 1992 and reached the end of its second stage in 1995. The Kazakhstan State Property Committee has responsibility for all three phases. In the first stage, housing and small enterprises employing fewer than 200 people were privatized. Most conversions of small enterprises were accomplished by auction to groups of employees, often under the leadership of the incumbent manager. Housing, which by 1995 was nearly all in private ownership, was privatized either by giving the residence outright to its current occupant or by payment of government-issued vouchers. The second stage entailed the privatization of almost everything except the republic's mineral wealth and industrial plants employing more than 5,000 people (such plants accounted for most of Kazakhstan's military-related industry).

Privatization of the largest state enterprises is the principal goal of stage three, which did not begin as scheduled in late 1995. Until that time, these enterprises were run as self-managing joint-stock companies in which the government of Kazakhstan was the largest stockholder. This interim stage, which was considered beneficial, required preparation of profit-and-loss statements in anticipation of full commercial operation sometime in the future. Meanwhile, 3,500 medium-sized firms, including 70 percent of state-owned industries, were offered for sale in a mass privatization program beginning in April 1994. These firms could be purchased with government-licensed investment funds.

Under Kazakhstan's privatization system, vouchers are issued to individual citizens. Vouchers then can be deposited in privatization investment funds, which in turn can buy up to 20 percent of large companies being privatized. The initial voucher issue reached an estimated 95 percent of citizens. After four auctions, in mid-1994 about 85 percent of forty-five small-to-medium-sized enterprises, mainly in light industry, machinery manufacturing, and fuel distribution, had been sold.

By the end of 1994, about 60 percent of enterprises were owned by individuals or cooperatives. (In 1990 the figure already had reached 40 percent, however.) The success of the privatization of small enterprises, together with the formation of new private enterprises, meant that in 1994 some 61 percent of retail trade occurred in the private sector, an increase of 17 percent over the 1993 figure. Large-enterprise privatization has been less successful, however. Nominally privatized enterprises often maintain close contact with government officials who permit firms to maintain outdated production practices and supply relationships, and even to keep unpaid workers on their rolls.

Distribution of vouchers among the 170 government-licensed investment funds also has been problematic. In 1994 and early 1995, twenty companies collected nearly 60 percent of the vouchers, while another nineteen funds accumulated more than 20 percent; half the funds received a total of only 4 percent of the vouchers. One fund, Butia-Kapital, received nearly 10 percent of the vouchers, the largest single holding. This fund was widely rumored to be controlled by a nephew of President Nazarbayev. Although proceeds from privatization amounted to an income of 242 million tenge for the state treasury in the first quarter of 1995, complaints persisted that objects of privatization were priced too low and that favored funds received "sweetheart" deals.

Privatization of land has been handled differently than that of industry because the concept of individual land ownership does not exist in Kazakhstan. Individuals and corporations can purchase only the right to use the land, and that right can be resold. Initial sale prices of state land are determined by the State Committee on Land Relations and Tenure. Government efforts to legalize a private land market have been stymied by both Russian and Kazak groups, each fearing that the other might gain control of the country's agriculture. By June 1995, some form of ownership or management change had occurred in 1,490 state farms, about three-quarters of the total remaining in operation. Many state farms, or portions of them, were converted into joint-stock companies that retained the same group of occupants and state-dominated arrangements for supply and marketing as under the previous nomenclature. The creation of small, individually managed farms was uncommon because capital, inputs, equipment, and credit were in very short supply for individuals attempting to start agricultural enterprises.

Banking and Finance

Restructuring of the state-controlled banking and financial systems that Kazakhstan inherited in 1991 has been a long, slow process. As in the Soviet era, the national bank continues to dominate the financial system, including currency management. Other commercial institutions have been established, but they play small roles in the country's financial life.

Banks

Kazakhstan's banking industry was created on the basis of a subsequently modified law enacted in April 1993. That law created a central institution, the National Bank of Kazakhstan (NBK), which has regulatory authority over a system of state, private, joint-stock, and joint banks. Licensed banks are authorized to perform all of the traditional banking functions.

The introduction of a modern banking system has not progressed smoothly. Scandals have involved swindles by bank employees, questionable loans, and the maintenance of heavy portfolios of nonproductive loans. Several bank failure scares also have occurred. Major modifications of banking regulations have been introduced several times. In June 1994, Kazakhstan instituted a fifteen-month program of financial and economic reform, tightening banking and credit laws, liberalizing price policies, and ending the granting of credits to state-owned institutions. Another short-term reform was introduced in March 1995, in part to tighten regulation of capital requirements and to increase the professionalism of the existing bank's operations. To that end, a system of partnership with foreign banks was introduced, pairing domestic banks with experienced foreign partners. Guidance for this bank reform is being provided by the IMF, as well as by international auditing firms such as Ernst and Young and Price Waterhouse.

In 1994 the national bank system included a State Export and Import Bank and a State Bank for Development, both of which functioned under full government control rather than as market institutions. Four large, state-owned banks controlled 80 percent of financial assets. Of the 200 small commercial banks in operation in 1994, the majority were attached to enterprises. About thirty private banks were licensed to deal in foreign exchange.

The aim of the 1995 reform was to create a republic-wide banking system, including ten to fifteen large banks with total capital of at least US$10 million, headquartered in Almaty and with branches throughout Kazakhstan; foreign branch banks, most of which would have single representative offices in Almaty; several dozen smaller banks, both in Almaty and in the provinces, with capital in the range of US$2-US$3 million; and savings banks, some with specialized purposes such as the Agricultural and Industrial Bank (Agroprombank).

In 1995 the NBK planned to release 80 percent of the credit funds it granted to an auction market, departing from the previous policy of rationing credit by directing it to designated enterprises. No stock exchange or capital markets existed as of 1995, although a law on securities and stock exchange had been adopted in 1991.

Fiscal Management

State revenue is derived primarily from various taxes, the introduction of which has been somewhat problematic. A fundamental revision of the national tax code in 1995 reduced the number of taxes from forty-five to eleven and the volume of prospective revenue by 17 percent. Five national corporate taxes remained after the reform, which reduced the corporate tax rate to 30 percent. Prior to that revision, the largest contributions to state income were business-profit taxes (15 percent); a uniform, 20 percent value-added tax (see Glossary), a personal income tax (ranging from 12 to 40 percent and accounting for 16 percent of tax income); and special-purpose revenue funds (17 percent). However, the system has suffered from chronic undercollection. The primary long-term goal of the 1995 tax reform was to encourage fuller compliance with tax laws. The 1996 budget called for reducing the deficit to 3.3 percent of GDP.

Prices, Wages, and Currency

The freeing of government price controls, followed by introduction of the tenge as Kazakhstan's independent currency unit, set off hyperinflation, which badly eroded real wages, pensions, and savings (see table 9). Introduced in November 1993 at approximately five to the United States dollar, the tenge fell to about fifty-six per dollar by late November 1994. Subsequently, the currency remained relatively stable, falling only to sixty-four per US$1 at the beginning of 1996. The tenge's stabilization was due in part to the government's determination to control the state budget, in part to the availability of an IMF stabilization fund, and in part to the backing of government reserves of US$1.02 billion in hard currency and gold. By 1995 inflation had decreased substantially from the levels of 1993 and 1994, when the rate was 1,880 percent, although the annualized rate for 1995 was estimated at midyear at 190 percent, well above the prime minister's target figure of 40 percent.

Inflation has strongly affected wages and family budgets. In July 1994, for example, nominal wages in the republic increased by an average of twenty times, but the costs of food, services, and goods increased by more than thirty-two times in the same month. As a result of such conditions, real wages in the republic declined by about one-third in the first half of 1994. The overall average monthly wage in the republic in February 1995 was 3,650 tenge, or about US$61 at the exchange rate of the time. In mid-1995, the overall average wage was 4,613 tenge, but the disparity between industrial and agricultural wages was growing steadily: the industrial average was 7,452 tenge, the agricultural average 2,309 tenge. Wages in service occupations such as education and health are quite low, and government employees in those occupations often are not paid on time. Chronic nonpayment of wages has caused strikes in industrial enterprises and coal mines.

Table 9. Central Asia: Cost of Living, 1990-93

Country and Category	1990	1991	1992	1993
Kazakhstan				
Food	n.a.	4.7	100	2,297
Clothing	n.a.	4.7	100	1,606
Rent	n.a.	n.a.	100	16,258
Average for all items	n.a.	3.3	100	2,265
Kyrgyzstan (all items)	100	185.0	954.0	n.a.
Tajikistan				
Food	101.8	194.4	1,450.5	n.a.
Alcoholic beverages	100.6	163.4	1,152.1	n.a.
Average for all items	104.0	193.0	1,153.9	n.a.
Turkmenistan (all items)[1]	104.2	202.5	592.9	n.a.
Uzbekistan (all items)[2]	100	205.0	627.7	951.1

Source: Based on information from *The Europa World Year Book 1995*, 2, London, 1995, 1737, 1825, 2952, 3071, 3364.

Notes: [1] All figures 1989.
[2] All figures 1993 except life expectancy (1989).

Many enterprises have made wage payments in merchandise rather than money; this practice has led to a large volume of merchandise resale at bazaars, either by workers or by private wholesalers. The actual level of consumer welfare is unknown because prices and the availability of goods change rapidly. Because Kazakhstan lacks a strong consumer-goods industry, imports have begun to replace CIS products, notably clothing, housewares, and electronics. In 1995 wage increases continued to lag behind the rising cost of living, causing spending power to decline by 2 to 3 percent per month. The greatest losses in real wages have been suffered in industrial (and mostly Russian) northern Kazakhstan. One consequence of declining purchasing power is that families now devote as much as 10 percent of their budgets to the purchase of foreign currency, presumably as a hedge against inflation. In 1995 the purchase of food became the largest family expenditure, exceeding 50 percent of average budgets. Even so, purchases of all categories of foodstuffs have declined in the republic, while purchases of nonfoodstuffs have dropped 40 percent or more.

International Financial Relations

Shortly after independence, Kazakhstan began seeking diversification of its commercial activities, which had focused completely on the Soviet Union until 1992. Because the regime has been stable and abundant natural resources make investment potentially profitable, the search for new foreign partners has been successful in many cases, although substantial limitations remained in the mid-1990s.

Foreign Investment

World Bank figures showed foreign direct investment in Kazakhstan of US$400 million in 1993, projected to rise to an annual average of about US$775 million by 1997. By mid-1994, fourteen British firms, fifty American firms, and twenty-four French firms were registered as investors. A March 1994 survey showed one foreign acquisition in the republic, twenty-five new economic projects, and seventy working joint ventures, with total foreign investment of $US10.44 billion. Average investment was computed at US$108.7 million, but that figure was distorted by Chevron's huge single investment in the Tengiz oil development project.

In the mid-1990s, Kazakhstan's investment climate was considered liberal compared with that of the other non-Baltic former Soviet republics. In December 1994, existing trade legislation was consolidated into the Law on Foreign Investments, which, among other things, offered foreign investors 100 percent ownership of enterprises and full conversion of profits into hard currency. Liberal tax incentives, including a five-year initial forgiveness of all corporate taxes, also have been implemented. Regulations have been loosened on the export of precious metals and on terms for foreign participation in oil field development. For these reasons, international investor ratings place Kazakhstan high among the former Soviet republics.

The international lending community also has been attracted to Kazakhstan. In 1994 the Paris Club of Western creditor countries committed US$1.33 billion for use in reconstructing Kazakhstan's industry and agriculture. The sum was the first large-scale foreign assistance received by the republic. Kazakhstan also received US$296.9 million in trade credits in 1994, US$220 million of which came from Japan. Projections called for Kazakhstan's external debt to peak at US$5.1 billion in 1996, then begin to decline. However, that figure was based on expectations of drastic increases in foreign oil sales by 1996, an eventuality made impossible by the intervening decline in output.

Foreign Trade

Traditionally, most of the goods that Kazakhstan produced for export went to markets in Russia and elsewhere in the Soviet Union. In 1990 some 88.7 percent of Kazakhstan's exports followed this route, including more than 70 percent of its industrial production and mined products and 27 percent of its agricultural production. By 1992 the trade situation among the CIS countries was characterized by the World Bank as "verging on the chaotic," with the old Soviet payments system deteriorating and a common currency, the ruble (see Glossary), showing uncertain value. That situation prompted Kazakhstan to undertake a vigorous search for diversified trade markets, and in fact its exports to the CIS declined by nearly 80 percent between 1990 and 1994. By 1994 Russia still accounted for 40 percent of Kazakhstan's total trade and for 74 and 80 percent of the republic's total CIS exports and imports, respectively. Kazakhstan's largest volume of non-Russian CIS trade is with Kyrgyzstan, Uzbekistan, Belarus, and Ukraine, all of which are net importers of Kazak goods. The most important West European trading partners are Germany, the Netherlands, Switzerland, the Czech Republic, and Italy (see table 10). Non-CIS Asian countries account for 11 percent of trade, with China the major partner in this category.

Table 10. Kazakhstan: Foreign Trade with Selected Countries, 1992-94

	1992	1993	1994
Imports			
Former Soviet Union			
Armenia	0.1	0.1	0.0
Azerbaijan	1.1	0.6	0.8
Belarus	4.6	3.0	1.9
Estonia	0.1	0.3	0.0
Georgia	0.3	0.4	0.1
Kyrgyzstan	3.2	1.3	0.9
Latvia	0.1	0.5	0.2
Lithuania	0.3	0.7	0.1
Moldova	0.2	0.8	0.1
Russia	72.4	70.9	89.3
Tajikistan	0.9	0.5	0.2
Turkmenistan	2.5	4.7	0.1
Ukraine	10.5	7.3	3.6
Uzbekistan	3.7	9.0	2.6
Exports			
Former Soviet Union[1]			
Armenia	0.1	0.0	0.0
Azerbaijan	1.7	3.2	2.0
Belarus	2.7	5.0	2.6
Estonia	0.1	0.0	0.1
Georgia	0.1	0.2	0.0
Kyrgyzstan	2.5	2.3	2.2
Latvia	0.3	0.2	1.2
Lithuania	0.6	0.5	1.3
Moldova	0.3	0.4	0.1
Russia	71.0	69.7	78.7
Tajikistan	1.2	1.4	0.6
Turkmenistan	3.3	2.1	0.7
Ukraine	9.7	8.1	5.2
Uzbekistan	6.5	6.9	5.3
Imports			
Other countries			
Austria	30	21	16
China	213	80	46
Czech Republic	4	48	n.a.
Finland	25	5	4
France	7	9	21
Germany	19	76	125
Hungary	27	23	14
Italy	30	21	37
Switzerland	15	18	40
Turkey	5	15	17
United Kingdom	23	19	17
United States	6	38	42
Exports			
Other Countries[2]			
Australia	835	940	809
Austria	1	21	30
Belgium	11	13	16
Bulgaria	18	22	9
China	237	172	85

	1992	1993	1994
Czech Republic[3]	80	19	14
Finland	43	9	1
France	19	7	5
Germany	123	131	65
Hungary	21	37	12
Italy	40	84	24
Japan	49	37	31
Korea, Democratic People's Republic of	18	22	3
Korea, Republic of	12	46	22
Netherlands	52	49	42
Poland	49	37	13
Slovakia[3]	80	30	11
Sweden	150	91	5
Switzerland	104	175	345
Turkey	16	56	40
United Kingdom	26	97	87
United States	101	145	121

Source: Based on information from World Bank, *Statistical Handbook 1995: States of the Former USSR*, Washington, 1995, 152-54.

Notes: [1] All figures 1993 except life expectancy (1990).
[2] All figures 1992 except life expectancy (1991).
[3] All figures 1993 except life expectancy (1989).

The predominant pattern of trade has continued from the Soviet era: exports are mostly raw materials, and imports are mostly manufactured goods. Ferrous and nonferrous metals--mainly rolled steel, copper, ferroalloys, zinc, titanium, and aluminum--account for 40 percent of export earnings, followed by oil and petroleum products (33 percent) and chemicals (10 percent). Energy products are also the largest import category, mainly because of the ongoing geographically determined exchange agreement that sends Russian oil from western Siberia to refineries in eastern Kazakhstan and oil from Kazakhstan's western oil fields to refineries across the border in Russia. Thus, in 1994 some 31 percent of imports were energy products, followed by machinery, equipment, and vehicles (29 percent); chemicals; and food. By 1994 private traders also imported large amounts of consumer products that did not appear in official statistics.

In 1994 Kazakhstan's total exports were worth US$3.076 billion, and its imports were worth US$3.488 billion. Comparison with 1993 is not meaningful because in that year unstable ruble values and heavy barter transactions skewed statistics. In fact, an estimated 70 percent of 1994 trade also was in the form of barter. Of the 1994 totals, US$1.266 billion, or 41 percent, of exports went to the "far abroad," beyond the CIS, and US$1.286 billion, or 37 percent, of imports came from the "far abroad." Experts forecast slightly lower overall export figures in 1995 because of restricted access to Russian pipelines. The trade deficit with non-CIS partners is financed by borrowing from international financial institutions. The deficit with CIS partners is financed simply by delaying payments to Russia.

TRANSPORTATION AND TELECOMMUNICATIONS

Kazakhstan's transportation and telecommunications networks are poorly developed because of the distance between population centers (see fig. 7) and because of the inhospitable terrain that separates them. Only the largest cities are linked by roads and railroad. Railroad lines carry the overwhelming bulk of freight traffic, and more than half of the passenger traffic moves by road. In 1996, two ministries were responsible for transportation: the Ministry of Transport and Communications for transport operation of railways, roads, and airlines; and the Ministry of Construction and Housing, for construction of highways and airport and port facilities.

Transportation

Overall transportation volume probably peaked in the late Soviet period, when enormous inefficiencies added time and distance to all types of movement. The postindependence correlation of prices to cost has meant abandonment of uneconomical transportation practices. The pipeline system, although crucial to the economic welfare of oil-rich Kazakhstan, remains without direct connection to potential customers in the West and elsewhere. The national telephone system serves only a small percentage of the population; domestic radio and television remain limited and state owned.

Roads

In 1994 and 1995, annual freight movement by road, which already accounted for less than 10 percent of Kazakhstan's freight haulage, declined more than 50 percent per year because of the shift to more efficient means of transport and the country's overall economic decline. In 1993 Kazakhstan counted about 400,000 road vehicles for freight transport, many of which were pieces of farm equipment. Available tractors and trailers are mostly small and in poor condition; the shortage of spare parts and the lack of a domestic truck-manufacturing industry hinder long-distance haulage.

The passenger bus fleet, which numbered 25,500 vehicles in 1991, has declined in numbers and quality since the last new buses were added in 1988. Spare parts are also a problem in bus maintenance, and local bus service is impeded by government caps on fares.

The basic road infrastructure (about 88,000 kilometers, of which about 83,000 kilometers are paved or gravel) serves the widely dispersed population and economic centers adequately. However, there is a shortage of road maintenance equipment, and construction and repair contracts are allocated to as many as seventy different companies and plants owned by the Ministry of Construction and Housing and the Ministry of Transport and Communications. As a result, construction and repair operations are disorganized and uneconomical.

Railroads

Kazakhstan Railways is the third largest rail system in the former Soviet Union, smaller only than the systems of Russia and Ukraine. In 1991 railroads carried 90 percent of Kazakhstan's freight and 30 percent of its passenger traffic. In 1993 the rail system included 14,148 kilometers of track, of which 3,050 kilometers were electrified. All track was 1,520-millimeter gauge. In 1993 the system carried about 39.7 million passengers and hauled about 517 million tons of freight, but haulage declined 42 percent in 1994, most notably in chemicals, cement, iron ore, and ferrous metals. Like the road system, Kazakhstan Railways suffers from a shortage of spare parts; as much as 95 percent of spare parts, equipment, and rolling stock must be purchased from Russia, Ukraine, and other countries. Repair plants for rolling stock are in poor condition and use outmoded equipment.

Pipelines

In 1992 Kazakhstan had 2,850 kilometers of pipeline for crude oil, 3,480 kilometers for natural gas, and 1,500 kilometers for refined products. The oil pipeline system was designed to ship domestic oil, most of which is in the western part of the republic, and to bring Russia's Siberian oil to Kazak refineries. Construction of a pipeline that would bring Kazakhstan's oil to world markets has proven a major obstacle in the development of the Tengiz field because of disagreements over routing, financing, and ownership. Russian control of Kazakhstan's only pipelines to the outside world has restricted oil exports to the West and discouraged foreign investment in the oil and gas industries. In 1995 Kazakhstan, Turkmenistan, and Azerbaijan, all of which have suffered export shutdowns in their cross-Russia pipelines, began discussing a massive pipeline project that would bring their products across China to the Pacific Ocean and into Japan.

Air Transport

Kazakhstan Airlines was founded in 1993 as a joint-stock company initially based on 100 aircraft that the republic received as its share when the Soviet Aeroflot fleet was divided among the former republics. Six private airline companies also operate within the republic. The republic airlines of Ukraine and Uzbekistan began service to Kazakhstan's regional airports in 1992, and Lufthansa of Germany and Turkish Airlines have begun international flights into Almaty. Air traffic between Kazakhstan and other CIS republics is handled mainly by Aeroflot. The airport at Almaty, Kazakhstan's only international facility, underwent a gradual modernization of instrumentation, air control, and communications facilities in the early 1990s; beginning in 1993, international traffic to and from Kyrgyzstan also moved through Almaty. In 1994, besides connections with CIS destinations, regular flights went to Frankfurt, Hannover, Vienna, Zurich, Istanbul, Delhi, Karachi, Tel Aviv, and Sharjah. In 1991 some 7.9 million passengers and about 36.4 million tons of freight passed through Kazak airports. In 1994 the republic had twenty commercial airports and another 132 classified as usable, of which forty-nine had permanent-surface runways and eight had runways longer than 3,600 meters.

Water Transport

The republic's two inland waterways, the Syrdariya in south-central Kazakhstan and the Ertis River in the northeast, have a total of 4,000 kilometers of waterway navigable by commercial craft. A state agency, the Kazakhstan River Fleet Industrial Association (Kazrechmorflot), administers river traffic. In 1992 the association's eleven water transport companies carried about 1.6 million passengers and about 7 million tons of freight.

Telecommunications

Experts consider Kazakhstan's telecommunications facilities inadequate to support the type of economic expansion sought in the mid-1990s. The Ministry of Transport and Communications is the only provider of telecommunications services; its responsibilities include management and regulation of all aspects of the republic's telephone, telex, telegraph, data communications, radio, television, and postal services.

In 1994 only seventeen of every 100 people in urban areas and 7.6 of every 100 people in rural areas had telephones. These figures were above average for Central Asia but lower than those for other CIS countries. Of the republic's total of about 2.2 million telephones, 184,000 were located in Almaty. Current equipment is utilized at a rate of 98 percent, leaving no room for expansion or new subscribers, although in 1992 the waiting list had about 1 million names.

Sixty breakdowns per 100 telephone lines occur annually, a very high rate. Because much of Kazakhstan's telephone equipment, most of which came from the Soviet Union and Eastern Europe, is obsolete, spare parts are scarce. In 1992 only 8 percent of exchanges used fiber-optic and digital equipment. International connections go through Moscow and via satellite links to Australia and Israel. In 1992 a total of 100 channels connected with countries outside the CIS, and 3,000 channels connected with CIS countries.

In 1994 there were about 4.75 million televisions and 10.17 million radios in Kazakhstan. Landlines and microwave carry radio broadcasts from other CIS republics and China; the International Telecommunications Satellite Organization (Intelsat) and the Russian Orbita satellite system provide satellite transmission of television broadcasts from other countries, and the Moscow gateway switch sends international radio broadcasts through eight telecommunications circuits. With Turkish aid, a new satellite ground station went into operation at Almaty in 1992.

Radio and television broadcasting is the exclusive domain of the Kazakhstan State Radio and Television Company. In 1995 the broadcasting system included three national and thirteen regional radio programs broadcast over fifty-eight stations, an irregular Moscow relay of the Voice of Russia and Radio Netherlands, Radio Almaty (a foreign broadcast service offering English, German, Kazak, and Russian programming), one domestic television channel available through eight regional stations, and relays of two Russian channels and Kyrgyz and Turkish programming in Almaty.

GOVERNMENT AND POLITICS

In 1995 Kazakhstan passed through a period of political turmoil that fundamentally changed the shape of the republic's government and political forces. The republic came under direct presidential rule in March 1995, and a new constitution adopted shortly thereafter strengthened the power of the executive. Presidential elections, originally scheduled for sometime in 1996, were postponed until December 2000 after a 1995 referendum provided the basis for such an extension.

Constitution

In May 1995, Nazarbayev convened a council of experts to draw up a new constitution under his guidance. The resulting constitution was adopted in August 1995 by a popular referendum. The official participation figure, 90 percent, and the fairness of this vote were contested by opposition groups. The constitution guarantees equal rights to all nationalities and prescribes both Kazak and Russian as "official" state languages, suitable for use in government documents and education. The president and the legislature, the Supreme Kenges (Supreme Soviet), are to be elected by universal adult suffrage for five-year terms. The president is head of state. The second component of the executive branch is the Council of Ministers, key members of which are presidential appointees. The prime minister, as head of the Council of Ministers, appoints the other ministers.

Structure of Government

The postindependence government was structured by the 1993 constitution with a strong executive branch, a parliament, and a judicial branch. In practice, the administration of Nursultan Nazarbayev dominated governance sufficiently to impel the writing of a new constitution providing justification for the one-man rule that developed in the early 1990s.

Executive Branch

The constitution formalizes the increased power that President Nazarbayev assumed upon the invalidation of parliament in early 1995. It continues the previous constitutional definition of Kazakhstan as a unitary state with a presidential form of government. The president is the highest state officer, responsible for naming the government--subject to parliamentary approval--and all other republic officials. The 1995 constitution expands the president's power in introducing and vetoing legislation. The government that the president appoints consists of the Council of Ministers, headed by a prime minister, and several state committees. In early 1996, after Nazarbayev had reshuffled the government in October 1995, the Council of Ministers included the heads of twenty-one ministries and nine state committees; the prime minister was Akezhan Kazhegeldin. In the October 1995 shift, Nazarbayev himself assumed the portfolio of the Ministry of National Security.

The new constitution does not provide for the position of vice president, although it permitted the incumbent vice president, Yerik Asanbayev, to remain in office until 1996. The president has the power to declare states of emergency during which the constitution can be suspended. The president is the sponsor of legislation and the guarantor of the constitution and of the proper functioning of government, with the power to override the decisions and actions of local authorities and councils. The only grounds on which a president can be removed are infirmity and treason, either of which must be confirmed by a majority of the joint upper and lower houses of the new parliament. In the event of such a removal from power, the prime minister would become the temporary president.

Legislative Branch

The 1993 constitution created a unicameral parliament, which was to replace the 350-seat Supreme Soviet when the mandates of that body's deputies expired in 1995. Composed overwhelmingly of career communists, the 1990 parliament had been a balky and turgid partner for the task of economic and political reform. Although he probably lacked the legal authority to do so, Nazarbayev pressured this parliament into a "voluntary" early dissolution in December 1993 in order to allow the seating of a smaller and presumably more pliant "professional parliament." Under the 1995 constitution, the parliament consists of two houses, the Senate and the Majlis, both operating in continuous session. Each of Kazakhstan's nineteen provinces and the city of Almaty, which has province status, have two senators. These are chosen for four-year terms by joint sessions of the provinces' legislative bodies. An additional seven senators are appointed directly by the president. In addition, ex-presidents automatically receive the status of senators-for-life. The Majlis has sixty-seven representatives, including one from each of fifty-five districts drawn to have roughly equal populations, and the Senate has forty seats. Direct elections for half the seats are held every two years. In the first election under the new parliamentary structure, all seats in both houses of parliament were contested in December 1995; runoff elections filled twenty-three seats in the Majlis for which the initial vote was inconclusive. International observers reported procedural violations in the Majlis voting. The new parliament, which was seated in January 1996, included sixty-eight Kazak and thirty-one Russian deputies; only ten deputies were women.

The initiative for most legislative actions originates with the president. If parliament passes a law that the president vetoes, a two-thirds vote of both houses is required to override the veto. A similar margin is needed to express no confidence in a prime minister, an action that requires the president to name a new prime minister and Council of Ministers.

Judicial System

The judicial system is the least developed of Kazakhstan's three branches of government. Although Minister of Justice Nagashibay Shaykenov objected strenuously, the constitution retains the practice of presidential appointment of all judges in the republic. The 1993 constitution specified terms of service for judges, but the 1995 document makes no mention of length of service, suggesting that judges will serve at the president's pleasure.

Under the 1993 constitution, lines of judicial authority were poorly defined, in part because the republic had three "highest courts"--the Supreme Court, the State Arbitrage Court, and the Constitutional Court--which among them employed a total of sixty-six senior judges. Many of these senior judges, as well as numerous judges in lower courts, had been retained from the Soviet era, when the judicial branch was entirely under the control of the central government. The 1995 constitution makes no provision for the State Abritrage Court, which had heard economic disputes among enterprises and between enterprises and government agencies. Provisions for the new judiciary clearly subordinate all other courts to the Supreme Court, which also has a consultative role in appointing senior judges.

Local Government

Kazakhstan is divided into nineteen provinces, and the city of Almaty has administrative status equal to that of a province. In turn, the provinces are divided into regions that consist of a number of settlement points. Each province and region and most settlements have their own elective councils, charged with drawing up a budget and supervising local taxation. Cities have their own local councils as well, and large cities are divided into regions, each of which has its own council.

The local legislatures lack the authority to choose the local executive, who is appointed directly by the president. The local executive has the job of ensuring that decisions of the national government are enforced and that the constitution is observed. Province and regional "heads of administration," known by the Russian term *glav* or the Kazak term *hakim*, are presidential appointees. The *hakim*, in turn, appoints the members of his staff, who are the department heads of the jurisdiction. The *hakim* also can reverse budgetary decisions of the local councils.

There has been considerable pressure, especially in the predominantly Russian north, to make the *hakim* posts elective rather than appointive. In 1994 Nazarbayev indicated that he would consider doing so, but the 1995 constitution provides only that the local councils can express no confidence in their *hakim* by a two-thirds vote. The president also has the power to override or revoke decisions taken by local councils; a *hakim* has the power to control budgetary decisions taken by the local council.

The Election of 1994 and its Aftermath

After the early dissolution in 1993 of Kazakhstan's first parliament, an election for the 177 seats of the new, "professional" parliament was held in March 1994. The election was so closely managed and restricted by the government that observers from the Organization for Security and Cooperation in Europe (OSCE; before 1995, the Conference on Security and Cooperation in Europe--CSCE--see Glossary) initially were reluctant to certify the election as fair.

Despite his careful electoral management, Nazarbayev netted a reliable bloc of only about sixty of the 177 seats. The remaining deputies quickly organized themselves into a "constructive" opposition bloc, a center-left configuration calling itself Respublika. It included a number of disparate political groups. A subgroup of Respublika organized a shadow cabinet to provide alternative viewpoints and programs to those of the government.

At the end of May 1994, the parliament passed a vote of no confidence in the government of Prime Minister Sergey Tereshchenko, who had been in office since 1991. Nazarbayev put off dismissing Tereshchenko, citing the provision of the 1993 constitution giving the president the right to name the prime minister, subject only to parliamentary confirmation. By midyear, however, parliament was in rebellion against the president, and a new faction of Respublika, including a broad range of communist, nationalist, and special-issue parties, demanded the resignations of Nazarbayev and Tereshchenko.

In mid-October, following a month-long scandal over the private dealings of Tereshchenko's ministers of internal affairs and the economy (the second of whom was indicted), Nazarbayev was finally forced to dismiss the Tereshchenko government. Nazarbayev named industrialist Akezhan Kazhegeldin to replace Tereshchenko. As chief of a northern industrial conglomerate, Kazhegeldin, a Kazak, was closely associated with the Russian-controlled sector of Kazakhstan prior to 1991.

Thus, by late 1994 parliament was emerging as a particular focus for anti-Nazarbayev sentiment. Although extremely unproductive itself, passing only seven laws during its year of existence, parliament severely impeded Nazarbayev's privatization programs, causing the complete cessation of privatization voucher distribution. At the end of 1994, the parliament issued its own alternative New Economic Policy, in competition with Nazarbayev's, and parliament also attempted to take over actual disbursement of funds for the state budget. At the same time, parliament was providing a forum for several skilled and well-financed men to position themselves for a challenge to Nazarbayev in the presidential election scheduled for 1996.

In March 1995, Kazakhstan's Constitutional Court ruled the 1994 parliamentary election invalid because of procedural irregularities that, among other things, waived certain requirements for pro-Nazarbayev candidates. After filing a token objection, Nazarbayev announced the dissolution of parliament and new elections to be held in two or three months. The Council of Ministers that had been approved by that parliament then resigned en masse. Using emergency powers granted him upon the dissolution of the 1990-93 parliament, Nazarbayev reappointed Prime Minister Kazhegeldin, who installed a new Council of Ministers. Unlike its virtually all-Kazak predecessor, the new body put the key Ministry of Finance under a Russian, Aleksandr Pavlov, and gave the Ministry of the Economy portfolio to a Middle Horde Kazak from the Russified north. One of Kazhegeldin's two new first deputy prime ministers was Kazak; the other was Russian. The new head of the Privatization Commission, Sarybay Kalmurzayev, also apparently was a Middle Horder. He not only began to permit privatization auctioneers to accept cash in addition to vouchers, but also began to give Russian companies rights of first refusal in privatization of large industrial plants, especially military ones. In April 1995, Nazarbayev staged a referendum that ratified extension of his presidency until December 2000 by a 95 percent majority. In December 1995, Nazarbayev issued a decree enabling him to annul any existing law, demand the government's resignation, or order new parliamentary elections. This step furthered the authoritarian direction of Kazakhstan's government.

Political Organizations

Economic and ethnic differentiation in Kazakhstan has led to the appearance of more than 2,000 social organizations, movements, political parties, and social action funds across a broad political spectrum. Although Nazarbayev prevented electoral participation by many opposition parties, the formation and reformation of parties and coalitions have occurred at a rapid pace in the postindependence years. In the parliamentary election of December 1995, thirty parties and other organizations registered candidates.

The President's Party

Significantly, the one type of party that has failed to thrive in Kazakhstan is a "presidential party" that would serve as a training ground for future officials, as well as a conduit for their advancement. Nazarbayev lost control of his first two attempts at forming parties, the Socialists and the People's Congress Party (NKK). The latter particularly, under the leadership of former Nazarbayev ally Olzhas Suleymenov, became a center of parliamentary opposition. Nazarbayev's third party, the People's Unity Party (SNEK), remained loyal to the president, although it was unable, even with considerable government help, to elect enough deputies to give Nazarbayev control of the 1994-95 parliament. SNEK formally incorporated itself as a political party in February 1995.

Other Parties

With the exception of SNEK and some smaller entities, such as the Republican Party and an entrepreneurial association known as For Kazakhstan's Future, most of Kazakhstan's parties and organizations have little or no influence on presidential decision making. Because privatization and the deteriorating economy have left most citizens much worse off than they were in the early 1990s, most of the republic's organizations and parties have an oppositional or antipresidential character.

The Communist Party of Kazakhstan, declared illegal in 1991, was allowed to re-register in 1993. Kazakhstan also has a small Socialist Democratic Party. Both parties made poor showings in the 1994 election, but two former communist organizations, the State Labor Union (Profsoyuz) and the Peasants' Union, managed to take eleven and four seats, respectively.

Nationalist Groups

At least four large Kazak nationalist movements were active in the mid-1990s. Three of them--Azat (Freedom), the Republican Party, and Zheltoksan (December)--attempted to form a single party under the name Azat, with the aim of removing "colonialist" foreign influences from Kazakhstan. The fourth movement, Alash (named for the legendary founder of the Kazak nation, as well as for the pre-Soviet nationalist party of the same name), refused to join such a coalition because it advocated a more actively nationalist and pro-Muslim line than did the other three parties. In the March 1994 election, Azat and the Republicans were the only nationalist parties to run candidates. They elected just one deputy between them.

Four exclusively Russian political organizations in Kazakhstan have nationalist or federative agendas. These are Yedinstvo (Unity), Civic Contract, Democratic Progress, and Lad (Harmony). Party registration procedures for the 1994 election made places on the ballot very difficult to obtain for the Russian nationalist groups. Although Lad was forced to run its candidates without party identification, four deputies were elected with ties to that party.

The Russian group most unsettling to the Nazarbayev government was the Cossacks, who were denied official registration, as well as recognition of their claimed status as a distinct ethnic group in the northeast and northwest. Not permitted to drill, carry weapons, or engage in their traditional military activities, Kazakhstan's Cossacks have, in increasing numbers, crossed the border into Russia, where restrictions are not as tight.

Opposition Coalitions

In 1994 parliament's success at countering presidential power encouraged the legislators, many of whom were connected with the former Soviet ruling elite, to use their training in the political infighting of Soviet bureaucracy to form effective antipresidential coalitions. Ironically, these coalitions were the only political groupings in the republic that transcended ethnic differences. The Respublika group was elastic enough to contain both Kazak and

Russian nationalists, and the Otan-Otechestvo organization forged a coalition of Kazaks, Russians, and even Cossacks who desired a return to Soviet-style political and social structures.

Nazarbayev and Political Prospects

Public opinion in Kazakhstan appears to have accepted the imposition of presidential rule, at least partly because the parliament Nazarbayev dissolved had focused on its own wages and benefits rather than on solving the nation's problems. In the short run, the imposition of direct presidential rule seemed likely to reduce ethnic tensions within the republic. Indeed, one of Nazarbayev's primary justifications for assuming greater power was the possibility that bolstered presidential authority could stem the growing ethnic hostility in the republic, including a general rise in anti-Semitism.

The ethnic constituency whose appeasement is most important is, however, the Russians, both within the republic and in Russia proper. Stability in Kazakhstan is overwhelmingly shaped by developments in Russia, especially as that country returns its attention to some measure of reintegration of the former Soviet empire. Because of Kazakhstan's great vulnerability to Russian political, economic, and military intervention, experts assume that Russian national and ethnic interests play a considerable part in Nazarbayev's political calculations (see Foreign Policy; National Security Prospects).

It also seems likely that Nazarbayev would use presidential rule to increase the linguistic and cultural rights of the republic's Russians. Although Nazarbayev had taken a firm stand on the issue of formal dual citizenship, a treaty he and Russia's president, Boris N. Yeltsin, signed in January 1995 all but obviated the language question by permitting citizens of the respective countries to own property in either republic, to move freely between them, to sign contracts (including contracts for military service) in either country, and to exchange one country's citizenship for the other's. When the Kazak parliament ratified that agreement, that body also voted to extend to the end of 1995 the deadline by which residents must declare either Kazakhstani or Russian citizenship. After the dissolution of that parliament, Kazakhstan considered extending the deadline until 2000, as Russia already had done.

In the mid-1990s, Nazarbayev seemed likely to face eventual opposition from Kazak nationalists if he continued making concessions to the republic's Russians. Such opposition would be conditioned, however, by the deep divisions of ethnic Kazaks along clan and family lines, which give some of them more interests in common with the Russians than with their ethnic fellows. The Kazaks also have no institutions that might serve as alternative focuses of political will. Despite a wave of mosque building since independence, Islam is not well established in much of the republic, and there is no national religious-political network through which disaffected Kazaks might be mobilized.

The lack of an obvious venue for expression of popular dissatisfaction does not mean, however, that none will materialize. Nazarbayev gambled that imposition of presidential rule would permit him to transform the republic's economy and thus placate the opposition through an indisputable and widespread improvement of living standards. Experts agree that the republic has the natural resources and industrial potential to make this a credible wager. But a number of conditions outside Nazarbayev's control, such as the political climate in Russia and the other Central Asian states, would influence that outcome. By dismissing parliament and taking upon himself the entire burden of government, Nazarbayev made himself the obvious target for the public discontent that radical transformations inevitably produce.

THE MEDIA

Kazakhstan has enjoyed the same flourishing of media as have most of the other former Soviet republics. To some extent, the republic also continues to be influenced by the Moscow media, although changes in currency and the simple passage of time are steadily reducing that influence. Also similar to the processes in other republics is a certain erosion of the freedom that the media enjoyed in the earlier days of independence. Although the government always has retained some control, there was a certain tendency to view the proper relationship between the media and government as adversarial. However, Nazarbayev steadily chipped away at Kazakhstan's central press, which as a result became more noticeably pro-government in 1994 and 1995. The 1995 constitution guarantees freedom of ideas and expression and explicitly bans censorship. In practice, however, the government influences the press in several ways. Government presses (the only ones available) have refused to publish private newspapers for various "technical" reasons; financial pressure has been brought through court cases or investigations of a given newspaper's sponsors; and, in some cases, outright censorship has been exercised for "security reasons." Strictly enforced laws forbid personal criticism of the president or members of the president's family.

The major official newspapers are the Russian-language *Kazakhstanskaya pravda* and *Sovety Kazakhstana*, which are supported by the government. Nominally, the former is the organ of the Council of Ministers and the latter that of the parliament. The newspaper *Ekspress K* has taken some independent positions, although in the mid-1990s the editor in chief was a senior official in SNEK, the presidential political party. The small-edition papers *Respublika* and *NKK* are somewhat more oppositional. The first was the organ of the Socialist Party until it was sold to commercial interests, and the second is the organ of the People's Congress Party. *Respublika* is said to be underfinanced, but *NKK* enjoys the resources of Olzhas Suleymenov's large Nevada-Semipalatinsk commercial organization. *Panorama*, perhaps the largest independent newspaper in the republic, is owned by some of the largest business interests in the republic and is oriented toward political and economic issues (on which it generally takes an objective view). The Karavan commercial organization publishes two newspapers, *Karavan* and *ABV* (short for Almaty Business News). The former inclines toward tabloid-style muckraking, while the latter is entirely commercial in character.

The electronic media remain under state control. Many private production companies exist, but access to television and radio is still controlled by the State Television and Radio Broadcasting Corporation (see Transportation and Telecommunications).

As it does most activities, ethnicity complicates media operations. Inevitably the nationality of the owners of a newspaper or television production company affects how its product is received. The most obvious example is that of the newspaper *Karavan*. Although its muckraking approach is similar to that taken by newspapers in Moscow and Bishkek, the fact that the paper is Russian-owned makes it seem, in the context of Kazakhstan, to be more vividly partisan. In early 1995, a fire in the *Karavan* warehouse prompted rumors of sabotage, which never were substantiated.

Human Rights

Considering the power available to the Nazarbayev regime, Kazakhstan's observation of international human-rights standards in the mid-1990s was given a relatively high rating. In one celebrated case of attempted censorship, historian Karishal Asanov was tried three times before being acquitted on a charge of defaming the president for an article he published in a Moscow newspaper.

Although antigovernment activities of the nationalist-religious group Alash have been actively discouraged, there have been no recorded instances of extrajudicial killings or disappearances, or of unsubstantiated grounds for arrest. Prisons are generally overcrowded because of the eruption of crime in the republic, but international organizations record no instances of torture or of deliberately degrading treatment.

The state security organs continue some of their Soviet-era ways; there have been complaints that proper procedures for search warrants are not always followed, and some credible accusations have been made about tampering with or planting evidence in criminal proceedings. In general, however, the republic's investigative and security organs seem to be making an effort to follow the constitution's guidance on the inviolability of person, property, and dwelling.

Free movement about the country is permitted, although residence is still controlled by the Soviet-era registration system, which requires citizens to have official permission to live in a particular city. In practice, this system has made it almost impossible for outsiders to move into Almaty.

The exercise of political rights in Kazakhstan is closely controlled, and the number of parties is limited by registration restrictions. Imposition of presidential rule and the general strengthening of the president's role have limited popular political participation. The Russian population has attempted to depict the imposition of language laws and the refusal to grant dual citizenship as violations of human rights, but these claims generally have not been accepted by the international community. Several Russian political groups and human rights alleged that irregularities in the August 1995 constitutional referendum invalidated the document's ratification on human rights grounds. The nine official foreign observers reported no major irregularities, however.

FOREIGN POLICY

From the onset of independence, President Nazarbayev sought international support to secure a place for Kazakhstan in the world community, playing the role of bridge between East and West, between Europe and Asia.

Almost immediately upon its declaration of independence, the republic gained a seat in the United Nations, membership in the CSCE, and a seat on the coordinating council of the North Atlantic Treaty Organization (NATO--see Glossary). The United States and other nations also gave Kazakhstan quick recognition, opening embassies in Almaty and receiving Kazakhstani ambassadors in return. Its status as an apparent nuclear power got Kazakhstan off to a fast start in international diplomacy. President Nazarbayev became a signatory to the Strategic Arms Reduction Treaty (START) and its so-called Lisbon Protocol by which Belarus, Kazakhstan, and Ukraine pledged to eliminate nuclear weapons in the 1990s. In addition, Nazarbayev was able to negotiate US$1.2 billion in prepayment by the United States against sale of the enriched uranium contained in Kazakhstan's warheads, as well as another US$311 million for maintenance and conversion of existing missile silos. Equally important was that the nuclear warheads prompted the United States to become a party to negotiations concerning the warheads between Kazakhstan and Russia. The United States eventually became a guarantor of the agreement reached by the two countries. In May 1995, the last nuclear warhead in Kazakhstan was destroyed at Semey, completing the program of removal and destruction of the entire former Soviet arsenal and achieving the republic's goal of being "nuclear free."

Under the leadership of Nazarbayev, who maintained personal control of foreign policy, Kazakhstan eagerly courted Western investment. Although foreign aid, most of it from Western nations, began as a trickle, significant amounts were received by 1994. In practice, however, Nazarbayev was ambivalent about moving too fully into a Western orbit.

Turkey

In the period shortly after independence, policy makers often discussed following the "Turkish model," emulating Turkey in incorporating a Muslim cultural heritage into a secular, Europeanized state. Turkey's president Turgut Özal made a state visit to Kazakhstan in March 1991 and hosted a return visit by Nazarbayev later the same year. Soon afterward Nazarbayev began to echo Turkish talk of turning Kazakhstan into a bridge between Muslim East and Christian West. In practice, however, the Turks proved to be more culturally dissimilar than the Kazakhstanis had imagined; more important, Turkey's own economic problems meant that most promises of aid and investment remained mostly just statements of intentions.

China

As Turkey proved itself a disappointment, President Nazarbayev began to speak with increasing enthusiasm about the Asian economic "tigers" such as Singapore, the Republic of Korea (South Korea), and Taiwan. Among the republic's first foreign economic advisers were Chan Young Bang, a Korean American with close ties to South Korea's major industrial families, and Singapore's former prime minister, Li Kwan Yew.

The most compelling model, however, was provided by China, which quickly had become Kazakhstan's largest non-CIS trading partner. The Kazakhstani leadership found the Chinese combination of rigid social control and private-sector prosperity an attractive one. China also represented a vast market and appeared quite able to supply the food, medicine, and consumer goods most desired by the Kazakhstani market.

However, the relationship with China has been a prickly one. Kazakhstan's fears of Chinese domination remain from the Soviet era and from the Kazaks' earlier nomadic history. A large number of Kazaks and other Muslims live in the Xinjiang Uygur Autonomous Region of China, just over the border. Direct rail and road links have been opened to Ürümqi in Xinjiang, and Chinese traders in Kazakhstan are prominent in the thriving barter between the two nations. However, China is plainly nervous about any contact that would encourage separatist or nationalist sentiments among its own "captive peoples." For its part, Kazakhstan has expressed unease about the large numbers of Chinese who began buying property and settling in the republic after the end of Soviet rule. Kazakhstan also has reacted angrily but without effect to Chinese nuclear tests at Lob Nor, China's main testing site, located within 300 kilometers of the common border.

The Middle East

Nazarbayev was hesitant to court investment from the Middle East, despite high levels of Turkish and Iranian commercial activity in Central Asia. Unlike the other Central Asian republics, Kazakhstan initially accepted only observer status in the Muslim-dominated ECO, largely out of concern not to appear too "Muslim" itself. Over time, however, the president moved from being a professed atheist to proudly proclaiming his Muslim heritage. He has encouraged assistance from Iran in developing transportation links, from Oman in building oil pipelines, from Egypt in building mosques, and from Saudi Arabia in developing a national banking system.

Russia and the CIS

Most of Kazakhstan's foreign policy has, not unnaturally, focused on the other former Soviet republics and, particularly, on the potential territorial ambitions of Russia. Since Gorbachev's proposal for a modified continuation of the Soviet Union in late 1991, Kazakhstan has supported arrangements with Russia that guarantee the republic's sovereignty and independence, including a stronger and institutionally complex CIS.

As the CIS failed to develop a strong institutional framework, Nazarbayev attempted to achieve the same end in another way, proposing the creation of a Euro-Asian Union that would subordinate the economic, defense, and foreign policies of individual member states to decisions made by a council of presidents, an elective joint parliament, and joint councils of defense and other ministries. Citizens of member nations would hold union citizenship, essentially reducing the independence of the individual member republics to something like their Soviet-era status. The proposal, however, met with little enthusiasm, especially from Russia, whose support was crucial to the plan's success.

Nazarbayev pursued bilateral trade and security agreements with each of the former republics and in September 1992 unsuccessfully attempted to have Kazakhstan broker a cease-fire between Armenia and Azerbaijan that also would set a precedent for settling interrepublic and interregional strife in the former republics. Nazarbayev also participated in the fitful efforts of the five Central Asian leaders to create some sort of regional entity; the most promising of these was a free-trade zone established in 1994 among Uzbekistan, Kyrgyzstan, and Kazakhstan.

Kazakhstan also has contributed to efforts by Russia and Uzbekistan to end the civil war in Tajikistan. Kazakhstani troops were part of a joint CIS force dispatched to protect military objectives in and around the Tajikistan's capital, Dushanbe. Although Nazarbayev and Uzbekistan's President Islam Karimov warned in 1995 that their countries soon would consider withdrawal if peace talks made no progress, the multinational CIS force remained in place in early 1996.

NATIONAL SECURITY

Kazakhstan's national security policy remains closely associated with that of Russia, partly because the military forces of Kazakhstan have developed more slowly than planned and partly because of long-standing habits of interdependence. The internal security organization of police, prisons, intelligence gathering, and criminal justice remains substantially as it was in the Soviet era.

Military Establishment

At independence Kazakhstan had no army because defense and security needs always had been met by the Soviet army. Initially Nazarbayev, unlike many of his fellow new presidents, argued that his country should function without an independent army, assuming that collective security needs would continue to be met by armies under CIS command. Even when the Russian military establishment changed its oath of service to refer solely to Russia rather than to the CIS, Nazarbayev continued the policy of drafting youth into the CIS forces rather than those of the republic. Even though the republic's strategic thinkers saw Kazakhstan as the intersection of three potential military theaters--Europe, the Near East, and the Far East--in the first years of independence, the republic was thought to require only a national guard of no more than 2,500 men, whose duties were envisioned as primarily ceremonial.

When Russia transformed the troops on its soil into a Russian army in the spring of 1992, Kazakhstan followed suit by nationalizing the former Soviet Fortieth Army, which remained in Kazakhstan, creating the formal basis for a Kazakhstani national defense force (see table 11).

Table 11. Central Asia: Military Budgets and Personnel, 1992-95 (budgets in millions of United States dollars)

Country	1992	1993	1994	1995
Kazakhstan				
Budget	1,600	707	450	297
Personnel	63,000	44,000	40,000	40,000
Kyrgyzstan				
Budget	47	51	57	13
Personnel	8,0001	12,000	12,000	12,000
Tajikistan				
Budget	107	110	115	67
Personnel	6,0001	3,000	3,000	3,000
Turkmenistan				
Budget	114	143	153	61
Personnel	34,0001	28,0001	28,0001	11,0001
Uzbekistan				
Budget	420	390	375	315
Personnel	15,0001	40,000	39,000	25,000

Source: Based on information from *The Military Balance, 1993-1994,* London, 1993, 140, 144-45; *The Military Balance, 1994-1995*, London, 1994, 156-57, 162-63; *The Military Balance, 1995-1996*, London, 1995, 160-61, 165-67; and *The Worldwide Directory of Defense Authorities 1996*, 2, Bethesda, 1996.

Command Structure

The armed forces established in 1992 are subordinate to the Ministry of Defense and to the president in his capacities as commander in chief and chairman of the National Security Council. The second-ranking military office is chief of the General Staff. The General Staff consists of deputy defense ministers for personnel, ground forces, air defense, and airborne forces. The president's main advisory body for national defense is the National Security Council, which includes the prime minister, the first deputy prime minister, the minister of foreign affairs, the chairman of the Committee for Defense of the Constitution, the chairman of the State Committee for Emergency Situations, the minister of defense, the commander of the Border Troops, the commander of the ground forces, and the minister of internal affairs. When it is active, parliament has a four-member Committee for National Security and Defense for coordination of defense policy with the executive branch.

Force Structure

In the mid-1990s, plans called for developing a military force of 80,000 to 90,000 personnel, including ground forces, air forces, and a navy (for deployment in the Caspian Sea). In 1996 the army included about 25,000 troops, organized into two motorized rifle divisions, one tank division, and one artillery brigade. Attached to that force were one multiple rocket launcher brigade, one motorized rifle regiment, and one air assault brigade. Overall army headquarters are at Semey, with division headquarters at Ayagöz, Sary Ozyk, Almaty, and Semey.

According to national defense doctrine, Kazakhstan has a minimal requirement for naval forces. In late 1993, Kazakhstan received about 25 percent of the patrol boats and cutters in Russia's Caspian Sea Flotilla, which subsequently constituted the entire naval force. In 1993 naval bases were planned for Fort Shevchenko on the Caspian Sea and at Aral, north of the Aral Sea, but a scarcity of funds delayed completion. Likewise, naval air bases were planned for Aqtau and the Buzachiy Peninsula on the Caspian Sea and at Saryshaghan on Lake Balkhash.

In 1995 the air force included an estimated 15,000 troops. After the withdrawal in 1994 of forty Tu-95MS nuclear-capable bombers, the Kazakhstan Air Force was left with 133 combat aircraft, whose offensive capability relied on MiG-23, MiG-27, MiG-29, and Su-24 fighters with support from An-24 and An-26 transport and MiG-25 surveillance aircraft. Thirty air bases are scattered throughout the republic. Since 1992 Kazak pilots have received little air training because units have been staffed at only 30 to 50 percent of operational levels.

Officer Cadre

Creating the projected national armed forces has proved more difficult than expected. Since independence, the officer corps, which was overwhelmingly Slavic in the early 1990s, has suffered a severe loss of manpower. In 1992 nearly two-thirds of the company and battalion commanders in Kazakhstan had to be replaced as Russian-speaking officers took advantage of CIS agreements permitting transfer to other republics. When these transfers occurred, almost no Kazak officers were available as replacements. In the entire Soviet period, only three Kazaks had graduated from the Military Academy of the General Staff, and only two had earned advanced degrees in military science.

Kazaks have dominated the top administrative positions in the post-Soviet military establishment. In addition to Minister of Defense Sagadat Nurmagambetov, President Nazarbayev appointed two Kazak colonels as deputy ministers of defense and a Kazak general to head the Republic National Guard (the guard unit responsible for protecting the president and other dignitaries as well as antiterrorist operations). Kazakhstan's first National Security Council consisted of seven Kazaks, one Russian, and one Ukrainian. In October 1994, both Slavs left office and were replaced by ethnic Kazaks. Despite a secret call-up of officers in reserve, by the fall of 1993 Kazakhstan was short at least 650 officers, while the Border Troops Command, 80 percent of whose officers were non-Kazak, was understaffed by 45 percent.

Border Troops

Kazakhstan's extensive land borders are highly vulnerable to penetration by international smugglers, illegal immigrants, and terrorists. In 1992 the Eastern Border Troops District of the former Soviet Union was dissolved; this action resulted in the formation of the Kazakhstan Border Troops Command under a Kazak general. After this transition, overall control of border security remained with the National Security Committee, formerly the Kazakhstan Committee for State Security (KGB). The border troops commander is a member of the National Security Committee and a member of the Council of CIS Border Troops Commanders, which was established in 1993 to foster regional cooperation. Cooperation with Russia, with which Kazakhstan shares roughly half its borders, is the primary goal of border policy, and several agreements provide for Russian aid. Cooperative agreements also are in effect with the other four Central Asian republics.

Kazakhstan's border troops force is estimated at 5,000 to 6,000 personnel. Troops are trained at the Almaty Border Troops School (formerly run by the KGB) or under a cooperative agreement at four Russian facilities. Headquarters are at Almaty, with several subordinate commands, including a coastal patrol squadron headquartered at Atyrau on the north Caspian Sea coast.

Training and Recruitment

Exacerbating the severe shortage of trained military personnel is the virtual absence of higher-level military training facilities. The only two such schools in existence, the general All Arms Command School and the Border Troops Academy, both in Almaty, are capable of graduating only about 200 junior officers a year, and in 1993 three-quarters of those left the republic. There were also three military secondary boarding schools--in Almaty, Shymkent, and Qaraghandy--and a civil aviation school in Aqtöbe, which is to be converted to a military flight school sometime after 2000.

There are indications of severe problems in filling the ranks of the armed services. Some accounts indicate that as many as 20,000 soldiers were absent without leave from the army in 1993, and desertion and low morale among conscripts continued to be a major problem in the mid-1990s. Another concern is the deteriorating physical condition of inductees, one-third of whom are said to be unfit for conscription. Discipline appears to be problematic as well. In 1993 more than 500 crimes by soldiers were reported in Almaty Province alone; members of the Kazakhstani peacekeeping force in Tajikistan reportedly have robbed and raped villagers they were sent to protect. At the command level, in 1993 one general was dismissed for selling weapons and other military goods.

Military Infrastructure

The quality of military support installations declined in the first years of the post-Soviet period. For instance, the chief planner of Kazakhstan's Institute for Strategic Studies has estimated that only in the next century will the republic have the capability to use air-to-surface missiles for defensive purposes. In addition, sensitive facilities inherited by military authorities from the Soviet army all are said to be on the point of collapse. Facilities in bad repair include nuclear test and storage facilities at Kökshetau, the BN-350 breeder-reactor at Aqtau, and a tracking and monitoring station at Priozersk. Even the first Kazak cosmonaut, who was sent into space with great pomp in June 1994, was in fact a Russian citizen and career officer in the Russian air force, as were his two "Ukrainian" shipmates.

Before the dissolution of the Soviet Union, Kazakhstan was the most significant site of military-industrial activity in Central Asia. The republic was home to roughly 3 percent of Soviet defense facilities, including more than fifty enterprises and 75,000 workers, located mostly in the predominantly Russian northern parts of the country.

A plant in Öskemen fabricated beryllium and nuclear reactor fuel, and another at Aqtau produced uranium ore. Plants in Oral manufactured heavy machine guns for tanks and antiship missiles. In Petropavl, one plant produced SS-21 short-range ballistic missiles, and other plants manufactured torpedoes and naval communications equipment, support equipment for intercontinental ballistic missiles (ICBMs), tactical missile launcher equipment, artillery, and armored vehicles. There was a torpedo-producing facility in Almaty as well. Chemical and biological weapons were produced in Aksu, and chemical weapons were manufactured in Pavlodar.

By 1994 most of Kazakhstan's defense plants had ceased military production. All of them required component parts from inaccessible sources outside Kazakhstan, principally in Russia. Even more important, the Russian military-industrial complex was itself in collapse, so that Kazakhstan's military enterprises no longer could rely on Russian customers. In addition, the great majority of key workers at all these facilities were ethnic Slavs, the most employable of whom moved to Russia or other former Soviet republics.

Substantial elements of Kazakhstan's military-production infrastructure nevertheless remain in the republic. In addition, in early 1992 the army nationalized all of the standard-issue Soviet military equipment remaining on the republic's soil. An unknown percentage of this equipment is still in use in Kazakhstan, and another portion of it likely has been sold to other countries. Since independence, at least one new ship, a cruiser named in honor of Nazarbayev, has been commissioned.

The weapons of greatest concern to the world, however, have been the 1,350 nuclear warheads that remained in Kazakhstan when the Soviet Union disbanded. Although two other new states--Ukraine and Belarus--also possessed "stranded" nuclear weapons, the Kazakhstani weapons attracted particular international suspicion, and unsubstantiated rumors reported the sale of warheads to Iran. Subsequent negotiations demonstrated convincingly, however, that operational control of these weapons always had remained with Russian strategic rocket forces (see Foreign Policy). All of the warheads were out of Kazakhstan by May 1995.

Kazakhstan's other military significance was as a test range and missile launch site. The republic was the location of only about 1 percent of all Soviet test ranges, but these included some all Soviet Union's largest and most important, especially in the aerospace and nuclear programs. Test sites included a range at Vladimirovka used to integrate aircraft with their weapons systems; a range at Saryshaghan for flight testing of ballistic missiles and air defense systems; a similar facility at Emba; and the Semipalatinsk Nuclear Weapons Proving Grounds, which was the more important of the two major nuclear testing facilities in the Soviet Union. In the four decades of its existence, there were at least 466 nuclear explosions at Semipalatinsk.

The other major Soviet military facility on Kazakhstani soil was the Baykonur space launch facility, the home of the Soviet space exploration program and, until 1994, Russia's premier launch site for military and intelligence satellites. Kazakhstan and Russia debated ownership of the facility, while the facility itself suffered acute deterioration from the region's harsh climate and from uncontrolled pilfering. In 1994 Russia formally recognized Kazakhstan's ownership of the facility, although a twenty-year lease ratified in 1995 guaranteed Russia continued use of Baykonur.

Military Doctrine

In 1992 Kazakhstan adopted a three-stage defense doctrine, calling for creation of administrative, command, and support organizations in 1992, restructuring of field forces between 1993 and 1996, and a modernization process leading to establishment of a fully professional military force by 2000. In 1992 Minister of Defense Sagadat Nurmagambetov abandoned the last goal as impractical, calling rather for a combination of conscripts and contract service personnel. In the summer of 1994, Kazakhstan's Institute for Strategic Studies called for the complete abandonment of the official defense doctrine. The existing doctrine was criticized for being based on outmoded Soviet precepts that combined fear of hostile military encirclement with a commitment to peace that approached pacificism.

The institute argued that Kazakhstan should instead base its defense policies on the assumption that the republic likely would find itself amid border confrontations involving CIS nations, an expansionist China, and Islamic neighbors with enhanced power and ambition. To prepare for such events, the institute recommended de-emphasizing military development and instead pursuing multinational defense agreements along the lines of Nazarbayev's proposed Euro-Asian Union or, absent that, a military alliance with Russia and active pursuit of NATO membership. Kazakhstan became a member of NATO's Partnership for Peace in 1994.

Following the appearance of the institute's evaluation, the Ministry of Defense has acknowledged that the second of its original goals--restructuring of field forces by 1996--likely could not be achieved. This admission meant that Kazakhstan's dependence upon Russia likely would become even greater. In January 1995, the two countries signed agreements committing them to creation of "unified armed forces." To deflect criticism that such an agreement was inimical to national sovereignty, Nazarbayev likened the new arrangement to the Warsaw Pact and NATO, as distinct from the formation of a single armed force. At the same time, Russia formally took up shared responsibility for patrol of Kazakhstan's international borders (under a nominally joint command), which in practice meant the border with China.

Law Enforcement Systems

Kazakhstan's police, court, and prison systems are based, largely unchanged, on Soviet-era practices, as is the bulk of the republic's criminal code. Major legislative changes have concentrated on commercial law, with a view to improving the atmosphere for foreign investment. Formal responsibility for observation of the republic's laws and for protection of the state's interests is divided among the National Security Committee (successor to the Kazak branch of the KGB), the Ministry of Internal Affairs, and the Office of the Procurator General. Intelligence and counterintelligence are the responsibility of the National Security Committee. The police (still called the militia) and prisons are the responsibility of the Ministry of Internal Affairs. The Office of the Procurator General, formerly charged with investigation and prosecution of unlawful acts, was removed from its investigative capacity by the 1995 constitution. Investigation of crimes shifted to the Ministry of Internal Affairs, which also is responsible for fire protection, automotive inspection, and routine preservation of order. As of 1992, Kazakhstan became a member of the International Criminal Police Organization (Interpol), and Kazakhstani authorities have worked particularly closely with the law enforcement agencies of Russia, Belarus, Uzbekistan, Ukraine, and Kyrgyzstan.

Courts

The present court system functions at three levels: local courts, which handle petty crimes such as pickpocketing and vandalism; province-level courts, which handle offenses such as murder, grand larceny, and organized crime; and the Supreme Court, to which decisions of the lower courts are appealed. Until mid-1995, the Constitutional Court ruled as final arbiter on the constitutionality of government laws and actions in cases of conflict.

The present constitution provides guarantees of legal representation for persons accused of a crime, including free representation if necessary, but this right appears to be little recognized by authorities or realized by the public. Pretrial detention is permissible, and a suspect may be held for three days before being charged. After being charged, an accused individual may be held for up to a year before being brought to trial. There is no system of bail; accused individuals remain incarcerated until tried.

Both the police and the National Security Committee have the right to violate guarantees of privacy (of the home, telephone, mail, and banks) with the sanction of the procurator general. The theoretical requirement for search warrants and judicial orders for wiretaps and other violations of privacy often is ignored in practice. When the 1995 constitution was approved, a United States official criticized its lack of protection of civil and human rights. Before the approval referendum, Nazarbayev had announced the dissolution of the Constitutional Court, which he replaced in October with a Constitutional Council whose decisions the president could veto.

Prisons

The Kazakhstani prison system came under attack from human rights organizations in the mid-1990s. In the late Soviet period, eighty-nine labor camps, ten prisons, and three psychiatric hospitals (under the administration of the Ministry of Internal Affairs) were known to be operating in the republic. At least two of the prisons, at Öskemen and Semey, date from tsarist days. There also were at least four special prisons for women and children, at Pavlodar, Zhambyl, and Chamalghan. The facilities remaining from the Soviet period are badly overcrowded and understaffed. According to a 1996 report from the Ministry of Internal Affairs, government funding of prisons is less than half the amount required, and corruption and theft are common throughout the prison system. The total prison population in 1996 was 76,000, and about 1,300 died of tuberculosis in 1995. Health conditions are extremely poor. Overcrowding has been exacerbated by an explosion of crime among the country's youth and by President Nazarbayev's ongoing policy of harsh sentences for convicted criminals.

Crime

In the early and mid-1990s, crime was increasing at an alarming rate. The police were badly understaffed, overworked, and underfinanced. In 1995 police in Almaty received no pay for three months. A significant drain of personnel has occurred since independence, as investigators and police officers either move to other republics or enter other lines of work offering higher pay. Even before independence, militia authorities complained that staffing was more than 2,000 below full force. In numerous instances, police officers themselves have been involved in crime, especially in such potentially lucrative branches of law enforcement as highway patrol and customs inspection. Under these circumstances, public respect for the police declined seriously.

Since independence Kazakhstan has suffered an enormous increase in crime of almost all types. One indication of this explosion has been a series of measures ordered by President Nazarbayev in September 1995, aimed primarily at ending corruption in the police force. The incidence of reported crimes has grown by about 25 percent in every year since independence, although in the first months of 1995 the growth rate slowed to about 16 percent. The average crime rate for the republic is about 50 crimes per 10,000 population, but the rate is significantly higher in Qaraghandy, North Kazakhstan, East Kazakhstan, Aqmola, Pavlodar, and Almaty. Crime-solving rates have fallen to under 60 percent across the republic and to as low as 30 percent in cities such as Qaraghandy and Temirtau.

Particular increases have been noted in violent crimes and in crimes committed by teenagers and young men. Contract murders and armed clashes between criminal groups increased noticeably in 1995 and were cited by Nazarbayev as a reason for tightening police procedures. Although Soviet crime statistics were not especially reliable, it is still revealing that in 1988 only 5 percent of the republic's convicts were under thirty years of age, but by 1992 that figure had risen to 58 percent. In addition, there has been an enormous increase in official malfeasance and corruption, with bribe taking reported to be nearly ubiquitous.

Narcotics

Kazakhstan offers natural conditions favorable to accelerated narcotics use and trade. Many parts of the country offer excellent growing conditions for cannabis and opium poppies, and the country is located on the route to lucrative markets in the West. Until it ceased production in 1991, Kazakhstan's Shymkent plant was the Soviet Union's only supplier of medicinal opiates. The Ministry of Internal Affairs estimated narcotics production and traffic to be 30 percent higher in 1993 than in the previous year. The focus of attention for that ministry, which coordinates the republic's antinarcotics program, is the Chu Valley in south central Kazakhstan, where an estimated 138,000 hectares of cannabis and an unknown area of opium poppy fields are under cultivation, providing exports for international smugglers. Because of low funding, efforts to eradicate cannabis and poppy cultivation virtually ceased in 1995.

Almaty has become a crossroads for opiates and hashish from southwest Asia. This role has resulted in large part from lax customs controls and the city's position as a transportation hub. In 1994 an estimated 1.4 tons of morphine base from Afghanistan were stored in Almaty.

An active government narcotics control program began in 1993, although limited personnel and funding have handicapped its efforts. In 1994 only 400 police, 100 sniffer dogs, and twelve special investigators were active. Most Ministry of Internal Affairs interdiction occurs along the Chinese border. Cooperation has been sought with the narcotics programs of other Central Asian states and Russia. In 1993 and 1994, Russian forces made eradication sweeps through the Chu Valley, but Russian helicopter support ceased in 1994. Antinarcotics agreements have been signed with Turkey, Pakistan, China, and Iran. Kazakhstan also has requested United States aid in drafting narcotics provisions in a new penal code.

Domestic use of narcotics has been confined largely to areas of production, notably around Shymkent. Although only 10,700 addicts were registered in 1991, experts believe the actual number to be much higher. The use of homemade opiates increased significantly in the early 1990s. The Ministry of Health runs a center offering treatment and prevention programs. However, by 1994 lack of resources had made treatment on demand impossible and stimulated reorganization of the program.

National Security Prospects

Like the other four Central Asian republics (with the possible exception of Uzbekistan), Kazakhstan lacks the resources to create an independent military establishment or an effective internal security force. By 1995 policy makers, headed by President Nazarbayev, had recognized the need to remain under the umbrella of Russian military protection, a status reinforced by a number of bilateral treaties and expected to become further institutionalized in future years. The poor state of internal security was a crisis that eluded control in the mid-1990s, despite authoritarian measures by Nazarbayev. But Kazakhstan has committed itself to encouraging foreign investment in the effort to salvage the national economy. To provide an appropriate atmosphere for such commercial activity, improved internal security, perhaps with substantial Western assistance, is a necessary step.

GLOSSARY

Bolshevik Revolution

Coup organized by Vladimir I. Lenin and carried out by the Bolshevik radical group of the Russian Social Democratic Labor Party to overthrow the Provisional Government of Russia in November 1917. Also known as the October Revolution.

Commonwealth of Independent States (CIS)

Official designation of the former republics of the Soviet Union that remained loosely federated in economic and security matters after the Soviet Union disbanded as a unified state in 1991. Members in 1996 were Armenia, Azerbaijan, Belarus, Georgia, Kazakhstan, Kyrgyzstan, Moldova, Russia, Tajikistan, Turkmenistan, Ukraine, and Uzbekistan.

Conventional Forces in Europe (CFE) Treaty

An agreement signed in 1990 by members of the Warsaw Pact and the North Atlantic Treaty Organization (NATO--*q.v.*) to establish parity in conventional weapons between the two organizations from the Atlantic to the Urals. Included a strict system of inspections and information exchange. In 1995 Russia requested exemptions for forces stationed in the Caucasus region, and substantial changes were negotiated by the thirty signatory nations in 1997.

Economic Cooperation Organization (ECO)

Established in 1985, an economic union of Islamic countries to promote regional cooperation in trade, transportation, communications, culture, and overall economic development. Members in 1996 were Afghanistan, Azerbaijan, Iran, Kazakhstan, Kyrgyzstan, Pakistan, Tajikistan, Turkey, the "Turkish Republic of Northern Cyprus," Turkmenistan, and Uzbekistan.

glasnost

Russian term, literally meaning "public voicing." Applied in the Soviet Union beginning in 1987 to official permission for public discussion of issues and public access to information, initially intended as a means for the regime of Mikhail S. Gorbachev to publicize the need for political and economic reform.

gross domestic product (GDP)

The total value of goods and services produced exclusively within a nation's domestic economy, in contrast to the gross national product (GNP--*q.v.*). Normally computed over one-year periods.

gross national product (GNP)

The total value of goods and services produced within a country's borders and the income received from abroad by residents, minus payments remitted abroad by nonresidents. Normally computed over one-year periods.

hard currency

National currencies that are freely convertible and traded on international currency markets.

International Monetary Fund (IMF)

Established with the World Bank (*q.v.*) in 1945, a specialized agency affiliated with the United Nations and responsible for stabilizing international exchange rates and payments. Its main function is to provide loans to its members (including industrialized and developing countries) when they experience balance of payments difficulties. These loans frequently have conditions that require substantial internal economic adjustments by the recipients, most of which are developing countries.

Iranian

Linguistically, a subgroup of the Indo-Iranian branch of Indo-European languages, which in modern times includes Persian (*q.v.*)--the most widely used--Pushtu, Kurdish (*q.v.*) dialects, and Ossetic. In the Middle Iranian stage of the group's development (third century B.C. to tenth century A.D.), the chief languages were Parthian, Pahlavi (middle Persian), and Soghdian.

Kurdish

Term referring to a mainly Muslim people speaking an Indo-European language similar to Persian. Kurds constitute significant minorities in Iran, Iraq, and Turkey, with smaller groups in Armenia and Syria. Despite international proposals in response to minority persecution, never united in a single state.

manat

Beginning in 1993, national currency of Turkmenistan. Inflation rapid in 1994 and 1995. In January 1996, official rate 200 per US$1.

Manichaeism

A dualistic religious movement founded in Persia, third century A.D., incorporating elements of Christianity and Iranian and Indian religions.

net material product (NMP)

In countries having centrally planned economies, the official measure of the value of goods and services produced within the country. Roughly equivalent to the gross national product (*q.v.*), NMP is based on constant prices and does not account for depreciation.

New Economic Policy (Novaya ekonomicheskaya politika--NEP)

Instituted in 1921 by Vladimir I. Lenin, program allowing peasants in the Soviet Union to sell produce on an open market and small enterprises to be privately owned and operated. Officially ended in 1929 with enforcement of national central planning of all economic activities.

North Atlantic Treaty Organization (NATO)

During the postwar period until the dissolution of the Soviet Union in 1991, the primary collective defense agreement of the Western powers against the military presence of the Warsaw Pact nations in Europe. Founded in 1949. Its military and administrative structure remained intact after 1991, but early in 1994 the Partnership for Peace offered partial membership to all former Warsaw Pact nations and former republics of the Soviet Union.

Organization for Security and Cooperation in Europe (OSCE)
Beginning in 1995, the name of the former Conference on Security and Cooperation in Europe (CSCE). Established in 1972 as an international forum for negotiation, the organization consisted of fifty-three member nations in 1996, including all European countries. The Charter of Paris (1990) changed the CSCE from an ad hoc forum to an organization with permanent institutions. In 1992 the CSCE took on new roles in conflict mediation, including crises in the former Yugoslavia, the Caucasus region, and Nagorno-Karabakh. Beginning in 1994, Russia advocated CSCE/OSCE as the chief European peacekeeping agency in preference to possible NATO expansion.

perestroika
Russian term meaning "restructuring." Applied in the late 1980s to an official Soviet program of revitalization of the Communist Party of the Soviet Union (CPSU), the economy, and the society by adjusting economic, social, and political mechanisms in the central planning system. Identified with the tenure of Mikhail S. Gorbachev as leader of the Soviet Union.

Persian
As a language, a member of the Iranian subgroup in the Indo-European language family. The official language of modern Iran and spoken widely in Afghanistan. Middle Persian (Pahlavi) was used between the third century B.C. and the ninth century A.D. and was the official language of the Sassanid Empire that ruled parts of Central Asia from the third century to the sixth century A.D. Modern Persian is called Farsi by native speakers.

ruble
Currency of the Soviet Union; then, beginning in 1992, of Russia. In February 1997, the exchange rate was 5,670 rubles to US$1.

ruble zone
Currency exchange arrangement by which former republics of the Soviet Union continued using the ruble as their national currency, forcing dependence on Russian currency valuations and economic developments elsewhere in the Commonwealth of Independent States (*q.v.*). In 1993 all Central Asian republics except Tajikistan established national currencies independent of the ruble.

Shia
The smaller of the two great divisions of Islam, supporting the claims of Ali to leadership of the Muslim community, in opposition to the Sunni (*q.v.*) view of succession to Muslim leadership--the issue causing the central schism within Islam.

som

Beginning in 1993, currency of Kyrgyzstan and Uzbekistan. In 1996 average exchange rate of Uzbekistani som was thirty-five to US$1; of Kyrgyzstani som, eleven to US$1.

Sunni

The larger of the two fundamental divisions of Islam, opposed to the Shia (*q.v.*) on the issue of succession to Muslim leadership.

Tajikistani ruble

Beginning in 1995, currency of Tajikistan. In January 1996, exchange rate 284 rubles per US$1.

tenge

Beginning in 1993, currency of Kazakhstan. In January 1996, exchange rate sixty-four tenge to US$1.

value-added tax (VAT)

A tax applied to the additional value created at a given stage of production and calculated as a percentage of the difference between the product value at that stage and the cost of all materials and services purchased or introduced as inputs.

World Bank

Informal name for a group of four affiliated international institutions: the International Bank for Reconstruction and Development (IBRD); the International Development Association (IDA); the International Finance Corporation (IFC); and the Multilateral Investment Guaranty Agency (MIGA). The four institutions are owned by the governments of the countries that subscribe their capital for credit and investment in developing countries; each institution has a specialized agenda for aiding economic growth in target countries. To participate in the World Bank group, member states first must belong to the International Monetary Fund (IMF--*q.v.*).

World Trade Organization (WTO)

Established 1995 as successor to the General Agreement on Tariffs and Trade (GATT), aimed at liberalizing and securing international trade. Formed in the Uruguay Round of trade negotiations, the WTO had 115 member nations in 1996, and fifteen others applied WTO rules to their trade policies. Administered by a general council, trade dispute negotiation panel, and secretariat.

Zoroastrianism

Religion founded in the sixth century B.C. by the Iranian prophet Zoroaster. With monotheistic and dualistic aspects, it influenced subsequently founded religions, including Christianity and Islam. Now practiced most widely by Persian immigrants in India.

BIBLIOGRAPHY

"Central Asia," *Current History*, 93, April 1994, 145-86.

"Central Asia: Five-State Commonwealth Set Up," *Current Digest of the Post-Soviet Press*, 45, February 3, 1993, 1-8.

"Central Asia: Patterns of Change, Past, Present, and Future," *Harvard International Report*, 15, Spring 1993, 6-12.

"Konflikt na granitse Kirgizii i Tadzhikistana" (Conflict on the Border of Kyrgyzia and Tajikistan), *Turkestan* [Ashgabat], 1990, No. 1, 5.

"Natsional'nyy vopros i mezhnatsional'nyye otnosheniya v SSSR: Istoriya i sovremennost'" (The National Question and Inter-national Relations in the USSR: History and the Present). *Voprosy istorii*, 1989, No. 5, 3-97.

"Russia: World Drugs Capital?" *The Economist Foreign Report*, April 27, 1995, 3-4.

"Uzbekistan," *Central Asia Monitor*, 1996, No. 3, entire issue.

1995 Britannica Book of the Year. Chicago: 1995.

Abduvakhitov, Abdujabar. "Independent Uzbekistan: A Muslim Community in Development." Pages 293-306 in Michael Bourdeaux, ed., *The Politics of Religion in Russia and the New States of Eurasia*. Armonk, New York: M.E. Sharpe, 1995.

Adshead, Samuel Adrian M. *Central Asia in World History*. New York: St. Martin's Press, 1993.

Ahmed, Akbar, and David Hart, eds. *Islam in Tribal Societies*. London: Routledge and Kegan Paul, 1984.

Akademiya nauk SSSR. Institut etnografii. *Sotsial'no-kul'turnyy oblik sovetskikh natsiy* (The Social-Cultural Aspect of the Soviet Nations). Moscow: Nauka, 1986.

Akademiya nauk Tadzhikskoy SSR. *Istoriya tadzhikskogo naroda* (A History of the Tajik People), 3. Moscow: Nauka, 1965.

Akademiya nauk Tadzhikskoy SSR. *Tadzhikistan: priroda i resursy* (Tajikistan: Nature and Resources). Dushanbe: Donish, 1982.

Akademiya nauk Tadzhikskoy SSR. *Tadzhikskaya Sovetskaya Sotsialisticheskaya Respublika* (The Tajik Soviet Socialist Republic). Ed., M.S. Asimov. Dushanbe: 1974.

Akbarzadeh, Shahram. "Nation Building in Uzbekistan," *Central Asian Survey* [Abingdon, United Kingdom], 15, March 1996, 23-32.

Akchurin, Marat. "Soviet Muslims: Seeking Reform, Not Revolution," *World and I*, 6, October 1991, 86-93.

Akiner, Shirin, ed. *Central Asia: 130 Years of Russian Dominance, an Historical Overview*. Durham: Duke University Press, 1994.

Akiner, Shirin, ed. *Economic and Political Trends in Central Asia*. New York: Routledge & Kegan Paul, 1992.

Akiner, Shirin. *Islamic Peoples of the Soviet Union: An Historical and Statistical Handbook*. New York: Kegan Paul International, 1986.

Akiner, Shirin. *Islamic Peoples of the Soviet Union: An Historical and Statistical Handbook*. New York: Routledge, 1986.

Alikhanov, B. B., and S. S. Tursunov, *Ekonomicheskiye problemy okhrany okruzhayushchey sredy v usloviyakh Uzbekistana* (Economic Problems of Environmental Protection in the Conditions of Uzbekistan). Tashkent: State Committee on Hydrology, 1990.

Allworth, Edward, ed. *Central Asia: 120 Years of Russian Rule*. Durham: Duke University Press, 1989.

Allworth, Edward, ed. *Central Asia: A Century of Russian Rule*. New York: Columbia University Press, 1967.

Allworth, Edward, ed. *Muslim Communities Reemerge: Historical Perspectives*. Durham: Duke University Press, 1994.

Allworth, Edward, ed. *The Nationality Question in Soviet Central Asia*. New York: Praeger, 1973.

Alptekin, Erkin. "Chinese Policy in Eastern Turkestan," *Institute of Muslim Minority Affairs Journal*, 13, January 1992, 185-95.

Amnesty International. *Tadzhikistan*. London: 1993.

Anderson, John. "Authoritarian Political Development in Central Asia: The Case of Turkmenistan," *Central Asian Survey* [Abingdon, United Kingdom], 14, No. 4, 1995, 509-28.

Andreyev, M.S. "Po etnografii tadzhikov: Nekotoryye svedeniya" (On the Ethnography of the Tajiks: Some Information). Pages 151-77 in *Tadzhikistan*. Tashkent: Obshchestvo dlya izucheniya Tadzhikistana i iranskikh narodnostey za yego predelami, 1925.

Andreyev, Nikolai. "Central Asia: From Marx to Mohammed," *New Times International* [Moscow], No. 39, 1992, 19-22.

Andreyev, Nikolai. "What Future for Uzbekistan, Kirgizia, Turkmenia?" *Current Digest of the Post-Soviet Press*, 44, July 22, 1992, 8-11.

Atkin, Muriel. "Islamic Assertiveness and the Waning of the Old Soviet Order," *Nationalities Papers*, 20, No. 1, Spring 1992, 55-72.

Atkin, Muriel. "Religious, National, and Other Identities in Central Asia." Pages 46-72 in Jo Ann Gross, ed., *Muslims in Central Asia*. Durham: Duke University Press, 1992.

Atkin, Muriel. "Tajikistan: Ancient Heritage, New Politics." Pages 361-83 in Ian Bremmer and Ray Taras, eds., *Nation and Politics in the Soviet Successor States*. Cambridge: Cambridge University Press, 1993.

Atkin, Muriel. "The Survival of Islam in Soviet Tajikistan," *Middle East Journal*, 43, No. 4, Autumn 1989, 605-18.

Atkin, Muriel. *The Subtlest Battle: Islam in Soviet Tajikistan*. Philadelphia: Foreign Policy Research Institute, 1989.

Aziz, Sartaj. "The Rediscovery of Central Asia," *Economics Review* [Karachi], 23, June 1992, 15-17.

Azv'yalova, L.V., O.A. Agafonova, and L.A. Semakina. *Zagryazneniye atmosfery Sredney Azii tyazhelymi metallami* (Atmospheric Pollution by Heavy Metals in Central Asia). Tashkent: State Committee on Hydrology, 1991.

Bachmann, Berta. *Memories of Kazakhstan: A Report on the Life Experiences of a German Woman in Russia*. Lincoln, Nebraska: American History Society, 1983.

Bacon, Elizabeth E. *Central Asians under Russian Rule: A Study in Culture Change*. Ithaca: Cornell University Press, 1980.

Baldick, Julian. *Imaginary Muslims: The Uwaysi Sufis of Central Asia*. Irvington: New York University Press, 1994.

Banuazizi, Ali, and Myron Weiner, eds. *The New Geopolitics of Central Asia and Its Borderlands*. Bloomington: Indiana University Press, 1994.

Bartol'd, Vasilii Vladimirovich. "A History of the Turkman People (An Outline)." Pages 73-170 in *Four Studies on the History of Central Asia* III. Trans., V. and T. Minorsky. Leiden: E.J. Brill, 1962.

Bartol'd, Vasilii Vladimirovich. *Histoire des Turcs d'Asie centrale.* Trans., M. Donskis. Philadelphia: Porcupine Press, 1977.

Bartol'd, Vasilii Vladimirovich. *Turkestan Down to the Mongol Invasion.* London: Lazac, 1968.

Barylski, Robert V. "The Caucasus, Central Asia, and the Near-Abroad Syndrome," *Central Asia Monitor,* No. 4, 1993, 31.

Basilov, Vladimir Nikolayevich. "Honor Groups in Traditional Turkmenian Society." Pages 220-43 in Akbar Ahmed and David Hart, eds., *Islam in Tribal Societies.* London: Routledge and Kegan Paul, 1984.

Basilov, Vladimir Nikolayevich. "Popular Islam in Central Asia and Kazakhstan," *Journal of the Institute of Muslim Minority Affairs*, 8, No. 1, 1987, 7-17.

Batalden, Stephen K., and Sandra L. Batalden. *The Newly Independent States of Eurasia: Handbook of Former Soviet Republics.* Phoenix: Oryx, 1993.

Baumann, Robert F. *Russian-Soviet Unconventional Wars in the Caucasus, Central Asia, and Afghanistan.* Fort Leavenworth, Kansas: Combat Studies Institute, 1993.

Becker, Seymour. "National Consciousness and the Politics of the Bukharan People's Counciliar Republic." Pages 159-67 in Edward Allworth, ed., *The Nationality Question in Soviet Central Asia.* New York: Praeger, 1973.

Becker, Seymour. *Russia's Protectorates in Central Asia: Bukhara and Khiva, 1865-1924.* Cambridge: Harvard University Press, 1968.

Bennigsen, Alexandre, and S. Enders Wimbush. *Muslims of the Soviet Empire.* Bloomington: Indiana University Press, 1986.

Bennigsen, Alexandre. *Mystics and Commissars: Sufism in the Soviet Union.* London: Hurst, 1985.

Berdi Murat, Aman. "Turkmenistan and the Turkmen." Pages 262-82 in Zev Katz, ed., *Handbook of Major Soviet Nationalities.* New York: Free Press, 1975.

Bilan du Monde: l'Année économique et sociale 1995. Ed., Jacques-François Simon. Paris: Le Monde, 1996.

Blank, Stephen. "Energy, Economics, and Security in Central Asia: Russia and Its Rivals," *Central Asian Survey*, 14, No. 3, 1995, 373-406.

Bohr, Annette. "Health Catastrophe in Karakalpakstan," *Report on the USSR* [Munich], 1, July 21, 1989, 37-38.

Bourdeaux, Michael, ed. *The Politics of Religion in Russia and the New States of Eurasia.* Armonk, New York: M.E. Sharpe, 1995.

Bradley, Catherine. *Kazakhstan.* Brookfield, Connecticut: Millbrook Press, 1992.

Bregel, Yuriy. "Nomadic and Sedentary Elements among the Turkmens," *Central Asiatic Journal*, 25, Nos. 1-2, 1981, 5-37.

Bregel, Yuriy. "The Peoples of Southern Turkmenistan and Khorasan in the 17th and 18th Centuries," *Central Asian Review*, 8, No. 3, 1960, 264-72.

Bremmer, Ian, and Ray Taras, eds. *Nation and Politics in the Soviet Successor States.* Cambridge: Cambridge University Press, 1993.

Brezhnev, Leonid. *Virgin Lands: Two Years in Kazakhstan, 1954-55.* Tarrytown, New York: Elsevier Science, 1982.

Brown, Bess. "Central Asia: The First Year of Unexpected Statehood," *RFE/RL Research Report* [Munich], 2, No. 1, January 1, 1993, 25-36.

Brown, Bess. "National Security and Military Issues in Central Asia." Pages 234-52 in Bruce Parrott, ed., *State Building and Military Power in Russia and the New States of Eurasia.* Armonk, New York: M.E. Sharpe, 1995.

Brown, Bess. "Three Central Asian States Form Economic Union," *RFE/RL Research Report* [Munich], 3, No. 11, April 1, 1994, 33-35.

Broxup, Marie. "Islam in Central Asia since Gorbachev," *Asian Affairs* [London], 18, October 1987, 283-93.

Canfield, Robert L., ed. *Turko-Persia in Historical Perspective.* Cambridge: Cambridge University Press, 1991.

Carlisle, Donald S. "Power and Politics in Soviet Uzbekistan: From Stalin to Gorbachev." Pages 93-130 in William Fierman, *Soviet Central Asia: The Failed Transformation.* Boulder, Colorado: Westview Press, 1991.

Carrère D'Encausse, Hélène. *Islam and the Russian Empire: Reform and Revolution in Central Asia.* Berkeley: University of California Press, 1989.

Carrère d'Encausse, Hélène. *Réforme et révolution chez les Musulmans de l'Empire russe.* Paris: Librarie Armand Colin, 1966.

Chalidze, F. "Aral Sea Crisis: A Legacy of Soviet Rule," *Central Asia Monitor*, 1992, No. 1, 30-34.

Clark, Susan L. "The Central Asian States: Defining Security Priorities and Developing Military Forces." Pages 177-206 in Michael Mandelbaum, ed., *Central Asia and the World: Kazakhstan, Uzbekistan, Tajikistan, Kyrgyzstan, and Turkmenistan.* New York: Council on Foreign Relations Press, 1994.

Clark, Susan L. *Security in Russia and Eurasia: The New National Militaries and Emerging Defense Policies.* Boulder, Colorado: Westview Press, 1995.

Colton, Timothy J., and Robert C. Tucker, eds. *Patterns in Post-Soviet Leadership.* Boulder, Colorado: Westview Press, 1995.

Commonwealth of Independent States. Statistical Committee. *Strany-chleny Sodruzhestva nezavisimykh gosudarstv: Statisticheskiy yezhegodnik* (The Member Nations of the Commonwealth of Independent States: A Statistical Yearbook). Moscow: Finansovyy inzhiniring, 1992.

Corbin, Henry. "Nasir-i Khusrau and Iranian Isma'ilism." Pages 520-42 in Richard N. Frye, ed., *The Cambridge History of Iran*, 4. Cambridge: Cambridge University Press, 1975.

Critchlow, James. *Nationalism in Uzbekistan.* Boulder, Colorado: Westview Press, 1991.

Dannreuther, Roland. *Creating New States in Central Asia.* Adelphi Paper No. 288. London: Brassey's for International Institute for Strategic Studies, 1994.

Dave, Bhavna. "A New Parliament Consolidates Presidential Authority," *Transition*, March 22, 1996, 33-37.

Dave, Bhavna. "Kazakhstan Staggers under Its Nuclear Burden," *Transition*, November 17, 1995, 12-13.

Davis, Christopher M. "Health Care Crisis: The Former Soviet Union," *RFE/RL Research Report* [Munich], 2, No. 40, October 8, 1993, 35-43.

Dawisha, A.I., and Karen Dawisha, eds. *The Foreign Policy Interests of Russia and the New States of Eurasia.* Armonk, New York: M.E. Sharpe, 1995.

Dawisha, Karen, and Bruce Parrott. *Russia and the New States of Eurasia: The Politics of Upheaval.* Port Chester, New York: Cambridge University Press, 1994.

Demidov, Sergey Mikhaylovich. *Istoriya religioznykh verovaniy narodov Turkmenistana* (A History of the Religious Faiths of Turkmenistan). Ashgabat: Ylym, 1990.

Deweese, Devin. *Islamization and Native Religion in the Golden Horde.* University Park: Pennsylvania State University Press, 1994.

Dienes, Leslie. "Economic Geographic Relations in the Post-Soviet Republics," *Post-Soviet Geography*, 34, October 1993, 497-529.

Diller, Daniel C., ed. *Russia and the Independent States.* Washington: Congressional Quarterly, 1993.

Diuk, Nadia, and Adrian Karatnycky. *The Hidden Nations: The People Challenge the Soviet Union.* Fairfield, New Jersey: William Morrow, 1990.

Doolotaliyev, S. "Some Issues in the Development of the Sary-Dzhaz Mining Industrial Center, Kirghiz SSR," *Sovetskaya Geografiya*, 30, May 1989, 371-4.

Dorian, James P. "The Kazakh Oil Industry: A Potential Critical Role in Central Asia," *Energy Policy*, 22, August 1994, 685-98.

Drobizheva, L.M. "Kul'tura i mezhnatsional'yye otnosheniya v SSSR" (Culture and International Relations in the USSR), *Voprosy istorii* [Moscow], 1979, No. 11, 3-15.

Drobizheva, Leokadia, et al., eds. *Ethics Conflict in the Post-Soviet World: Case Studies and Analysis.* Armonk, New York: M. E. Sharpe, 1996.

Durdyyev, Marat, and Shukhrat Kadyrov. *Turkmeny mira* (Turkmen of the World). Ashgabat: Kharp, 1991.

Dzharylgasimova, R.Sh., and L.S. Tolstova, eds. *Etnicheskiye protsessy u natsional'nykh grupp Sredney Azii i Kazakhstana* (Ethnic Processes in the National Groups of Central Asia and Kazakhstan). Moscow: Nauka, 1980.

Dzhikiyev, Ata. *Ocherki proiskhozhdeniya i formirovaniya turkmenskogo naroda v epokhu srednovekov'ya* (Essays on the Origin and Formation of the Turkmen People in the Middle Ages). Ashgabat: Ylym, 1991.

Economist Intelligence Unit. *Country Report: Georgia, Armenia, Azerbaijan, Central Asian Republics.* London: 1994.

Economist Intelligence Unit. *Country Report: Kazakhstan, Kyrgyz Republic, Tajikistan, Turkmenistan, Uzbekistan* [London], No. 1, 1996.

Eickelman, Dale F., ed. *Russia's Muslim Frontiers: New Directions in Cross-Cultural Analysis.* Bloomington: Indiana University Press, 1993.

Elebayeva, Aynur B. "The Osh Incident: Problems for Research," *Post-Soviet Geography*, 33, February 1992, 78-86.

Ellis, C.H. *The Transcaspian Episode, 1918-1919.* London: Hutchinson, 1963.

Encyclopedia Iranica, 5. Costa Mesa, California: Mazda, 1990.

Entsiklopediyai sovetii Tojik (Soviet Tajik Encyclopedia). Dushanbe: Sarredaktsiyai ilmii entsiklopediyai sovetii Tojik, 1978-1987.

Evans, John L. *Russia and the Khanates of Central Asia to 1865.* New York: Associated Faculty Press, 1982.

Fane, Daria. "Ethnicity and Regionalism in Uzbekistan: Maintaining Stability Through Authoritarian Control." Pages 271-302 in Leokadia Drobizheva, et al., eds. *Ethnic Conflict in the Post- Soviet World: Case Studies and Analysis.* Armonk, New York: M.E. Sharpe, 1996.

Farmayan, Hafez. "Turkoman Identity and Presence in Iran," *Iran*, 4, Summer 1981, 45-63.

Fedorova, T.I. *Goroda Tadzhikistana i problemy rosta i razvitiya* (Cities of Tajikistan and Problems of Growth and Development). Dushanbe: Irfon, 1981.

Feldman, Walter. "Interpreting the Poetry of Makhtumquli." Pages 167-89 in Jo-Ann Gross, ed., *Muslims in Central Asia: Expressions of Identity and Change*. Durham: Duke University Press, 1992.

Ferdinand, Peter, ed. *The New States of Central Asia and Their Neighbors*. New York: Council on Foreign Relations Press, 1994.

Feshbach, Murray, and Alfred Friendly, Jr. *Ecocide in the USSR: Health and Nature under Siege*. New York: Basic Books, 1992.

Fierman, William, ed. *Soviet Central Asia: The Failed Transformation*. Boulder, Colorado: Westview Press, 1991.

Fierman, William. "Independence and the Declining Priority of Language Law Implementation in Uzbekistan." Pages 205-30 in Yaacov Ro'i, ed., *Muslim Eurasia: Conflicting Legacies*. London: Frank Cass, 1995.

Forsythe, Rosemarie. "The Politics of Oil in the Caucasus and Central Asia," *Adelphi Papers*, 300, May 1996, whole issue.

Freidin, Gregory. "Coup II," *The New Republic*, 205, No. 16, October 14, 1991, 16-18.

Friedman, L. "Ethnic and National Composition of Population in Newly Independent Countries of the Middle East and Caucasus," *Central Asia Today*, 1993, No. 1, 56-60.

Frye, Richard N. "The Samanids." Pages 136-61 in Richard N. Frye, *The Cambridge History of Iran*. Cambridge: Cambridge University Press, 1975.

Frye, Richard N. *Bukhara: The Medieval Achievement*. Norman: University of Oklahoma Press, 1965.

Frye, Richard N., ed. *The Cambridge History of Iran*. Cambridge: Cambridge University Press, 1975.

Fuller, Graham. "Central Asia: The Quest for Identity," *Current History*, 93, April 1994, 145-49.

Fuller, Graham. "The Emergence of Central Asia," *Foreign Policy*, Spring 1990, 49-67.

Fuller, Graham. *Central Asia: The New Geopolitics*. Santa Monica, California: Rand, 1992.

Furtado, Charles F., and Henry R. Huttenback, eds. "The Ex-Soviet Nationalities Without Gorbachev," *Nationalities Papers*, 20, Fall 1992, 1-124.

Geldiyev, B., S.P. Tokarev, and T. Sakhatliyev. *Razvitiye promyshlennosti Turkmenistana za 50 let* (The Development of Industry in Turkmenistan over 50 Years). Ashgabat: Turkmenistan, 1974.

Ghorban, Narsi. "The Role of the Multinational Oil Companies in the Development of Oil and Gas Resources in Central Asia and the Caucasus," *Iranian Journal of International Affairs*, 5, Spring 1993, 1-15.

Gleason, Gregory. "Central Asia: Land Reform and the Ethnic Factor," *RFE/RL Research Report* [Munich], 2, No. 3, 1993, 28-33.

Gleason, Gregory. "The Political Economy of Dependency under Socialism: The Asian Republics in the USSR," *Studies in Comparative Communism*, 24, December 1991, 335-53.

Gleason, Gregory. "The Struggle for Control over Water in Central Asia: Republican Sovereignty and Collective Action." *RFE/RL Report on the USSR* [Munich], 3, No. 25, June 21, 1991, 11-19.

Gleason, Gregory. *An Introduction to the History of the Turkic Peoples*. Wiesbaden: Otto Harrasowitz, 1992.

Goetz, Roland, and Uwe Halbach. *Informationen über eine unbekannte Republik, I-II*. Berichte des Bundesinstituts für ostwissenschaftliche und internationale Studien. Cologne: 1995.

Goron, Leonard, and Alex Pravda, eds. *Who's Who in Russia and the New States*. London: I.B. Tauris, 1993.

Gretsky, Sergei. "Civil War in Tajikistan and Its International Repercussions," *Critique*, Spring 1995, 3-24.

Gretsky, Sergei. "Qadi Akbar Turajonzoda," *Central Asia Monitor*, 1994, No. 1, 16-24.

Gretsky, Sergei. "Russia and Tajikistan." Pages 231-51 in A.Z. Rubinstein and O.M. Smolansky, eds. *Regional Power Rivalries in the New Eurasia: Russia, Turkey, and Iran*. Armonk, New York: M.E. Sharpe, 1995.

Gross, Jo-Ann, ed. *Muslims in Central Asia: Expressions of Identity and Change*. Durham: Duke University Press, 1992.

Grousset, Rene. *The Empire of the Steppes*. Trans., N. Walford. New Brunswick: Rutgers University Press, 1970.

Haghayeghi, Mehrdad. *Islam and Politics in Central Asia*. New York: St. Martin's Press, 1995.

Hale, Henry. "Islam, State-building, and Uzbekistan Foreign Policy," Pages 136-72 in Ali Banuazizi and Myron Weiner, eds., *The New Geopolitics of Central Asia and Its Borderlands*. Bloomington: Indiana University Press, 1994.

Hambly, Gavin, ed. *Central Asia*. New York: Delacorte Press, 1969.

Helsinki Watch. *Conflict in the Soviet Union*. New York: Human Rights Watch, 1991.

Henley, John S., and George B. Assaf. "Re-Integrating the Central Asian Republics into the World Economy," *Intereconomics*, 30, September-October 1995, 235-45.

Henze, Paul B. *Whither Turkestan?* Santa Monica, California: Rand, 1992.

Hitchins, Keith. "Modern Tajik Literature." Pages 454-75 in E. Yarshater, ed., *Persian Literature*. Albany: Bibliotheca Persica, 1988.

Hooson, David. *The Soviet Union: People and Regions*. Belmont, California: Wadsworth, 1966.

Horton, Scott, and Tatiana Geller. "Investing in Uzbekistan's Natural Resources Sector," *Central Asia Monitor*, 1996, No. 1, 25-35.

Horton, Scott, and Tatiana Geller. "Secured Transactions in Uzbekistan," *Central Asia Monitor*, 1996, No. 2, 21-7.

Hostler, Charles Warren. *The Turks of Central Asia*. Westport, Connecticut: Praeger, 1993.

Howard, G. "The Caspian Oil and Gas Oasis: Turkmenistan," *Russian Oil and Gas Guide*, 3, No. 1, 1994, 54-58.

Institute for National Strategic Studies. *Strategic Assessment 1995: U.S. Security Challenges in Transition*. Washington: GPO, 1995.

International Monetary Fund. *Economic Review: Turkmenistan*. Washington: 1992.

International Monetary Fund. *Turkmenistan*. Washington: 1994.

Irons, William. "The Turkmen of Iran: A Brief Research Report," *Iranian Studies*, 2, Winter 1969, 27-38.

Irons, William. *The Yomut Turkmen: A Study of Social Organization among a Central Asian Turkic-Speaking Population*. Ann Arbor: University of Michigan Press, 1975.

Istoriya kul'turnogo stroitel'stva v Tadzhikistane, 1917-1977 gg (The History of Cultural Construction in Tajikistan, 1917-1977, 2.) Dushanbe: Donish, 1983.

Istoriya Turkmenskoy SSR (History of the Turkmen SSR). Ashgabat: Akademiya nauk Turkmenskoy SSR, 1957.

Janabel, Jiger. "When National Ambition Conflicts with Reality: Studies on Kazakhstan's Ethnic Relations," *Central Asian Survey*, 15, No. 1, March 1996, 5-22.

Jane's Sentinel Regional Security Assessment: Commonwealth of Independent States. Ed., Paul Beaver. Coulsdon, United Kingdom: Jane's Information Group, 1994.

Kaiser, Robert J. *The Geography of Nationalism in Russia and the USSR*. Princeton: Princeton University Press, 1994.

Karasik, Theodore, ed. *USSR Facts and Figures Annual 1992*. Gulf Breeze, Florida: Academic International Press, 1992.

Karasik, Theodore. *Azerbaijan, Central Asia, and Future Persian Gulf Security*. Santa Monica, California: Rand, 1993.

Karpat, Kemal. "The Foreign Policy of the Central Asian States, Turkey, and Iran," *OSCE Bulletin*, 3, No. 1, Winter 1994-95, 17-30.

Katz, Zev, ed. *Handbook of Major Soviet Nationalities*. New York: Free Press, 1975.

Kedzie, Christopher R. *Stumbling Blocks and Stepping Stones: The Crossing from Soviet Domination to Self Rule in the Republics of Central Asia*. Santa Monica, California: Rand, 1994.

Keller, S. "Islam in Soviet Central Asia, 1917-1930: Soviet Policy and the Struggle for Control," *Central Asian Survey* [Abingdon, United Kingdom], 11, No. 1, 1992, 25-50.

Khrushchev, Anatoliy Timofeyevich, and O.D. Chuvilkin. "Resursy gaza gosudarstv Tsentral'noy Azii: Ekonomiko-geograficheskiye aspekty" (Gas Resources of the States of Central Asia: Economic-Geographic Aspects), *Vestnik Moskovskogo universiteta: Geografiya* [Moscow], 1994, No. 4, 51-57.

Kirpichenko, V. "Khozyaystvennyye svyazi stran-chlenov SNG" (Economic Relations of CIS Member States). *Ekonomist* [Moscow], 1993, No. 4, 53-62.

Kojaoglu, T. "The Existence of a Bukharan Nationality in the Recent Past." Pages 151-8 in Edward Allworth, ed., *The Nationality Question in Soviet Central Asia*. New York: Praeger, 1973.

Konyukhov, V.G. *Ekologicheskaya obstanovka v Uzbekistanskoy SSR i mery po yeye uluchsheniyu* (The Ecological Situation in the Uzbek SSR and Measures to Improve It). Tashkent: State Committee on Environmental Protection, 1990.

Korsunskiy, L. "Podzemnyy atomnyy gulag deystvuyet" (An Underground Atomic Gulag Is in Operation). *Stolitsa* [Moscow] 1992, No. 35, 22-6.

Krader, Lawrence. *Peoples of Central Asia*. Uralic and Altaic Series, No. 26. Bloomington: Indiana University Press, 1963.

Landau, Jacob M. *Pan-Turkism: From Irredentism to Cooperation*. Bloomington: Indiana University Press, 1995.

Lawyers' Committee for Human Rights. Freedom of Association Project. *Karimov's Way: Freedom of Association and Assembly in Uzbekistan*. Briefing Paper No. 1. New York: 1994.

Lipski, Andrei. "The Community of Central Asia: Inside or Outside the CIS?" *International Affairs* [Moscow], October 1993, 51-5.

Lubin, Nancy. "Islam and Ethnic Identity in Central Asia: A View from Below." Pages 53-70 in Yaacov Ro'i, ed., *Muslim Eurasia: Conflicting Legacies*. London: Frank Cass, 1995.
Lubin, Nancy. "Leadership in Uzbekistan and Kazakhstan: The Views of the Led." Pages 217-34 in Timothy J. Colton and Robert C. Tucker, eds., *Patterns in Post-Soviet Leadership*. Boulder, Colorado: Westview Press, 1995.
Lubin, Nancy. "Uzbekistan." Pages 289-306 in Philip R. Pryde, ed., *Environmental Resources and Constraints in the Former Soviet Republics*. Boulder, Colorado: Westview Press, 1995.
Lubin, Nancy. "Uzbekistan: The Challenges Ahead," *Middle East Journal*, 43, No. 4, Autumn 1989, 619-34.
Lubin, Nancy. *Central Asians Take Stock*. Washington: United States Institute of Peace Press, 1995.
Lubin, Nancy. *Labour and Nationality in Soviet Central Asia: An Uneasy Compromise*. Princeton: Princeton University Press, 1985.
Maier, Frith. *Trekking in Russia and Central Asia: A Traveler's Guide*. Seattle: Mountaineers Books, 1994.
Maksudov, Sergey. "On Infant Mortality in Turkmenistan," *Central Asia Monitor*, 1992, No. 1, 26-30.
Malik, Hafeez, ed. *Central Asia: Its Strategic Importance and Future Prospects*. New York: St. Martin's Press, 1994.
Mandelbaum, Michael, ed. *Central Asia and the World: Kazakhstan, Uzbekistan, Tajikistan, Kyrgyzstan, and Turkmenistan*. New York: Council on Foreign Relations Press, 1994.
Manz, Beatrice F., ed. *Central Asia in Historical Perspective*. Boulder, Colorado: Westview Press, 1994.
Martin, Keith. "Environment: Central Asia's Forgotten Tragedy," *RFE/RL Research Report* [Munich], 3, No. 29, July 29, 1994, 35-48.
Mesbahi, Mohiaddin, ed. *Central Asia and the Caucasus after the Soviet Union: Domestic and International Dynamics*. Gainesville: University Press of Florida, 1994.
Micklin, Philip. "The Aral Sea Crisis: Introduction to the Special Issue," *Post-Soviet Geography*, 33, No. 5, May 1992, 269-82.
Micklin, Phillip P. *The Water Management Crisis in Soviet Central Asia*. The Carl Beck Papers in Russian and East European Studies, No. 905. Pittsburgh: University of Pittsburgh Press, 1992.
Migranyan, Andranik. "Russia and the Near Abroad," *Current Digest of the Post-Soviet Press*, 47, March 9, 1994, 1-4 and March 16, 1994, 6-11.
Monogarova, L.F. "Evolyutsiya natsional'nogo samosoznaniya pripamirskikh narodnostey" (The Evolution of National Self-Awareness of the Pamiri Peoples). Pages 125-35 in *Etnicheskiye protsessy u natsional'nykh grupp Sredney Azii i Kazakhstana*. Moscow: Nauka, 1980.
Nahaylo, Bohdan, and Viktor Swoboda. *Soviet Disunion*. New York: The Free Press, 1990.
Narody mira: Etnograficheskiye ocherki (Peoples of the World: Ethnographic Sketches). Moscow: Nauka, 1963.
Naumkin, Vitaly. *State, Religion, and Society in Central Asia: A Post-Soviet Critique*. London: Ithaca Press, 1993.
Nissman, David B. "Iran and Soviet Islam: The Azerbaijan and Turkmen SSRs," *Central Asia Survey* [Abingdon, United Kingdom], 2, No. 4, 1983, 45-60.

Olcott, Martha Brill. "Central Asia's Islamic Awakening," *Current History*, 93, April 1994, 150-54.

Olcott, Martha Brill. "The Basmachi or Freemen's Revolt in Turkestan 1918-1924," *Soviet Studies*, 33, No. 3, July 1981, 352-69.

Olcott, Martha Brill. "The Myth of 'Tsentral'naia Aziia'," *Orbis*, 38, No. 3, Summer 1995, 549-66.

Olcott, Martha Brill. *Central Asia's New States: Independence, Foreign Policy, and Regional Security*. Washington: United States Institute of Peace Press, 1996.

Olcott, Martha Brill. *The Kazakhs*. 2d ed. Studies of Nationalities in the USSR. Stanford, California: Hoover Institution Press, 1995.

Paksoy, G.B., ed. *Central Asia Reader: The Rediscovery of History*. Armonk, New York: M.E. Sharpe, 1994.

Park, A.G. *Bolshevism in Turkestan, 1917-1927*. New York: Columbia University Press, 1957.

Pierce, Richard A. *Russian Central Asia, 1867-1917*. Berkeley: University of California Press, 1960.

Pilkington, John. "Kyrgyzstan: A Tale of Two Journeys," *Geographical Magazine*, 65, April 1993, 8-12.

Pipes, Daniel. "The Politics of the 'Rip Van Winkel' States: The Southern Tier States of the Ex-Soviet Union Have Moved the Borders of the Middle East North," *Middle East Insight*, 10, November-December 1993, 30-40.

PlanEcon. *Review and Outlook for the Former Soviet Republics*. Washington: 1995.

Plyshevskiy, B. "Ekonomicheskoye polozheniye gosudarstv SNG" (The Economic Situation of the CIS States), *Ekonomist* [Moscow], 1993, No. 4, 63-75.

Polat, Abdumannob. "Uzbekistan: Does the Government Want a Dialogue with the Opposition," *Caspian Crossroads*, Winter 1995, 26-28.

Polyakov, Sergey Petrovich. *Etnicheskaya istoriya severo-zapadnoy Turkmenii v sredniye veka* (The Ethnic History of Northwest Turkmenia in the Middle Ages). Ashgabat: 1973.

Pomfret, Richard. *The Economies of Central Asia*. Princeton: Princeton University Press, 1995.

Posner, Michael. *Human Rights and Legal Issues in Uzbekistan*. New York: Lawyers' Committee for Human Rights, 1993.

Potter, William C. "The 'Sapphire' File: Lessons for International Nonproliferation Cooperation," *Transition*, 1, November 17, 1995, 14-19.

Pryde, Ian. "Kyrgyzstan: Secularism vs. Islam," *World Today*, 48, November 1992, 208-11.

Pryde, Ian. "Kyrgyzstan: The Trials of Independence," *Journal of Democracy*, 5, January 1994, 109-20.

Pryde, Philip R., ed. *Environmental Resources and Constraints in the Former Soviet Republics*. Boulder, Colorado: Westview Press, 1995.

Rakowska-Harmstone, Teresa. *Russia and Nationalism in Central Asia: The Case of Tadzhikistan*. Baltimore: Johns Hopkins Press, 1970.

Rashid, Ahmed. *The Resurgence of Central Asia: Islam or Nationalism?* Karachi: Oxford University Press, 1994.

Rashid, Ahmed. *The Resurgence of Central Asia: Islam or Nationalism?* Atlantic Highlands, New Jersey: Zed Books, 1994.

Ro'i, Yaacov, ed. *Muslim Eurasia: Conflicting Legacies*. London: Frank Cass, 1995.

Rotor, Igor. "Kyrgyzstan: Capitalist Experiment in Central Asia," *Current Digest of the Post-Soviet Press*, 44, April 8, 1992, 4-5.

Rubin, Barry M. "The Fragmentation of Tajikistan," *Survival*, 35, No. 4, Winter 1993-1994, 71-91.

Rubinstein, Alvin Z. "The Geopolitical Pull on Russia," *Orbis*, 38, No. 3, Summer 1995, 567-84.

Rubinstein, Alvin Z., and Oles M. Smolansky, eds. *Regional Power Rivalries in the New Eurasia: Russia, Turkey, and Iran*. Armonk, New York: M.E. Sharpe, 1995.

Rumer, Boris Z. *Soviet Central Asia: "A Tragic Experiment."* Winchester, Massachusetts: Unwin Hyman, 1990.

Rumer, Boris Z. *Soviet Central Asia: A "Tragic Experiment."* Boston: Unwin Hyman, 1989.

Rywkin, Michael. *Moscow's Muslim Challenge: Soviet Central Asia*. Armonk, New York: M.E. Sharpe, 1990.

Sagers, Matthew J. "News Notes," *Post-Soviet Geography*, 33, No. 3, 1992, 190.

Saray, Mehmet. *The Turkmens in the Age of Imperialism: A Study of the Turkmen People and Their Incorporation into the Russian Empire*. Ankara: Turkish Historical Society, 1989.

Sharipov, I. *Zakonomernosti formirovaniya sotsialisticheskikh obshchestvennykh otnosheniy v Tadzhikistane* (The Regularity of the Formation of Socialist Social Relations in Tajikistan). Dushanbe: Donish, 1983.

Shlapentokh, Vladimir, Munir Sendich, and Emil Payin, eds. *The New Russian Diaspora: Russian Minorities in the Former Soviet Republics*. Armonk, New York: M.E. Sharpe, 1994.

Shome, Parthasarathi, and Julio Escolano. "The State of Tax Policy in the Central Asian and Transcaucasian Newly Independent States," *Bulletin of International Fiscal Documentation*, 48, April 1994, 159-66.

Shukurov, E., ed. *Discovery of Kyrghyzstan*. Bishkek: International Foundation "A Discovery of Kyrghyzstan," 1993.

Shukurov, Maksud Rakhmatullayevich. *Kul'turnaya zhizn' Tadzhikistana* (The Cultural Life of Tajikistan). Dushanbe: Irfon, 1980.

Simon, Gerhard. *Nationalism and Policy Toward the Nationalities in the Soviet Union*. Trans., K. Forster and O. Forster. Boulder, Colorado: Westview Press, 1991.

Sizov, Andrey Yevgen'yevich. "Ekonomika Rossii i drugikh stran SNG v nachale 90-kh godov" (The Economy of Russia and the Other Countries of the CIS at the Beginning of the 1990s). *Mirovaya ekonomika i mezhdunarodnyye otnosheniya* [Moscow], 1993, No. 7, 20-29.

Smirnov, Yu. "Strannyy Islam" (Strange Islam), *Pamir*, No. 2, 1988, 104-25.

Soviet Union. Central Statistical Administration. *Chislennost' i sostav naseleniy SSSR* (Size and Composition of the Populations of the USSR). Moscow: Finansy i statistika, 1984.

Soviet Union. State Committee on Statistics. *Chislennost' naseleniya soyuznykh respublik po gorodskim poseleniyam i rayonam* (Size of the Population of the Union Republics by Urban Settlement and District). Moscow: Informatsionno-izdatel'skiy tsentr Goskomstata SSSR, 1991.

Soviet Union. State Committee on Statistics. *Demograficheskiy yezhegodnik SSSR 1990* (Demographic Yearbook of the USSR 1990). Moscow: Finansy i statistika, 1990.

Soviet Union. State Committee on Statistics. *Soyuznyye respubliki: Osnovnyye ekonomicheskiye i sotsial'nyye pokazateli* (The Union Republics: Basic Economic and Social Indicators). Moscow: Informatsionno-izdatel'skiy tsentr Goskomstata SSSR, 1991.

Sparks, John. *Realms of the Russian Bear: A Natural History of Russia and the Central Asian Republics*. Waltham, Massachusetts: Little Brown, 1992.

Staar, S. Frederick. "Making Eurasia Stable," *Foreign Affairs*, 75, January-February 1996, 80-92.

Starr, S. Frederick, ed. *The Legacy of History in Russia and the New States of Eurasia*. Armonk, New York: M.E. Sharpe, 1994.

Subtelny, E. "The Cult of Holy Places: Religious Practices among Soviet Muslims," *Middle East Journal*, 43, No. 4, 1989, 593-604.

Symon, L. "Tadzhikistan: A Developing Country in the Soviet Union," *Asian Affairs*, 61, pt. 3, October 1974, 249-56.

Szporluk, Roman, ed. *National Identity and Ethnicity in Russia and the New States of Eurasia*. Armonk, New York: M.E. Sharpe, 1994.

Tadjbakhsh, Shahrbanou. "Causes and Consequences of the Civil War," *Central Asia Monitor*, 1993, No. 1, 10-14.

Tadjbakhsh, Shahrbanou. "The 'Tajik Spring' of 1992," *Central Asia Monitor*, No. 2, 1993, 21-9.

Tadzhikistan. Tashkent: Obshchestvo dlya izucheniya Tadzhikistana i iranskikh narodnostey za yego predelami, 1925.

Tajik SSR. Supreme Soviet. Presidium. "Soobshcheniye komissii Prezidiuma Verkhovnogo Soveta Tadzhikskoy SSR po proverke sobytiy 12-14 fevralya 1990 g. v Dushanbe" (Report of the Commission of the Presidium of the Supreme Soviet of the Tajik SSR on Examining the Events of February 12-14, 1990, in Dushanbe), *Sogdiana* [Dushanbe],1990. No. 3, entire issue.

The Europa World Year Book 1993, 2. London: Europa, 1993.

The Europa World Year Book 1994, 2. London: Europa, 1994.

The Europa World Year Book 1995, 2. London: Europa, 1995.

The Europa World Year Book 1996, 2. London: Europa, 1996.

The FirstBook [sic] *of Demographics for the Republics of the Former Soviet Union, 1951-1990*. Shady Side, Maryland: New World Demographics, 1992.

The Military Balance 1992-1993. London: International Institute for Strategic Studies, 1992.

The Military Balance 1993-1994. London: International Institute for Strategic Studies, 1993.

The Military Balance 1994-1995. London: International Institute for Strategic Studies, 1994.

The Military Balance 1995-1996. London: International Institute for Strategic Studies, 1995.

The Statesman's Year-Book 1992-1993. Ed., Brian Hunter. New York: St. Martin's Press, 1992.

The Statesman's Year-Book 1993-1994. Ed., Brian Hunter. New York: St. Martin's Press, 1993.

The Statesman's Year-Book 1994-1995. Ed., Brian Hunter. New York: St. Martin's Press, 1994.

The Statesman's Year-Book 1995-1996. Ed., Brian Hunter. New York: St. Martin's Press, 1995.

Thomas, Paul. *The Central Asian States: Tajikistan, Uzbekistan, Kyrgyzstan, Turkmenistan*. Brookfield, Connecticut: Millbrook Press, 1992.

Turkmenenforschung (Research on the Turkmen), 1-15. Hamburg and Berlin: Reinhold Schletzer Verlag, 1979-93.

Tyson, David, and Larry Clark. *Turkmen: Language Competencies for Peace Corps Volunteers in Turkmenistan*. Washington: GPO, 1994.

Undeland, Charles, and Nicholas Platt. *The Central Asian Republics: Fragments of Empire, Magnets of Wealth*. New York: Asia Society, 1994.

United Nations. Department for Economic and Social Information and Policy Analysis. *Demographic Yearbook 1993*. New York: 1995.

United Nations. Department for Economic and Social Information and Policy Analysis. *Demographic Yearbook 1994*. New York: 1996.

United States. Agency for International Development. Center for Health Information. *USAID Health Profile: Turkmenistan*. Arlington, Virginia: USAID, 1992.

United States. Bureau of International Narcotics Matters. *International Narcotics Strategy Report March 1996*. Washington: GPO, 1996.

United States. Central Intelligence Agency. *Handbook of International Economic Statistics 1995*. Washington: GPO, 1995.

United States. Central Intelligence Agency. *Handbook of International Economic Statistics 1992*. Washington: GPO, 1992.

United States. Central Intelligence Agency. *Kazakhstan: An Economic Profile*. Springfield, Virginia: National Technical Information Service, 1993.

United States. Central Intelligence Agency. *Piecing Together Central Asia: A Look at Key Leaders*. Washington: GPO, 1993.

United States. Central Intelligence Agency. *The World Factbook 1994*. Washington: GPO, 1994.

United States. Central Intelligence Agency. *The World Factbook 1995*. Washington: GPO, 1995.

United States. Central Intelligence Agency. *Turkmenistan: An Economic Profile*. Springfield, Virginia: National Technical Information Service, 1993.

United States. Congress. 103d, 2d Session. House of Representatives. Foreign Affairs Subcommittee on Europe and the Middle East. Prepared testimony of Holly Burkhalter of Human Rights Watch/Helsinki, Sept. 22, 1994. Washington: GPO, 1994.

United States. Congress. 103d, 2d Session. House of Representatives. Subcommittee on International Security, International Operations, and Human Rights. Testimony from Pamela B. Cohen, National President, and Micah H. Naftalin, National Director of the Union of Councils, April 26, 1994. Washington: GPO, 1994.

United States. Congress. Commission on Security and Cooperation in Europe. *Report on the Helsinki Commission Visit to Armenia, Azerbaijan, Tajikistan, Uzbekistan, Kazakhstan, and Ukraine*. Washington: GPO, 1992.

United States. Congress. Commission on Security and Cooperation in Europe. *Human Rights and Democratization in the Newly Independent States of the Former Soviet Union*. Washington: GPO, 1993.

United States. Department of Agriculture. Economic Research Service. *Former USSR: Agriculture and Trade Report 1991*. Washington: GPO, 1992.

United States. Department of Agriculture. Economic Research Service. *Former USSR: Agriculture and Trade Report 1992*. Washington: GPO, 1993.

United States. Department of Commerce. Business Information Service for the Newly Independent States. *Commercial Overview of Turkmenistan*. Washington: 1993.

United States. Department of State. Bureau of International Narcotics Matters. *International Narcotics Strategy Report March 1996*. Washington: GPO, 1996.

United States. Department of State. *Country Reports on Human Rights Practices for 1993*. (Report submitted to United States Congress, 103d, 2d Session, House of Representatives, Committee on Foreign Affairs, and Senate, Committee on Foreign Relations.) Washington: GPO, 1994.

Uzbekistan. State Committee on Projections and Statistics. *Chislennost', sostav i dvizheniye naseleniya Respubliki Uzbekistan* (The Size, Composition, and Movement of the Population of the Republic of Uzbekistan). Tashkent: 1992.

Uzbekistan. State Committee on Projections and Statistics. *Okhrana zdorov'ya v respublike Uzbekistana* (Health Protection in the Republic of Uzbekistan). Tashkent: 1991.

Vaisman, Demian. "Regionalism and Clan Loyalty in the Political Life of Uzbekistan." Pages 105-22 in Yaacov Ro'i, ed., *Muslim Eurasia: Conflicting Legacies*. London: Frank Cass, 1995.

Veselovskiy, Vladimir Glebovich, et al. *Arkhitektura sovetskogo Tadzhikistana* (The Architecture of Soviet Tajikistan). Moscow: Stroyizdat, 1987.

Vinnikov, Ya. R. "Natsional'nyye i etnograficheskiye gruppy Sredney Azii po dannym etnicheskoy statistiki" (The National and Ethnographic Groups of Central Asia According to Ethnic Statistical Data). Pages 11-42 in R. Sh. Dzharylgasimova and L.S. Tolstova, eds., *Etnicheskiye protsessy u natsional'nykh grupp Sredney Azii i Kazakhstana*. Moscow: Nauka, 1980.

WEFA Group. *Eurasia Economic Outlook February 1996*. Eddystone, Pennsylvania: 1996.

Wheeler, Geoffrey. *The Modern History of Soviet Central Asia*. New York: Praeger, 1964.

Wixman, Ronald. *Peoples of the USSR: An Ethnographic Handbook*. Armonk, New York: M.E. Sharpe, 1984.

Wolfson, Zeev. "Central Asian Environment: A Dead End," *Environmental Policy Review*, 4, No. 1, January 1990, 29-46.

World Bank. *Kazakhstan: Agricultural Sector Review*. Washington: 1994.

World Bank. *Kazakhstan: The Transition to a Market Economy*. Washington: 1993.

World Bank. *Kyrgyz Republic: Agricultural Sector Review*. Washington: 1995.

World Bank. *Kyrgyz Republic: Economic Report*. Washington: 1994.

World Bank. *Kyrgyz Republic: Energy Sector Review*. Washington: 1995.

World Bank. *Kyrgyz Republic: National Environmental Action Plan*. Washington: 1995.

World Bank. *Kyrgyz Republic: Poverty Assessment and Strategy*. Washington: 1995.

World Bank. *Kyrgyzstan: Social Protection in a Reforming Economy*. Washington: 1993.

World Bank. *Kyrgyzstan: The Transition to a Market Economy*. Washington: 1993.

World Bank. *Statistical Handbook 1995: States of the Former USSR*. Washington: 1995.

World Bank. *Turkmenistan*. World Bank Country Study. Washington: 1994.

World Bank. *Uzbekistan: An Agenda for Economic Reform*. Washington: 1993.

World Radio TV Handbook 1996. Ed., Andrew G. Sennitt. Amsterdam: Billboard, 1996.

Worldwide Directory of Defense Authorities 1996, 1. Ed., Kenneth Gause. Bethesda, Maryland: Worldwide Government Directories, 1996.

Worldwide Directory of Defense Authorities, 2. Ed., Kenneth Gause. Bethesda, Maryland: Worldwide Government Directories, 1996.

Wright, R. "Report from Turkestan," *New Yorker*, April 6, 1992, 53-75.
Yarshater, Ehsan, ed. *Persian Literature*. Albany: Bibliotheca Persica, 1988.
Yekayev, Orazpolat. *Turkmenistan i turkmeny v kontse XV-pervoy polovine XVI v* (Turkmenistan and the Turkmen at the End of the Fifteenth-First Half of the Sixteenth Centuries). Ashgabat: Ylym, 1981.

Chapter 7

KYRGYZSTAN: A COUNTRY STUDY*

Glenn E. Curtis (Editor)

HISTORICAL BACKGROUND

Elevated to the status of a union republic by Joseph V. Stalin in 1936, the Kyrgyz Soviet Socialist Republic was until 1990 one of the poorest, quietest, and most conservative of all the Soviet republics. It was the Kyrgyz Republic that celebrated the election of a sheepherder as president of its parliamentary executive committee, the Presidium, in 1987. Three years later, however, that quiescence ended, and Kyrgyzstan's history as a separate nation began.

Kyrgyzstan began the new phase of its existence by declaring independence in August 1991. At that point, it possessed a combination of useful resources and threatening deficiencies. Geographic location fits in both categories; landlocked deep inside the Asian continent, Kyrgyzstan has minimal natural transportation routes available to serve its economic development, and its isolation has been an obstacle in the campaign to gain international attention. On the other hand, Kyrgyzstan also is isolated from most of the Asian trouble spots (excepting Tajikistan), making national security a relatively low priority. The natural resources that Kyrgyzstan possesses--primarily gold, other minerals, and abundant hydroelectric power--have not been managed well enough to make them an asset in pulling the republic up from the severe economic shock of leaving the secure, if limiting, domain of the Soviet Union.

In the mid-1990s, the most ambitious economic and political reform program in Central Asia caused more frustration than satisfaction among Kyrgyzstan's citizens, largely because the republic inherited neither an economic infrastructure nor a political tradition upon which to base the rapid transitions envisioned by President Askar Akayev's first idealistic blueprints. Although some elements of reform (privatization, for example) went into place quickly, the absence of others (credit from a commercial banking system, for example) brought the overall system to a halt, causing high unemployment and frustration. By 1995, democratic reform seemed a victim of that frustration, as Akayev increasingly sought to use personal executive

---

* Excerpted from the Library of Congress Country Studies Website at: http://lcweb2.loc.gov/frd/cs/cshome.html.

power in promoting his policies for economic growth, a pattern that became typical in the Central Asian countries' first years of independence.

Since independence Kyrgyzstan has made impressive strides in some regards such as creating genuinely free news media and fostering an active political opposition. At the same time, the grim realities of the country's economic position, which exacerbate the clan- and family-based political tensions that have always remained beneath the surface of national life, leave long-term political and economic prospects clouded at best. Kyrgyzstan has no desire to return to Russian control, yet economic necessity has forced the government to look to Moscow for needed financial support and trade.

Background

The modern nation of Kyrgyzstan is based on a civilization of nomadic tribes who moved across the eastern and northern sections of present-day Central Asia. In this process, they were dominated by, and intermixed with, a number of other tribes and peoples that have influenced the ultimate character of the Kyrgyz people.

Early History

Stone implements found in the Tian Shan mountains indicate the presence of human society in what is now Kyrgyzstan as many as 200,000 to 300,000 years ago. The first written records of a Kyrgyz civilization appear in Chinese chronicles beginning about 2000 B.C. The Kyrgyz, a nomadic people, originally inhabited an area of present-day northwestern Mongolia. In the fourth and third centuries B.C., Kyrgyz bands were among the raiders who persistently invaded Chinese territory and stimulated the building of the original Great Wall of China in the third century B.C. The Kyrgyz achieved a reputation as great fighters and traders. In the centuries that followed, some Kyrgyz tribes freed themselves from domination by the Huns by moving northward into the Yenisey and Baikal regions of present-day south-central Siberia.

The first Kyrgyz state, the Kyrgyz Khanate, existed from the sixth until the thirteenth century A.D., expanding by the tenth century southwestward to the eastern and northern regions of present-day Kyrgyzstan and westward to the headwaters of the Ertis (Irtysh) River in present-day eastern Kazakhstan. In this period, the khanate established intensive commercial contacts in China, Tibet, Central Asia, and Persia.

In the meantime, beginning about 1000 B.C., large tribes collectively known as the Scythians also lived in the area of present-day Kyrgyzstan. Excellent warriors, the Scythian tribes farther west had resisted an invasion by the troops of Alexander the Great in 328-27 B.C. The Kyrgyz tribes who entered the region around the sixth century played a major role in the development of feudalism.

The Kyrgyz reached their greatest expansion by conquering the Uygur Khanate and forcing it out of Mongolia in A.D. 840, then moving as far south as the Tian Shan range--a position the Kyrgyz maintained for about 200 years. By the twelfth century, however, Kyrgyz domination had shrunk to the region of the Sayan Mountains, northwest of present-day Mongolia, and the Altay Range on the present-day border of China and Mongolia. In the same period, other Kyrgyz tribes were moving across a wide area of Central Asia and mingling with other ethnic groups (see Ethnic Traditions).

Mongol Domination

The Mongols' invasion of Central Asia in the fourteenth century devastated the territory of Kyrgyzstan, costing its people their independence and their written language. The son of Chinggis (Genghis) Khan, Dzhuchi, conquered the Kyrgyz tribes of the Yenisey region, who by this time had become disunited. For the next 200 years, the Kyrgyz remained under the Golden Horde and the Oriot and Jumgar khanates that succeeded that regime. Freedom was regained in 1510, but Kyrgyz tribes were overrun in the seventeenth century by the Kalmyks, in the mid-eighteenth century by the Manchus, and in the early nineteenth century by the Uzbeks.

The Kyrgyz began efforts to gain protection from more powerful neighboring states in 1758, when some tribes sent emissaries to China. A similar mission went to the Russian Empire in 1785. Between 1710 and 1876, the Kyrgyz were ruled by the Uzbek Quqon (Kokand) Khanate, one of the three major principalities of Central Asia during that period (see fig. 3). Kyrgyz tribes fought and lost four wars against the Uzbeks of Quqon between 1845 and 1873. The defeats strengthened the Kyrgyz willingness to seek Russian protection. Even during this period, however, the Kyrgyz occupied important positions in the social and administrative structures of the khanate, and they maintained special military units that continued their earlier tradition of military organization; some Kyrgyz advanced to the position of khan.

Russian Control

In 1876 Russian troops defeated the Quqon Khanate and occupied northern Kyrgyzstan. Within five years, all Kyrgyzstan had become part of the Russian Empire, and the Kyrgyz slowly began to integrate themselves into the economic and political life of Russia. In the last decades of the nineteenth century, increasing numbers of Russian and Ukrainian settlers moved into the northern part of present-day Kyrgyzstan. Russian specialists began large-scale housing, mining, and road construction projects and the construction of schools. In the first years of the twentieth century, the presence of the Russians made possible the publication of the first books in the Kyrgyz language; the first Kyrgyz reader was published in Russia in 1911. Nevertheless, Russian policy did not aim at educating the population; most Kyrgyz remained illiterate, and in most regions traditional life continued largely as it had before 1870.

By 1915, however, even many Central Asians outside the intelligentsia had recognized the negative effects of the Russian Empire's repressive policies. The Kyrgyz nomads suffered especially from confiscation of their land for Russian and Ukrainian settlements. Russian taxation, forced labor, and price policies all targeted the indigenous population and raised discontent and regional tension. The Kyrgyz in Semirech'ye Province suffered especially from land appropriation. The bloody rebellion of the summer of 1916 began in Uzbekistan, then spread into Kyrgyzstan and elsewhere. Kazaks, Turkmen, Uzbeks, and Kyrgyz participated. An estimated 2,000 Slavic settlers and even more local people were killed, and the harsh Russian reprisals drove one-third of the Kyrgyz population into China.

Into the Soviet Union

Following a brief period of independence after the 1917 Bolshevik Revolution (see Glossary) toppled the empire, the territory of present-day Kyrgyzstan was designated the Kara-Kyrghyz Autonomous Region and a constituent part of the Union of Soviet Socialist Republics (Soviet Union) in 1924. In 1926 the official name changed to the Kyrgyz Autonomous Republic before the region achieved the status of a full republic of the Soviet Union in 1936.

Recent History

In the late 1980s, the Kyrgyz were jolted into a state of national consciousness by the reforms of Soviet leader Mikhail S. Gorbachev and by ethnic conflict much closer to home. As democratic activism stirred in Kyrgyzstan's cities, events in Moscow pushed the republic toward unavoidable independence.

Ethnic Conflict

The most important single event leading to independence grew from an outburst of ethnic friction. From the perspective of the Kyrgyz, the most acute nationality problem long had been posed by the Uzbeks living in and around the city of Osh, in the republic's southwest. Although Kyrgyzstan was only about 13 percent Uzbek according to the 1989 census, almost the entire Uzbek population was concentrated in Osh Province. Tensions very likely had existed between the Kyrgyz and the Uzbeks throughout the Soviet period, but Moscow was able to preserve the image of Soviet ethnic harmony until the reforms of Gorbachev in the mid-1980s. In the general atmosphere of *glasnost* (see Glossary), an Uzbek-rights group called Adalat began airing old grievances in 1989, demanding that Moscow grant local Uzbek autonomy in Osh and consider its annexation by nearby Uzbekistan.

The real issue behind Adalat's demand was land, which is in extremely short supply in the southernmost province of Osh. To protect their claims, some Osh Kyrgyz also had formed an opposing ethnic association, called Osh-aimagy (Osh-land). In early June 1990, the Kyrgyz-dominated Osh City Council announced plans to build a cotton processing plant on a parcel of land under the control of an Uzbek-dominated collective farm in Osh Province.

The confrontation that erupted over control of that land brought several days of bloody riots between crowds led by the respective associations, killing at least 320 Kyrgyz and Uzbeks in Osh. The precise cause and sequence of events in early June 1990 is disputed between Uzbek and Kyrgyz accounts. Scores of families were left homeless when their houses were burned out. The government finally stopped the rioting by imposing a military curfew.

Because the telephone lines remained open in the otherwise blockaded city, news of the violence spread immediately to Frunze. In the capital, a large group of students marched on the headquarters of the Communist Party of Kyrgyzia (CPK), which also served as the seat of government, in the center of the city. In the violent confrontation that ensued, personal injuries were minimized by effective crowd control, and the riotous crowd eventually was transformed into a mass meeting.

Democratic Activism

The Osh riots and the subsequent events in Frunze quickly brought to the surface an undercurrent of political discontent that had been forming among both the intelligentsia and middle-level party officials. A loose affiliation of activists calling themselves the Democratic Movement of Kyrgyzstan (DDK) began to organize public opinion, calling among other things for the resignation of Absamat Masaliyev, who was president of the republic's parliament, the Supreme Soviet, as well as a member of the Soviet Union's Politburo and the head of the CPK. The DDK called for Masaliyev's resignation because he was widely viewed as having mishandled the Osh riots.

Democratic activists erected tents in front of the party headquarters, maintaining pressure with a series of hunger strikes and highly visible public demonstrations. The continuing atmosphere of crisis emboldened CPK members, who also wished to get rid of the reactionary Masaliyev. Four months later, in a presidential election prescribed by Gorbachev's reform policies, Masaliyev failed to win the majority of Supreme Soviet votes required to remain in power.

The Rise of Akayev

With none of the three presidential candidates able to gain the necessary majority in the 1990 election, the Supreme Soviet unexpectedly selected Askar Akayev, a forty-six-year-old physicist, who had been serving as head of the republic's Academy of Sciences. Although he had served for a year in a science-related post on the Central Committee of the Communist Party of the Soviet Union (CPSU) and was a party member, Akayev was the first president of a Soviet republic who had not held a high party position.

At the same meeting of the Supreme Soviet, the deputies changed the name of the republic to Kyrgyzstan. They also began to speak seriously of seeking greater national sovereignty (which was formally declared on November 20, 1990) and of attaining political domination of the republic by the Kyrgyz, including the establishment of Kyrgyz as the official language.

By mid-summer 1991, the Kyrgyz were beginning to make serious moves to uncouple the government from the CPSU and its Kyrgyzstan branch. In early August, the Ministry of Internal Affairs of Kyrgyzstan, which governs the police and the internal security forces, announced a ban of all CPSU affiliation or activity within the ministry. Events elsewhere precluded a seemingly inevitable conflict with Moscow over that decision; in August 1991, the attention of the entire union moved to Moscow when reactionaries in Gorbachev's government attempted to remove him from power.

Unlike the leaders of the other four Central Asian republics, who temporized for a day about their course following the coup, Akayev condemned the plot almost immediately and began preparations to repel the airborne forces rumored to be on the way to Kyrgyzstan from Moscow. The quick collapse of the coup made the preparations unnecessary, but Akayev's declaration of support for Gorbachev and for the maintenance of legitimate authority gained the Kyrgyz leader enormous respect among the Kyrgyz people and among world leaders. On

August 30, 1991, days after the coup began, Akayev and the republic's Supreme Soviet declared Kyrgyzstan an independent nation, and the president threw the CPSU and its Kyrgyzstan branch out of the government. However, he did not go as far as officials in most of the other former Soviet republics, where the party was banned totally.

At the same time independence was declared, the republic's Supreme Soviet scheduled direct presidential elections for October 1991. Running unopposed, Akayev received 95 percent of the popular vote, thus becoming the country's first popularly elected president. The so-called Silk Revolution drew much international sympathy and attention. In December 1991, when the Belarusian, Russian, and Ukrainian republics signed the Tashkent Agreement, forming a commonwealth that heralded the dissolution of the Soviet Union, Akayev demanded that another meeting be held so that Kyrgyzstan might become a founding member of the Commonwealth of Independent States (CIS--see Glossary), as the new union was to be called.

The sympathy that Akayev had won for Kyrgyzstan earlier in his presidency served the country well once the world generally acknowledged the passing of the Gorbachev regime and the Soviet Union. Kyrgyzstan was recognized almost immediately by most nations, including the United States, whose secretary of state, James Baker, made an official visit in January 1992. A United States embassy was opened in the capital (which had reassumed its pre-Soviet name of Bishkek in December 1990) in February 1992. By early 1993, the new country had been recognized by 120 nations and had diplomatic relations with sixty-one of them.

Akayev's Early Years

Despite initial euphoria over the possibilities of independence and membership in the CIS, Akayev recognized that his country's economic position was extremely vulnerable and that the ethnic situation exacerbated that vulnerability. Thus, the Akayev administration devoted much attention to creating a legal basis of governance while struggling to keep the economy afloat.

In the first two years of his presidency, Akayev seemed to work effectively with the Supreme Soviet that had put him in office. By 1992, however, Akayev's good relations with the legislature had fallen victim to the rapidly declining economy, the failure of the CIS to become a functioning body, and the country's inability to attract substantial assistance or investment from any of the potential foreign partners whom he had courted so assiduously.

In advancing his reform programs, Akayev experienced particular difficulties in gaining the cooperation of entrenched local politicians remaining from the communist government apparatus. To gain control of local administration, Akayev imitated the 1992 strategy of Russia's president Boris N. Yeltsin by appointing individuals to leadership positions at the province, district, and city levels (see Structure of Government). Akayev filled about seventy such positions, the occupants of which were supposed to combine direct loyalty and responsibility to the president with a zeal to improve conditions for their immediate locales. The system became a source of constant scandal and embarrassment for Akayev, however. The most flagrant abuses came in Jalal-Abad Province (which had been split from neighboring Osh in spring 1991 to dilute political power in the south), where the new *akim*, the provincial governor, appointed members of his own family to the majority of the positions under his control and used state funds to acquire personal property. The situation in Jalal-

Abad aroused strong resentment and demonstrations that continued even after the governor had been forced to resign.

In 1992 and 1993, the public perception grew that Akayev himself had provided a model for the tendency of local leaders to put family and clan interests above those of the nation. Indeed, several prominent national government officials, including the head of the internal security agency, the heads of the national bank and the national radio administration, the minister of foreign affairs, and the ambassador to Russia, came from Akayev's home area and from Talas, the home district of his wife.

Akayev's loss of momentum was reflected in the debate over the national constitution, a first draft of which was passed by the Supreme Soviet in December 1992. Although draft versions had begun to circulate as early as the summer of 1992, the commission itself agreed on a definitive version only after prolonged debate. An umbrella group of opposition figures from the DDK also began drawing up constitutional proposals in 1992, two variations of which they put forward for public consideration.

Although broad agreement existed on the outlines of the constitution, several specific points were difficult to resolve. One concerned the status of religion. Although it was agreed that the state would be secular, there was strong pressure for some constitutional recognition of the primacy of Islam. Another much-debated issue was the role of the Russian language. Kyrgyz had been declared the official state language, but non-Kyrgyz citizens exerted pressure to have Russian assigned near-equal status, as was the case in neighboring Kazakhstan, where Russian had been declared the "official language of interethnic communication." The issue of property ownership was warmly debated, with strong sentiment expressed against permitting land to be owned or sold. Another important question was the role of the president within the new state structure.

The proposed constitution was supposed to be debated by the full Supreme Soviet (as the new nation's parliament continued to call itself after independence) and by a specially convened body of prominent citizens before its acceptance as law. However, some members of the democratic opposition argued that a special assembly of Kyrgyz elders, called a *kuraltai*, should be convened to consider the document. A final draft of the constitution was passed by the Supreme Soviet in May 1993, apparently without involvement of a *kuraltai*.

In drafting a final document, the Supreme Soviet addressed some of the most controversial issues that had arisen in predraft discussions. Specific passages dealt with transfer and ownership of property, the role of religion in the government, the powers of the president, and the official language of the country (see Constitution).

Akayev had spoken of the need to have a presidential system of government--and, indeed, the constitution sets the presidency outside the three branches of government, to act as a sort of overseer ensuring the smooth functioning of all three. However, by the mid-1990s dissatisfaction with the strong presidential model of government and with the president himself was growing. With economic resources diminished, political infighting became commonplace. Although the prime minister and others received blame for controversial or unsuccessful policy initiatives, President Akayev nonetheless found himself increasingly isolated politically amid growing opposition forces.

Although the "democratic" opposition that had helped bring Akayev to power had grown disenchanted, its constituent factions were unable to exert serious pressure on the president because they could not agree on ideology or strategy. In October 1992, the main democratic opposition party Erk (Freedom) fractured into two new parties, Erkin and Ata-Meken

(Fatherland). More serious opposition originated within the ranks of the former communist elite. Some of this opposition came directly from the ranks of the reconstituted and still legal CPK (see Political Parties).

In January 1993, Akayev made an unusually harsh statement to the effect that he had been misled by his economic advisers and that Kyrgyzstan's overtures to the outside world had only raised false hopes. The continuing outflow of ethnic Russians (who constitute the greater part of Kyrgyzstan's technicians), the war in Tajikistan (which has driven refugees and "freedom fighters" into Kyrgyzstan), the growing evidence of wide-scale official corruption and incompetence, rising crime, and--more than anything else--the spectacular collapse of the economy increasingly charged the country's political atmosphere in the first half of the 1990s.

PHYSICAL ENVIRONMENT

The smallest of the newly independent Central Asian states, Kyrgyzstan is about the same size as the state of Nebraska, with a total area of about 198,500 square kilometers. The national territory extends about 900 kilometers from east to west and 410 kilometers from north to south. Kyrgyzstan is bordered on the southeast by China, on the north and west by Kazakhstan, and on the south and west by Uzbekistan and Tajikistan. One consequence of the Stalinist division of Central Asia into five republics is that many ethnic Kyrgyz do not live in Kyrgyzstan. Three enclaves, legally part of the territory of Kyrgyzstan but geographically removed by several kilometers, have been established, two in Uzbekistan and one in Tajikistan (see fig. 8). The terrain of Kyrgyzstan is dominated by the Tian Shan and Pamir mountain systems, which together occupy about 65 percent of the national territory. The Alay range portion of the Tian Shan system dominates the southwestern crescent of the country, and, to the east, the main Tian Shan range runs along the boundary between southern Kyrgyzstan and China before extending farther east into China's Xinjiang Uygur Autonomous Region. Kyrgyzstan's average elevation is 2,750 meters, ranging from 7,439 meters at Pik Pobedy (Mount Victory) to 394 meters in the Fergana Valley near Osh. Almost 90 percent of the country lies more than 1,500 meters above sea level.

Topography and Drainage

The mountains of Kyrgyzstan are geologically young, so that the physical terrain is marked by sharply uplifted peaks separated by deep valleys (see fig. 9). There is also considerable glaciation. Kyrgyzstan's 6,500 distinct glaciers are estimated to hold about 650 billion cubic meters of water. Only around the Chu, Talas, and Fergana valleys is there relatively flat land suitable for large-scale agriculture.

Because the high peaks function as moisture catchers, Kyrgyzstan is relatively well watered by the streams that descend from them. None of the rivers of Kyrgyzstan are navigable, however. The majority are small, rapid, runoff streams. Most of Kyrgyzstan's rivers are tributaries of the Syrdariya, which has its headwaters in the western Tian Shan along the Chinese border. Another large runoff system forms the Chu River, which arises in northern Kyrgyzstan, then flows northwest and disappears into the deserts of southern Kazakhstan. Ysyk-Köl is the second largest body of water in Central Asia, after the Aral Sea, but the saline lake has been shrinking steadily, and its mineral content has been rising gradually. Kyrgyzstan has a total of about 2,000 lakes with a total surface area of 7,000 square kilometers, mostly located at altitudes of 3,000 to 4,000 meters. Only the largest three, however, occupy more than 500 square kilometers. The second- and third-largest lakes, Songköl and Chatyr-Köl (the latter of which also is saline), are located in the Naryn Basin.

Natural disasters have been frequent and varied. Overgrazing and deforestation of steep mountain slopes have increased the occurrence of mudslides and avalanches, which occasionally have swallowed entire villages. In August 1992, a severe earthquake left several thousand people homeless in the southwestern city of Jalal-Abad.

Climate

The country's climate is influenced chiefly by the mountains, Kyrgyzstan's position near the middle of the Eurasian landmass, and the absence of any body of water large enough to influence weather patterns. Those factors create a distinctly continental climate that has significant local variations. Although the mountains tend to collect clouds and block sunlight (reducing some narrow valleys at certain times of year to no more than three or four hours of sunlight per day), the country is generally sunny, receiving as much as 2,900 hours of sunlight per year in some areas. The same conditions also affect temperatures, which can vary significantly from place to place. In January the warmest average temperature (-4°C) occurs around the southern city of Osh, and around Ysyk-Köl. The latter, which has a volume of 1,738 cubic kilometers, does not freeze in winter. Indeed, its name means "hot lake" in Kyrgyz. The coldest temperatures are in mountain valleys. There, readings can fall to -30°C or lower; the record is -53.6°C. The average temperature for July similarly varies from 27°C in the Fergana Valley, where the record high is 44°C, to a low of -10°C on the highest mountain peaks. Precipitation varies from 2,000 millimeters per year in the mountains above the Fergana Valley to less than 100 millimeters per year on the west bank of Ysyk-Köl.

Environmental Problems

Kyrgyzstan has been spared many of the enormous environmental problems faced by its Central Asian neighbors, primarily because its designated roles in the Soviet system involved neither heavy industry nor large-scale cotton production. Also, the economic downturn of the early 1990s reduced some of the more serious effects of industrial and agricultural policy. Nevertheless, Kyrgyzstan has serious problems because of inefficient use and pollution of water resources, land degradation, and improper agricultural practices.

Water Resources

Although Kyrgyzstan has abundant water running through it, its water supply is determined by a post-Soviet sharing agreement among the five Central Asian republics. As in the Soviet era, Kyrgyzstan has the right to 25 percent of the water that originates in its territory, but the new agreement allows Turkmenistan and Uzbekistan unlimited use of the water that flows into them from Kyrgyzstan, with no compensation for the nation at the source. Kyrgyzstan uses the entire amount to which the agreement entitles it, but utilization is skewed heavily in favor of agricultural irrigation. In 1994 agriculture accounted for about 88 percent of total water consumption, compared with 8 percent by industry and 4 percent by municipal water distribution systems. According to World Bank (see Glossary) experts, Kyrgyzstan has an adequate supply of high-quality water for future use, provided the resource is prudently managed.

Irrigation is extremely wasteful of water because the distribution infrastructure is old and poorly maintained. In 1993 only an estimated 5 percent of required maintenance expenditures was allocated. Overall, an estimated 70 percent of the nation's water supply network is in need of repair or replacement. The quality of drinking water from this aging system is poorly monitored--the water management staff has been cut drastically because of inadequate funds. Further, there is no money to buy new water disinfection equipment when it is needed. Some aquifers near industrial and mining centers have been contaminated by heavy metals, oils, and sanitary wastes. In addition, many localities rely on surface sources, making users vulnerable to agricultural runoff and livestock waste, which seep gradually downward from the surface. The areas of lowest water quality are the heavily populated regions of the Chu Valley and Osh and Jalal-Abad provinces, and areas along the rivers flowing into Ysyk-Köl.

In towns, wastewater collection provides about 70 percent of the water supply. Although towns have biological treatment equipment, as much as 50 percent of such equipment is rated as ineffective. The major sources of toxic waste in the water supply are the mercury mining combine at Haidarkan; the antimony mine at Kadamzai; the Kadzyi Sai uranium mine, which ceased extraction in 1967 but which continues to leach toxic materials into nearby Ysyk Köl; the Kara-Balta Uranium Recovery Plant; the Min Kush deposit of mine tailings; and the Kyrgyz Mining and Metallurgy Plant at Orlovka.

Land Management

The most important problems in land use are soil erosion and salinization in improperly irrigated farmland. An estimated 60 percent of Kyrgyzstan's land is affected by topsoil loss, and 6 percent by salinization, both problems with more serious long-term than short-term effects. In 1994 the size of livestock herds averaged twice the carrying capacity of pasturage land, continuing the serious overgrazing problem and consequent soil erosion that began when the herds were at their peak in the late 1980s (see Agriculture). Uncertain land tenure and overall financial insecurity have caused many private farmers to concentrate their capital in the traditional form--livestock--thus subjecting new land to the overgrazing problem.

The inherent land shortage in Kyrgyzstan is exacerbated by the flooding of agricultural areas for hydroelectric projects. The creation of Toktogol Reservoir on the Naryn River, for example, involved the flooding of 13,000 hectares of fertile land. Such projects have the additional effect of constricting downstream water supply; Toktogol deprives the lower reaches of the Syrdariya in Uzbekistan and the Aral Sea Basin of substantial amounts of water. Because the Naryn Basin, where many hydroelectric projects are located, is very active seismically, flooding is also a danger should a dam be broken by an earthquake. Several plants are now in operation in zones where Richter Scale readings may reach eleven.

The Aral Sea

In response to the internationally recognized environmental crisis of the rapid desiccation of the Aral Sea, the five states sharing the Aral Sea Basin (Kazakhstan, Kyrgyzstan,

Tajikistan, Turkmenistan, and Uzbekistan) are developing a strategy to end the crisis. The World Bank and agencies of the United Nations (UN) have developed an Aral Sea Program, the first stage of which is funded by the five countries and external donors. That stage has seven areas of focus, one of which--land and water management in the upper watersheds--is of primary concern to Kyrgyzstan. Among the conditions detrimental to the Aral Sea's environment are erosion from deforestation and overgrazing, contamination from poorly managed irrigation systems, and uncontrolled waste from mining and municipal effluents. Kyrgyzstan's National Environmental Action Plan (NEAP) has addressed these problems as part of its first-phase priorities in cooperation with the Aral Sea Program.

Environmental Policy Making

The NEAP, adopted in 1994, is the basic blueprint for environmental protection. The plan focuses on solving a small number of critical problems, collecting reliable information to aid in that process, and integrating environmental measures with economic and social development strategy. The initial planning period is to end in 1997. The main targets of that phase are inefficient water resource management, land degradation, overexploitation of forest reserves, loss of biodiversity, and pollution from inefficient mining and refining practices.

Because of severe budget constraints, most of the funds for NEAP operations come from international sources, including official institutions such as the World Bank and the Asian Development Bank and numerous international nongovernmental organizations. Implementation is guided by a committee of state ministers and by a NEAP Expert Working Group, both established in 1994 by executive order. A NEAP office in Bishkek was set up with funds from Switzerland.

The main environmental protection agency of the Kyrgyzstani government is the State Committee on Environmental Protection, still known by its Soviet-era acronym, Goskompriroda. Established by the old regime in 1988, the agency's post-Soviet responsibilities have been described in a series of decrees beginning in 1991. In 1994 the state committee had a central office in Bishkek, one branch in each of the seven provinces, and a total staff of about 150 persons. Because of poorly defined lines of responsibility, administrative conflicts often occur between local and national authorities of Goskompriroda and between Goskompriroda and a second national agency, the Hydrometeorological Administration (Gidromet), which is the main monitoring agency for air, water, and soil quality. In general, the vertical hierarchy structure, a relic of Soviet times, has led to poor coordination and duplication of effort among environmental protection agencies.

POPULATION

The population of Kyrgyzstan is divided among three main groups: the indigenous Kyrgyz, the Russians who remained after the end of the Soviet Union, and a large and concentrated Uzbek population. Topography divides the population into two main segments, the north and the south. Each has differing cultural and economic patterns and different predominant ethnic groups.

Demographic Characteristics

The censuses of 1979 and 1989 indicated annual population growth of a little over 2 percent, with a birth rate of 30.4 per 1,000 in 1989. The estimated birth rate in 1994 was twenty-six per 1,000, the death rate seven per 1,000, with a rate of natural increase of 1.9 percent (see table 1). In 1993 average life expectancy was estimated at sixty-two years for males, seventy years for females--the second lowest rate among the former Soviet republics. In 1993 the infant mortality rate was estimated at 47.8 deaths per 1,000 live births. Early marriage and large family size have combined to make Kyrgyzstan's population a relatively young one. In 1989, some 39.5 percent of the population was below working age, and only 10.1 percent was of pension age. The 1989 census indicated that only about 38 percent of the country's population was urbanized (see table 2).

Table 1. Central Asia: Demographic Indicators, 1989-93

Indicator	Kazakhstan	Kyrgyzstan	Tajikistan	Turkmenistan	Uzbekistan
Live births	316,369	128,352	186,504	124,992	711,000
Birth rate	18.7	28.6	32.5	34.9	33.3
Deaths	156,253	32,163	49,326	27,609	139,900
Death rate*	9.2	7.2	8.6	7.7	6.5
Life expectancy, male	63.8	64.6	66.8	61.8	66.0
Life expectancy, female	73.0	72.7	71.7	68.4	72.1
Marriages	146,161	40,818	53,946	34,890	235,900
Marriage rate*	8.6	9.1	0.9	9.8	11.0
Divorces	45,516	8,043	5,293	4,940	29,953
Divorce rate*	2.7	1.8	0.9	1.4	1.5

Source: Based on information from United Nations, Department for Economic and Social Information and Policy Analysis, *Demographic Yearbook 1994*, New York, 1996, 140-43.
Note: * Per 1,000 population.

Table 2. Central Asia: Population Distribution, 1989-92 (in thousands)

Population Group	Kazakhstan	Kyrgyzstan	Tajikistan	Turkmenistan*	Uzbekistan*
Urban male	4,577	800	813	783	3,937
Urban female	5,029	881	842	808	4,104
Urban total	9,606	1,681	1,655	1,591	8,041
Urban percentage	57.6	37.9	32.5	43.9	40.6
Rural male	3,539	1,383	1,717	952	5,847
Rural female	3,576	1,388	1,720	980	5,922
Rural total	7,115	2,771	3,437	1,932	11,769
Total male	8,116	2,183	2,530	1,735	9,784
Total female	8,605	2,269	2,562	1,788	10,026
14 and younger	5,248	1,673	2,187	n.a.	8,083
15 to 39	6,851	1,794	1,996	1,453	8,029
50 to 64	3,623	756	717	510	2,894
65 and older	999	228	192	132	804

Source: Based on information from United Nations, Department for Economic and Social Information and Policy Analysis, *Demographic Yearbook 1994*, New York, 1996, 240-45.
Note: * All figures 1989.

Ethnic Groups

In 1993 the population of Kyrgyzstan was estimated at 4.46 million, of whom 56.5 percent were ethnic Kyrgyz, 18.8 percent were Russians, 12.9 percent were Uzbeks, 2.1 percent were Ukrainians, and 1.0 percent were Germans (see table 3). The rest of the population was composed of about eighty other nationalities. Of some potential political significance are the Uygurs. That group numbers only about 36,000 in Kyrgyzstan, but about 185,000 live in neighboring Kazakhstan. The Uygurs are also the majority population in the Xinjiang Uygur Autonomous Region of China, whose population is about 15 million, located to the northeast of Kyrgyzstan. In November 1992, the Uygurs in Kyrgyzstan attempted to form a party calling for establishment of an independent Uygurstan that also would include the Chinese-controlled Uygur territory. The Ministry of Justice denied the group legal registration.

Table 3. Central Asia: Ethnic Composition, Selected Years, 1989-94 (in percentages)

Country and Ethnic Group	1989	1991	1993	1994
Kazakhstan				
Kazak	39.7	41.9	43.2	44.3
Russian	37.8	37.0	36.5	35.8
Ukrainian	5.4	5.2	5.2	5.1
German	5.8	4.7	4.1	3.6
Uzbek	2.0	2.1	2.2	2.2
Tatar	2.0	2.0	2.0	2.0
Kyrgyzstan				
Kyrgyz	52.4	n.a.	56.5	n.a.
Russian	21.5	n.a.	18.8	n.a.
Uzbek	12.9	n.a.	12.9	n.a.
Ukrainian	2.5	n.a.	2.1	n.a.
German	2.4	n.a.	1.0	n.a.
Tajikistan				
Tajik	62.3	63.8	n.a.	n.a.
Uzbek	23.5	24.0	n.a.	n.a.
Russian	7.6	6.5	n.a.	n.a.
Tatar	1.4	1.4	n.a.	n.a.
Turkmenistan				
Turkmen	72.0	n.a.	73.3	n.a.
Russian	9.8	n.a.	9.5	n.a.
Uzbek	9.0	n.a.	9.0	n.a.
Kazak	2.0	n.a.	2.5	n.a.
Uzbekistan				
Uzbek	71.4	73.0	n.a.	n.a.
Russian	8.3	7.7	n.a.	n.a.
Tajik	4.7	4.8	n.a.	n.a.
Kazak	4.1	n.a.	n.a.	n.a.
Tatar	2.4	2.3	n.a.	n.a.

Source: Based on information from *The Europa World Year Book 1994*, 2, London, 1994, 1679; *The Europa World Year Book 1995*, 2, London, 1995, 1679, 1735, 1823, 2950, 3070, 3363; United States, Central Intelligence Agency, *The World Factbook 1994*, Washington, 1994, 210, 222, 385, 403, 420; and *1995 Britannica Book of the Year*, Chicago, 1995, 726, 746.

Between 1989 and 1993, a significant number of non-Kyrgyz citizens left the republic, although no census was taken in the early 1990s to quantify the resulting balances among ethnic groups. A considerable portion of this exodus consisted of Germans repatriating to Germany, more than 8,000 of whom left in 1992 alone. According to reports, more than 30,000 Russians left the Bishkek area in the early 1990s, presumably for destinations outside Kyrgyzstan. In 1992 and 1993, refugees from the civil war in Tajikistan moved into southern Kyrgyzstan. In 1989 about 64,000 Kyrgyz were living in Tajikistan, and about 175,000 were living in Uzbekistan. Reliable estimates of how many of these people subsequently returned to Kyrgyzstan have not been available.

The Fergana Valley, which eastern Kyrgyzstan shares with Central Asian neighbors Uzbekistan and Tajikistan, is one of the most densely populated and agriculturally most heavily exploited regions in Central Asia. As such, it has been the point of bitter contention among the three adjoining states, both before and after the collapse of the Soviet Union. Members of the various ethnic groups who have inhabited the valley for centuries have managed to get along largely because they occupy slightly different economic niches. The sedentary Uzbeks and Tajiks traditionally have farmed lower-lying irrigated land while the nomadic Kyrgyz have herded in the mountains. However, the potential for ethnic conflict is ever present. Because the borders of the three countries zigzag without evident regard for the nationality of the people living in the valley, many residents harbor strong irredentist feelings, believing that they should more properly be citizens of a different country. Few Europeans live in the Fergana Valley, but about 552,000 Uzbeks, almost the entire population of that people in Kyrgyzstan, reside there in crowded proximity with about 1.2 million Kyrgyz.

Geographic Factors

Population statistics depict only part of the demographic situation in Kyrgyzstan. Because of the country's mountainous terrain, population tends to be concentrated in relatively small areas in the north and south, each of which contains about two million people. About two-thirds of the total population live in the Fergana, Talas, and Chu valleys. As might be expected, imbalances in population distribution lead to extreme contrasts in how people live and work. In the north, the Chu Valley, site of Bishkek, the capital, is the major economic center, producing about 45 percent of the nation's gross national product (GNP--see Glossary). The Chu Valley also is where most of the country's Europeans live, mainly because of economic opportunities. The ancestors of today's Russian and German population began to move into the fertile valley to farm at the end of the nineteenth century. There was a subsequent influx of Russians during World War II, when industrial resources and personnel were moved en masse out of European Russia to prevent their capture by the invading Germans. In the era of Soviet First Secretary Leonid I. Brezhnev, a deliberate development policy brought another in-migration. Bishkek is slightly more than 50 percent Kyrgyz, and the rest of the valley retains approximately that ethnic ratio. In the mid-1990s, observers expected that balance to change quickly, however, as Europeans continued to move out while rural Kyrgyz moved in, settling in the numerous shantytowns springing up around Bishkek. The direct distance from Bishkek in the far north to Osh in the southwest is slightly more than 300 kilometers, but the mountain road connecting those cities requires a drive of more than ten hours in summer conditions; in winter the high mountain passes are often closed. In the

Soviet period, most travel between north and south was by airplane, but fuel shortages that began after independence have greatly limited the number of flights, increasing a tendency toward separation of north and south (see Topography and Drainage; Transportation and Telecommunications).

The separation of the north and the south is clearly visible in the cultural mores of the two regions, although both are dominated by ethnic Kyrgyz. Society in the Fergana Valley is much more traditional than in the Chu Valley, and the practice of Islam is more pervasive. The people of the Chu Valley are closely integrated with Kazakhstan (Bishkek is but four hours by car from Almaty, the capital of Kazakhstan). The people of the south are more oriented, by location and by culture, to Uzbekistan, Iran, Afghanistan, and the other Muslim countries to the south.

Geographical isolation also has meant that the northern and southern Kyrgyz have developed fairly distinct lifestyles. Those in the north tend to be nomadic herders; those in the south have acquired more of the sedentary agricultural ways of their Uygur, Uzbek, and Tajik neighbors. Both groups came to accept Islam late, but practice in the north tends to be much less influenced by Islamic doctrine and reflects considerable influence from pre-Islamic animist beliefs. The southerners have a more solid basis of religious knowledge and practice. It is they who pushed for a greater religious element in the 1993 constitution (see Religion).

SOCIETY AND CULTURE

The ethnic identity of the Kyrgyz has been strongly linked to their language and to ethnic traditions, both of which have been guarded with particular zeal once independence provided an opportunity to make national policy on these matters. Less formally, the Kyrgyz people have maintained with unusual single-mindedness many elements of social structure and a sense of their common past. The name Kyrgyz derives from the Turkic *kyrk* plus *yz*, a combination meaning "forty clans."

Language

In the period after A.D. 840, the Kyrgyz joined other Turkic groups in an overall Turkification pattern extending across the Tian Shan into the Tarim River basin, east of present-day Kyrgyzstan's border with China. In this process, which lasted for more than two centuries, the Kyrgyz tribes became mixed with other tribes, thoroughly absorbing Turkic cultural and linguistic characteristics.

The forebears of the present-day Kyrgyz are believed to have been either southern Samoyed or Yeniseyan tribes. Those tribes came into contact with Turkic culture after they conquered the Uygurs and settled the Orkhon area, site of the oldest recorded Turkic language, in the ninth century (see Early History). If descended from the Samoyed tribes of Siberia, the Kyrgyz would have spoken a language in the Uralic linguistic subfamily when they arrived in Orkhon; if descended from Yeniseyan tribes, they would have descended from a people of the same name who began to move into the area of present-day Kyrgyzstan from the Yenisey River region of central Siberia in the tenth century, after the Kyrgyz conquest of the Uygurs to the east in the preceding century. Ethnographers dispute the Yeniseyan origin, however, because of the very close cultural and linguistic connections between the Kyrgyz and the Kazaks.

In the period of tsarist administration (1876-1917), the Kazaks and the Kyrgyz both were called Kyrgyz, with what are now the Kyrgyz subdenominated when necessary as Kara-Kyrgyz (black Kyrgyz). Although the Kyrgyz language has more Mongolian and Altaic elements than does Kazak, the modern forms of the two languages are very similar. As they exist today, both are part of the Nogai group of the Kipchak division of the Turkic languages, which belong to the Uralic-Altaic language family. The modern Kyrgyz language did not have a written form until 1923, at which time an Arabic-based alphabet was used. That was changed to a Latin-based alphabet in 1928 and to a Cyrillic-based one in 1940. In the years immediately following independence, another change of alphabet was discussed, but the issue does not seem to generate the same passions in Kyrgyzstan that it does in other former Soviet republics.

One important difference between Kyrgyzstan and Kazakhstan is that the Kyrgyz people's mastery of their own language is almost universal, whereas the linguistic phase of national identity is not as clear in the much larger area and population of Kazakhstan. As in Kazakhstan, mastery of the "titular" language among the resident Europeans of Kyrgyzstan is very rare. In the early 1990s, the Akayev government pursued an aggressive policy of introducing Kyrgyz as the official language, forcing the remaining European population to use Kyrgyz in most public situations. Public pressure to enforce this change was sufficiently strong that a Russian member of President Akayev's staff created a public scandal in 1992 by threatening to resign to dramatize the pressure for "Kyrgyzification" of the non-native population. A 1992 law called for the conduct of all public business to be converted fully to Kyrgyz by 1997. But in March 1996, Kyrgyzstan's parliament adopted a resolution making Russian an official state language alongside Kyrgyz and marking a reversal of earlier sentiment. Substantial pressure from Russia was a strong factor in this change, which was part of a general rapprochement with Russia urged by Akayev.

Ethnic Traditions

The Kyrgyz also have retained a strong sense of cultural tradition. Figures from the 1989 Soviet census show that Kyrgyz males were the least likely of the men of any Soviet nationality to marry outside their people (only 6.1 percent of their marriages were "international") and that Kyrgyz women did so in only 5.8 percent of marriages. Moreover, although the degree of such changes is difficult to measure, Kyrgyz "mixed" marriages seem uncommonly likely to assimilate in the direction of a Kyrgyz identity, with the non-Kyrgyz spouse learning the Kyrgyz language and the children assuming the Kyrgyz nationality. Even ordinary citizens are thoroughly familiar with the Kyrgyz oral epic, *Manas*, a poem of several hundred thousand lines (many versions are recited) telling of the eponymous Kyrgyz hero's struggles against invaders from the east. Many places and things in Kyrgyzstan, including the main airport, bear the name of this ancient hero, the one-thousandth anniversary of whose mythical adventures were cause for great national celebration in 1995.

Social Structure

The age-old geographic separation of pockets of the Kyrgyz population has tended to reinforce conservatism in all of the country's society. The modern Kyrgyz still apply great significance to family and clan origins. The majority of Kyrgyz continued a nomadic lifestyle until the Soviet campaigns of forcible collectivization forced them first into transitional settlements and then into cities and towns or state and collective farms in the 1930s. Within the centralized farm systems, however, many Kyrgyz continued to move seasonally with their herds. There has been strong resistance to industrial employment.

Clans

Kyrgyz identity in public and private life is said to be determined primarily by membership in one of three clan groupings known as "wings" (right, or *ong* ; left, or *sol* ; and *ichkilik*, which is neither) and secondarily by membership in a particular clan within a wing. The history of this grouping is unknown, although several legends explain the phenomenon. The left wing now includes seven clans in the north and west. Each of the seven has a dominant characteristic, and all have fought each other for influence. The Buguu warrior clan provided the first administrators of the Kyrgyz Republic under the Soviet Union; when the purges of Stalin eradicated their leaders in the 1930s, their place was taken by a second northern warrior clan, the Sarybagysh, who have provided most Kyrgyz leaders since that time, including Akayev. The right wing contains only one clan, the Adygine. Located in the south, the Adygine are considered the most genuinely Kyrgyz clan because of their legendary heritage. The southern Ichkilik is a group of many clans, some of which are not of Kyrgyz origin, but all of which claim Kyrgyz identity in the present.

Acutely aware of the roles each of the clans traditionally has played, the Kyrgyz are still very conscious of clan membership in competing for social and economic advantage. Support for fellow clan members is especially strong in the northern provinces. Kyrgyz men frequently wear traditional black-on-white felt headgear, which informs others of their clan status and the degree of respect to be accorded them. Larger clans are subdivided by origin and by the nobility of their ancestors; although there is no prohibition of advancement for those of non-noble descent, descent from a high-born extended family still is considered a social advantage.

Like other Central Asian groups, the Kyrgyz venerate history and see themselves as part of a long flow of events. A traditional requirement is the ability to name all the people in the previous seven generations of one's family. Clan identity extends this tradition even further, to the legendary origins of the Kyrgyz people. Kyrgyz clans are said to spring from "first fathers," most of whom appear in both oral legends and in history. Clan history and genealogy are entrusted to tribal elders, whose ongoing knowledge of those subjects makes falsification of lineage difficult. Because clan identity remains an important element of social status, however, Kyrgyz do sometimes claim to have descended from a higher branch of their clan than is actually the case.

Domestic Life

The Kyrgyz are classified as nomadic pastoralists, meaning that they traditionally have herded sheep, horses, or yaks, following the animals up and down the mountains as the seasons change. The basic dwelling is the yurt, a cylindrical felt tent easily disassembled and mounted on a camel or horse. The image of a yurt's circular smoke opening is the central design of Kyrgyzstan's flag. Various parts of the yurt have ritual significance. Because the herding economy continues in many parts of the country, the yurt remains a strong symbol of national identity. Families living in Western-style dwellings erect yurts to celebrate weddings and funerals.

Traditional domestic life centers on the flocks. The diet of the nomads is limited to mutton and noodles; fruit and vegetables are rare even in today's Kyrgyz cuisine. The most traditional dishes are *besh barmak*, a mutton stew, and roast lamb. For ceremonial meals, the lamb is killed without spilling its blood, and the head is served to the guest of honor, who slices portions of the eyes and ears and presents them to other guests to improve their sight and hearing. Horsemeat is eaten fresh and in sausages. Traditional beverages are *kumys*, fermented mare's milk, and two varieties of beer.

Family traditions continue to demonstrate the patriarchal and feudal character of a nomadic people. Family relations are characterized by great respect for older family members and the dominance of male heads of households. Traditional celebrations of special events retain the markings of religious and magical rites. For example, the cutting of a child's umbilical cord is celebrated with elaborate consumption of food and humorous games. The naming of a child and the cutting of the child's hair are conducted in such a way as to appease supernatural forces. The full observance of the most important family event, the wedding celebration, requires considerable expense that relatively few Kyrgyz can afford: payment for a bride, dowry, animal sacrifice, and an exchange of clothing between the relatives of the bride and the groom.

The Role of Women

In traditional Kyrgyz society, women had assigned roles, although only the religious elite sequestered women as was done in other Muslim societies. Because of the demands of the nomadic economy, women worked as virtual equals with men, having responsibility for chores such as milking as well as child-rearing and the preparation and storage of food. In the ordinary family, women enjoyed approximately equal status with their husbands. Kyrgyz oral literature includes the story of Janyl-myrza, a young woman who led her tribe to liberation from the enemy when no man in the tribe could do so. In the nineteenth century, the wife of Khan Almyn-bek led a group of Kyrgyz tribes at the time of the Russian conquest of Quqon.

In modern times, especially in the first years of independence, women have played more prominent roles in Kyrgyzstan than elsewhere in Central Asia. Since 1991 women have occupied the positions of state procurator (the top law enforcement official in the national government), minister of education, ambassador to the United States and Canada, and minister of foreign affairs. Women have also excelled in banking and business, and the editor of Central Asia's most independent newspaper, *Respublika*, is a woman. Roza Otunbayeva, who was minister of foreign affairs in 1996, has been mentioned frequently as a successor to Akayev.

Contemporary Culture

As the capital of a Soviet republic, Bishkek (which until 1990 had been named Frunze after the Soviet general who led the military conquest of the Basmachi rebels in the mid-1920s) was endowed with the standard cultural facilities, including an opera, ballet, several theater companies, and an orchestra, as well as a Lenin museum, national art and craft museums, and an open-air sculpture museum. Since independence, funding for those institutions has decreased dramatically, and the cultural facilities have also been hard hit by the departure of local Russians. It also is unclear whether younger Kyrgyz will continue their parents' substantial interest in classical music, which in the Soviet era led several generations to support the national orchestra.

In the Soviet-directed propagation of "all-union culture," Kyrgyz actors, directors, and dancers achieved fame throughout the Soviet Union. Chingiz Aitmatov, the republic's most prominent writer, became one of the best-known and most independent artists in the Soviet Union in the 1980s. The Kyrgyz film industry, which had been very productive while supported by Soviet government funds, essentially vanished after 1991. Film projects that survive, such as a large-scale production on the life of Chinggis Khan directed by noted Kyrgyz director T. Okeyev, do so through foreign financing (an Italian film company has supported production of the Okeyev film).

Perhaps the best indicator of the condition of the fine arts in postcommunist Kyrgyzstan is the fate of the open-air sculpture museum in Bishkek, which began suffering a series of thefts in early 1993. Because the targets were all bronze, presumably the sculptures were stolen for their value as metal, not as art. When a large statuary group commemorating Aitmatov's Ysyk-Köl Forum (a notable product of the early *glasnost* period) disappeared, the museum's remaining statues were removed to a more secure location.

RELIGION

The vast majority of today's Kyrgyz are Muslims of the Sunni (see Glossary) branch, but Islam came late and fairly superficially to the area. Kyrgyz Muslims generally practice their religion in a specific way influenced by earlier tribal customs. The practice of Islam also differs in the northern and southern regions of the country. Kyrgyzstan remained a secular state after the fall of communism, which had only superficial influence on religious practice when Kyrgyzstan was a Soviet republic. Most of the Russian population of Kyrgyzstan is atheist or Russian Orthodox. The Uzbeks, who make up 12.9 percent of the population, are generally Sunni Muslims.

The Introduction of Islam

Islam was introduced to the Kyrgyz tribes between the ninth and twelfth centuries. The most intense exposure to Islam occurred in the seventeenth century, when the Jungars drove the Kyrgyz of the Tian Shan region into the Fergana Valley, whose population was totally Islamic. However, as the danger from the Jungars subsided and Kyrgyz groups returned to their previous region, the influence of Islam became weaker. When the Quqon Khanate conquered the territory of the Kyrgyz in the eighteenth century, the nomadic Kyrgyz remained aloof from the official Islamic practices of that regime. By the end of the nineteenth century, however, most of the Kyrgyz population had been converted to at least a superficial recognition of Islamic practice.

Tribal Religion

Alongside Islam the Kyrgyz tribes also practiced totemism, the recognition of spiritual kinship with a particular type of animal. Under this belief system, which predated their contact with Islam, Kyrgyz tribes adopted reindeer, camels, snakes, owls, and bears as objects of worship. The sun, moon, and stars also played an important religious role. The strong dependence of the nomads on the forces of nature reinforced such connections and fostered belief in shamanism (the power of tribal healers and magicians with mystical connections to the spirit world) and black magic as well. Traces of such beliefs remain in the religious practice of many of today's Kyrgyz.

Knowledge of and interest in Islam are said to be much stronger in the south, especially around Osh, than farther north. Religious practice in the north is more heavily mixed with animism (belief that every animate and inanimate object contains a spirit) and shamanist practices, giving worship there a resemblance to Siberian religious practice.

Islam and the State

Religion has not played an especially large role in the politics of Kyrgyzstan, although more traditional elements of society urged that the Muslim heritage of the country be acknowledged in the preamble to the 1993 constitution. That document mandates a secular state, forbidding the intrusion of any ideology or religion in the conduct of state business. As in other parts of Central Asia, non-Central Asians have been concerned about the potential of a fundamentalist Islamic revolution that would emulate Iran and Afghanistan by bringing Islam directly into the making of state policy, to the detriment of the non-Islamic population. Because of sensitivity about the economic consequences of a continued outflow of Russians, President Akayev has taken particular pains to reassure the non-Kyrgyz that no Islamic revolution threatens (see Ethnic Groups). Akayev has paid public visits to Bishkek's main Russian Orthodox church and directed 1 million rubles from the state treasury toward that faith's church-building fund. He has also appropriated funds and other support for a German cultural center. The state officially recognizes Orthodox Christmas (but not Easter) as a holiday, while also noting two Muslim feast days, Oroz ait (which ends Ramadan) and Kurban ait (June 13, the Day of Remembrance), and Muslim New Year, which falls on the vernal equinox.

EDUCATION

In the mid-1990s, much of the Soviet-era education system remained in Kyrgyzstan, which had made a conscientious effort to educate all of its citizens before 1991 and continued to do so after that date. Substantial structural and curriculum changes were underway by

1995, however. The 1993 constitution continues the Soviet guarantee of free basic education at state institutions to all citizens; education is compulsory through grade nine. Free education at the vocational, secondary specialized, and higher levels also continues to be offered by the state to qualified individuals. The fundamentals of post-Soviet education policy were enumerated in the 1992 law on education, which established the Ministry of Education as the central administrative body of the national system. Although Soviet-era statistics indicated that 100 percent of the people between the ages of nine and forty-nine were literate, the actual literacy rate probably is somewhat less.

Education System

Once independence was achieved, the Ministry of Education began working energetically to revamp the old Soviet course of study. The ministry is responsible for developing curriculum, setting national standards and educational policy, developing certification examinations, and awarding degrees. The ministry is divided into departments for general education, higher education, and material support. Below the ministry level, the education hierarchy includes the six provinces and the separate city of Bishkek, representatives from each of which provide input to the ministry on local conditions. The level of basic local administration is the district (*rayon*), where the district education officer hires faculty and appoints school inspectors and methodology specialists.

General education is financed from district budgets, and the college preparatory and higher education programs are financed by the national budget. For the former category of expenditures, school principals negotiate their requirements with district officials, but the central government sets norms based on previous expenditures and on the relative resources of the provinces. In the last years of the Soviet period, Kyrgyzstani schools had a surplus of money, but available funds declined sharply beginning in 1992. Since that time, insufficient funds in local budgets have forced the Ministry of Education to make special requests for support from the Ministry of Economics and Finance.

Instruction

General education traditionally has been accessible to nearly all children in Kyrgyzstan. In primary and secondary grades, about 51 percent of students are female; that number increases to 55 percent in higher education, with a converse majority of males in vocational programs. There is little difference in school attendance between urban and rural areas or among the provinces. Higher education, however, has been much more available to the urban and more wealthy segments of the population. Because of a shortage of schools, 37 percent of general education students attend schools operating in two or three shifts. Construction of new facilities has lagged behind enrollment growth, the rate of which has been nearly 3 percent per year.

In line with the reform of 1992, children start school at age six and are required to complete grade nine. The general education program has three stages: grades one through four, grades five through nine, and grades ten and eleven. Students completing grade nine may continue into advanced or specialized (college preparatory) secondary curricula or into a technical and vocational program. The school year is thirty-four weeks long, extending from the beginning of September until the end of May. The instruction week is twenty-five hours long for grades one through four and thirty-two hours for grades five through eleven. In 1992 about 960,000 students were enrolled in general education courses, 42,000 in specialized secondary programs, 49,000 in vocational programs, and 58,000 in institutions of higher education. About 1,800 schools were in operation in 1992. That year Kyrgyzstan's state system had about 65,000 teachers, but an estimated 8,000 teachers resigned in 1992 alone because of poor salaries and a heavy work load that included double shifts for many. Emigration also has depleted the teaching staff. In 1993 the national pupil-teacher ratio for grades one through eleven was 14.4 to 1, slightly higher in rural areas, and considerably higher in the primary grades. The city of Bishkek, however, had a ratio of almost 19 to 1.

Curriculum

Post-Soviet curriculum reform has aroused much controversy in Kyrgyzstan. A fundamental question is the language of instruction, which has become increasingly Kyrgyz as non-indigenous citizens leave the country and textbooks in Kyrgyz slowly become available. The Ministry of Education has held competitions, supported by foreign donations, for the design of new textbooks in Kyrgyz. Until 1992 textbook production and distribution were inefficient and costly aspects of the education system. By the mid-1990s, the single, state-supported publisher of textbooks had gradually improved the quality and availability of its products. In 1992 the first major curriculum reform provided for mandatory foreign language study (English, French, or German) beginning in grade one; computer science courses in grades eight through eleven (a program hampered by lack of funds); and the replacement of Soviet ideology with concepts of market economy and ethnic studies. The reformed curriculum requirements also leave room for elective courses, and instructional innovation is encouraged.

Higher Education

In 1994 Kyrgyzstan had twenty-six institutions of higher learning, all but seven of which were located in Bishkek. Seven of the institutions were private and the remainder state-funded. Approximately 4,700 faculty were employed there, of which only 150 had doctoral degrees and 1,715 were candidates, the step below the doctorate in the Soviet system. The language of instruction remained predominantly Russian in the mid-1990s, although the use of Kyrgyz increased yearly. Long-term plans call for a more Western style of university study, so that, for example, the universities would begin to offer a baccalaureate degree. In 1992 President Akayev created a Slavic University in Bishkek to help Kyrgyzstan retain its population of educated Russians, for whom the increased "Kyrgyzification" of education was a reason to emigrate. Because Russian students from outside the Russian Federation had lost their Soviet-era right to free education in Russian universities, Akayev hoped to provide a Russian-language institution for Russian-speaking students from all the Central Asian states. The shortage of education funds in Kyrgyzstan brought strong objections to a project that did not promote the education of ethnic Kyrgyz students, however.

HEALTH AND WELFARE

In 1993 the World Bank reported that the population of Kyrgyzstan enjoyed better health care than most other countries with similar per capita income, which averaged US$3,410 per year for Kyrgyzstan's category in 1992. The current health conditions and health prospects of Kyrgyzstan's population are difficult to calculate, however, because of the sudden change that independence visited upon the medical community. Until 1991 Kyrgyzstan's medical system was financed through the Soviet Union's Ministry of Health, which guaranteed a health establishment equal to that of other Soviet republics. With the dissolution of the Soviet Union and the slow collapse of fiscal ties between Kyrgyzstan and Moscow, the medical community has inherited an aging but generally adequate physical plant. However, the system often lacks the vaccines, medicines, and other resources needed to maintain the health of the population.

Health Care System

Kyrgyzstan inherited the Soviet system of free universal health care, which in Kyrgyzstan's case generally provided sufficient numbers of doctors, nurses, and doctor's assistants, as well as medical clinics and hospitals. However, since 1991 citizens often have received inadequate care because medical personnel are not well trained; pharmaceuticals, medical supplies, and equipment are insufficient; and facilities are generally inadequate and unsanitary.

In 1991 Kyrgyzstan had 15,354 doctors, or 34.2 per 10,000 people. Paramedical workers totaled 42,448, or 94.6 per 10,000 people. Some 588 outpatient clinics were in operation, averaging 139 hours of patient visits per eight-hour shift. In addition, 246 general and twenty specialized hospitals were in operation; nearly one-third of all hospitals were located in Osh Province (which also had about one-third of the country's total population). By contrast, the capital city, Bishkek, had the fewest hospital facilities per capita of all regions, providing 1.55 general hospitals per 100,000 population. Like other Central Asian countries, Kyrgyzstan has continued the Soviet practice of state enterprises having their own clinics and sanatoriums. With the dissolution of the Soviet Union, Kyrgyzstan's residents lost the right to free treatment in the hospitals of other former republics, making unavailable many types of specialized treatment that the Soviet system had apportioned among adjacent republics.

Very few truly private health facilities have developed in the early post-Soviet period, and those that exist face very high licensing fees. Although it is illegal for state employees in the health field to diversify their activity into private practice, by 1993 many health workers were accepting unreported payments for providing additional treatment. In 1992 the maximum salary of a medical specialist such as a surgeon was only about 18 percent higher than the maximum salary of a technician or laboratory worker. Under such conditions, the rising cost of living in 1992 and 1993 forced many doctors to leave medicine for higher salaries in other professions.

Kyrgyzstan produces no vaccines of its own and almost no medicines or other pharmaceuticals. Drug availability is substantially higher at regional facilities than at smaller ones, but items such as antihistamines, insulin, antiseptics, vaccines, and some narcotics are either extremely scarce or extremely expensive. The other former Soviet republics now demand payment in United States dollars, which Kyrgyzstan does not have, for medical supplies. Because of the scarcity of vaccines, there is a greatly increased likelihood of epidemics of diseases such as diphtheria and measles. An outbreak of measles in Bishkek in early 1993 was said to be just below epidemic level. It has become common practice in hospitals and clinics to require patients to provide their own medicines for operations and other medical procedures. Because virtually the only available medicines are those for sale in the public bazaars, quality is questionable, and accidental poisonings caused by misuse and spoilage have been reported.

Kyrgyzstan's post-Soviet financial crisis has reduced government support of the Soviet-era health system, forcing government planners to formulate an ambitious health care delivery reform program. The center of the program is a transformation of the national health system into a system of public health insurance, in which compulsory employer fees and a health insurance tax on employees would support care for employees, and state contributions would support care for unemployed citizens. All employed citizens would be required to carry health insurance. All care providers would switch from the salary basis of the old system to a fee-for-service payment system. Because the banking, record-keeping, and tax systems of the country are not ready to support such a nationwide program, however, installation has lagged far behind the original timetable, which called for a pilot program in Bishkek in 1993.

Health Conditions

The main causes of adult deaths in Kyrgyzstan are, in order of occurrence, cardiovascular conditions, respiratory infections, and accidents (see table 4). Sexually transmitted diseases reportedly are very low in incidence; only five cases of acquired immune deficiency syndrome (AIDS) were recorded in 1992. In the early 1990s, major health hazards have been posed by growing shortages of chlorine to purify water supplies and the increasing danger of typhus outbreaks resulting from the closure of most of the country's public baths. In 1993 Kyrgyzstan suffered increasing cases of hepatitis and gastrointestinal infections, especially in the southern provinces of Osh and Jalal-Abad. The cause of such infections is believed to be the use of open water supplies contaminated by livestock and improper disposal of waste (see Environmental Problems). Although adults traditionally consume most of their water in the form of boiled tea, children have greater access to untreated water and foods.

Table 4. Central Asia: Incidence of Selected Diseases and Mortality, 1989-91

	Kazakhstan	Kyrgyzstan	Tajikistan	Turkmenistan	Uzbekistan
Viral hepatitis	465.6	710.8	918.3	735.1	1,074.5
Cancer	289.9	219.0	163.1	203.0	169.2
Tuberculosis*	65.8	53.3	44.4	63.6	46.1
Maternal mortality	53.1	42.7	38.9	55.2	42.8
Infant mortality	27.1	29.6	40.0	46.6	35.8

Source: Based on information from Christopher M. Davis, "Health Care Crisis: The Former Soviet Union," *RFE/RL Research Report* [Munich], 2, No. 40, October 8, 1993, 36.

Note: * All figures 1992 except life expectancy (1991).

Additional stress is placed on the population by the rising cost of food, which has reduced the quality and quantity of most people's diets. In 1993 meat consumption was reported to have dropped by 20 percent since 1990, intake of milk products by 30 percent, and consumption of fish (which was imported in the Soviet period) by 70 percent. The average caloric intake was reported to have decreased by about 12 percent since 1990. There are also frequent reports of deaths or injuries caused by tainted or falsely labeled food and drink, particularly alcoholic beverages, which are widely sold by extralegal private concerns. The rising cost of energy has meant insufficient heat for many apartments and public buildings. Naryn Province, the coldest and most remote part of the country, has been particularly affected. In that region, many buildings lack central heating, and residents have been forced to devise homemade stoves vented directly out the windows. In addition, the availability and range of ambulance services have been restricted severely by fuel shortages.

Social Welfare

Like the other former Soviet republics, Kyrgyzstan inherited a social welfare system that allocated benefits very broadly without targeting needy groups in society. In this system, nearly half of society received some sort of benefit, and many benefit payments were excessive. By necessity, the post-Soviet government has sought to make substantial reductions in state social protection payments, emphasizing identification of the most vulnerable members of society.

The Soviet Heritage

In 1991, the last year of the Soviet Union, the payment of pensions, child allowances, and other forms of support amounted to 18 percent of the Kyrgyz Republic's gross domestic product (GDP--see Glossary). At that point, about 600,000 pensioners and 1.6 million children received some form of payment. Eligibility requirements were extremely liberal, defined mainly by age and work history rather than by social position or contributions to a pension fund. This generous system failed to eliminate poverty, however; according to a 1989 Soviet survey, 35 percent of the population fell below the official income line for "poorly supplied" members of society. Thus poverty, which became an increasingly urgent problem during the economic decline of the transition period of the early 1990s, already was rooted firmly in Kyrgyzstan when independence was achieved.

Reforming Social Welfare

The Akayev government addressed the overpayment problem by reducing categorical subsidies and government price controls; by indexing benefits only partially as inflation raised the cost of living; and by targeting benefits to the most needy parts of society. Under the new program, child allowances went only to people with incomes below a fixed level, and bread price compensation went only to groups such as pensioners who lacked earning power. By 1993 such measures had cut government welfare expenses by more than half, from 57 percent of the state budget to 25 percent.

Nevertheless, the percentage of citizens below the poverty line grew rapidly in the early 1990s as the population felt the impact of the government's economic stabilization program (see Economic Reform). In addition, the Soviet system delegated delivery of many social services, including health, to state enterprises, which in the post-Soviet era no longer had the means to guarantee services to employees (or, in many cases, even to continue employing them). The state's Pension Fund (a government agency with the relatively independent status of a state committee) went into debt in 1994 because workers who retired early or worked only for a short period remained eligible for pensions and the poor financial state of enterprises made revenue collection difficult. The pension system is supported by payroll taxes of 33 percent on industries and 26 percent on collective and state farms. Besides retirement pensions, disability and survivors' benefits also are paid. Of the amount collected, 14 percent goes to the labor unions' Social Insurance Fund and the remainder to the Pension Fund. The standard pension eligibility age is sixty for men and fifty-five for women, but in 1992 an estimated 156,000 people were receiving benefits at earlier ages. In 1994 the minimum pension amount was raised to forty-five som (for value of the som--see Glossary) per month, the latest in a long series of adjustments that did not nearly keep pace with inflation's impact on the real value of the pension.

New pension legislation prepared in 1994 made enterprises responsible for the costs of early retirement; established a five-year minimum for pension eligibility; clearly separated the categories of work pensions from social assistance payments; abolished supplementary pension payments for recipients needing additional support; eliminated the possibility of receiving a pension while continuing to work (the position of an estimated 49,000 workers in 1992); and provided for long-term linkage of contributions made to pensions later received.

Child allowances are paid for children up to the age of eighteen, and a lump sum payment is made on the birth of a child. In 1991 child allowances consumed 6.7 percent of GDP; since that time, targeting of benefits has been a major concern in this category to reduce spending but cover vulnerable groups. The first alteration of eligibility standards occurred in 1993. Cash for this category is provided by direct transfers from the state budget combined with Pension Fund contributions.

Besides pensions and family allowances, Kyrgyzstani citizens also receive maternity benefits and sick pay covered by the Social Insurance Fund, which is managed by the Federation of Independent Labor Unions and the individual unions; it receives money only from its 14 percent share of payroll taxes, not from the state budget or individual contributions. All public and private employees are eligible for sick leave, with payments depending on length of service. The maternity allowance is a single payment equal to two months' minimum wage. World Bank experts consider the sick and maternity benefits excessive in relation to the state of the economy and the state budget.

In assessing the future of social assistance in Kyrgyzstan, experts predict that economic restructuring through the 1990s will increase the number of citizens requiring assistance from the state system. To meet such needs, thorough reform of the system--aimed mainly at tightening eligibility standards--will be necessary. It is also expected that Kyrgyzstan will require other methods of social assistance to provide for individuals who do not fall into existing categories, or for whom inflation erodes excessively the value of payments now received. The officially and unofficially unemployed (together estimated at 300,000 at the end of 1994) are an especially vulnerable group because of the unlikelihood of workers being reabsorbed rapidly into the country's faltering economy. (Unemployment benefits are paid for twenty-six weeks to those who register, but the number of "non-participants" is much greater than the number of registered unemployed.)

THE ECONOMY

In the first five years of independence, Kyrgyzstan's economy made more progress in market-oriented reform legislation but less progress in economic growth than the other four Central Asian states. This disparity was largely because Kyrgyzstan lacked the diversified natural resources and processing infrastructure that enable a national economy to survive the shutdown of some sectors by shifting labor and other inputs to new areas of production.

The economic system of Kyrgyzstan is undergoing a slow, painful, and uncertain transition. Once a highly integrated provider of raw materials for the centrally controlled economy of the Soviet Union, the republic's economy is reorienting itself toward processing its own raw materials and producing its own industrial products. During the late 1980s and early 1990s, however, industry accounted for only about one-third of the country's net material product (NMP--see Glossary) while employing less than one-fifth of the labor force. The primary emphasis of the economy remained agriculture, which accounted for about 40 percent of NMP and officially employed about one-third of the labor force. The transportation and communications sector employed only about 3.2 percent of the labor force in 1991. As in other Soviet republics, the vast majority of workers were employed by the state, while most of the remainder worked on private agricultural plots.

Role in the Soviet Economy

As part of the Soviet Union, Kyrgyzstan played a small but highly integrated role in the centrally controlled economy. Figures for 1990 show that agriculturally the republic contributed 1 percent or less of the total Soviet output of preserved vegetables, animal fats, plant oils, and meat, and 3 percent of the total Soviet output of beet sugar. Kyrgyzstan also produced small proportions of Soviet wine products and tobacco. Industrially, the republic supplied 1 to 2 percent of the Soviet Union's total output of cotton cloth, silk cloth, linen, and woolen cloth, and an equal proportion of ready-made clothing and shoes. Machine-assembly plants, steel plants, motor-assembly plants, and miscellaneous light industry contributed another 1 percent or less of the Soviet total. The only energy resources that Kyrgyzstan contributed in any volume were coal (0.5 percent of the Soviet total) and hydroelectric power (0.8 percent). Kyrgyzstan's radio-assembly and other electronic plants accounted for a small portion of the defense industry. A torpedo-assembly plant was located on the shores of Ysyk-Köl. One of the Soviet Union's two military airbases for the training of foreign pilots was located outside Bishkek.

Kyrgyzstan's largest role in the Soviet economy was as a supplier of minerals, especially antimony (in which the republic had a near monopoly), mercury, lead, and zinc. Of greatest significance economically, however, was gold, of which Kyrgyzstan was the Soviet Union's third-largest supplier.

Natural Resources

Soviet geologists have estimated Kyrgyzstan's coal reserves at about 27 billion tons, of which the majority remained entirely unexploited in the mid-1990s. About 3 billion tons of that amount are judged to be of highest quality. This coal has proven difficult to exploit, however, because most of it is in small deposits deep in the mountains. Kyrgyzstan also has oil resources; small deposits of oil-bearing shale have been located in southern Kyrgyzstan, and part of the Fergana oil and natural gas complex lies in Kyrgyzstani territory. In the Osh region, four pools of oil, four of natural gas, and four mixed pools have been exploited since the 1950s; however, the yield of all of them is falling in the 1990s. In 1992 their combined output was 112,000 tons of oil and 65 million cubic meters of natural gas, compared with the republic's annual consumption of 2.5 million tons of oil and 3 billion cubic meters of natural gas.

Kyrgyzstan's iron ore deposits are estimated at 5 billion tons, most containing about 30 percent iron. Copper deposits in the mountains are located in extremely complex mineral deposits, making extraction costly. The northern mountains also contain lead, zinc, molybdenum, vanadium, and bismuth. The south has deposits of bauxite and mercury; Kyrgyzstan was the Soviet Union's main supplier of mercury, but in the 1990s plummeting mercury prices have damaged the international market. A tin and tungsten mine was 80 percent complete in 1995. Kyrgyzstan had a virtual monopoly on supplying antimony to the Soviet Union, but post-Soviet international markets are small and highly specialized. Uranium, which was in high demand for the Soviet Union's military and atomic energy programs, no longer is mined in Kyrgyzstan.

The Soviet Union's largest gold mine was located at Makmal in Kyrgyzstan, and in the Soviet period Kyrgyzstan's 170 proven deposits put it in third place behind only Russia and Uzbekistan in gold production in the union. Two more promising deposits, at Kumtor and Jerui, have been discovered. Kumtor, said to be the seventh-largest gold deposit in the world with an estimated value of US$5.5 billion, is being explored by the Canadian Metals Company (Cameco), a uranium company, in a joint-venture operation. Gold deposits are concentrated in Talas Province in north-central Kyrgyzstan, where as much as 200 tons may exist; deposits in Makmal are estimated at sixty tons. Deposits adjacent to the Chatkal River in the northwest amount to an estimated 150 tons.

The terms of the agreement for Kumtor exploitation with Cameco, which gains one-third of profits from gold extraction, caused public concern in 1992. To improve control of the mineral-extraction and refining processes, and to address the uncontrolled movement of precious metals out of the country, President Akayev created a new administrative agency, Kyrgyzaltyn (Kyrgyzstan Gold), to replace Yuzhpolmetal, the Soviet-era body responsible for precious metals. In January 1993, Akayev also brought the country's antimony and mercury mines into Kyrgyzaltyn. The latter are especially important because mercury is used to refine gold. Control of the mercury mines makes more likely the realization of Akayev's hope that Kyrgyzstan will become more than just a supplier of raw materials.

Although Kyrgyzstan has one of the largest proven gold reserves in the world, in the early 1990s fuel and spare parts shortages combined with political disputes to hamper output (see Government and Politics). Production in 1994 was 3.5 tons, but the output goal for 1996 was ten tons.

Kyrgyzstan's major energy source, water, has also been discussed as a commercial product. The export of bottled mineral and fresh water was the object of several unrealized plans in the mid-1990s.

Agriculture

The condition of agriculture in Kyrgyzstan is determined by the state's continuing control of production, marketing, and prices, as well as by the republic-wide specialization mandated by the former Soviet Union to promote interdependence among the republics. Most agricultural production continues to occur in the state farm and collective farm systems, which are slowly being privatized. In the early post-Soviet years, government policy encouraged self-sufficiency in cereal grains to provide food security. Maintaining such self-sufficiency, however, has entailed continued government regulation such as compulsory marketing, which in turn has discouraged the development of diversified farm enterprise. The main agricultural regions are in the Fergana Valley (Osh and Jalal-Abad provinces), in the northern Chu and Talas valleys, and in the Ysyk-Köl basin in the northeast. In the early 1990s, income declined steadily in both state-run and privatized agricultural enterprises.

Agricultural Land

Kyrgyzstan has about 1.4 million hectares of arable land, which is only about 7 percent of the nation's total area. More than 70 percent of the arable area depends on irrigation for its productivity. In the Soviet period, only about 4 percent of agricultural land was owned privately, although private plots contributed a much higher percentage of overall output, especially in fruits and vegetables. In 1994 only an additional 6 percent of agricultural land had passed to some form of private ownership. The privatization of land was a difficult issue that was contested between President Akayev and more conservative government officials. The latter reflected the Soviet-era view that land should be common property protected and disposed of only by the state. More immediately, these officials represented the interests of state farm administrators, whose enterprises suffered greatly from post-Soviet economic shocks and redistribution of resources.

In 1992 and 1993, the land redistribution program also was hindered by poor cooperation between the national and local governments and by lack of clarity in the program outline. Nevertheless, by early 1993 some 165 of the 470 existing state and collective farms had been reorganized or privatized into about 17,000 peasant enterprises, cooperatives, or peasant associations. However, the state retained control over vital agricultural inputs and market distribution channels, meaning that private land users often lacked material support and that price controls limited the profitability of private farms. The privatization program was halted in early 1993, and a more comprehensive reform program was developed. In early 1995, the government offered debt relief to state and collective farms that expedited the availability of land to private farmers.

According to privatization law, state agricultural assets are distributed according to a share system in which all citizens have the right to a garden plot, but only individuals in the rural population have the right to occupy land and other agricultural assets formerly owned by state and collective farms. Recipients of shares can maintain the property as part of the collective, transfer it to a cooperative, or establish an individual farm. In the early 1990s, the former alternative was much more popular because of the perception that larger units offered greater security in a time of financial uncertainty. Private ownership of land remained illegal in 1995, but use rights are guaranteed for forty-nine years, and use rights can be bought, sold, and used as collateral for loans. In 1994 a new decree on land reform expanded and clarified the legal basis for the use and exchange of land and improved the administration of land privatization, which is the responsibility of the Ministry of Agriculture and Food.

Agricultural Production

In the post-Soviet years, Kyrgyzstan has continued to emphasize production of raw materials for industrial processing, a role assigned to the republic in the Soviet system. An estimated 62 percent of the population is rural (see Population). The chief crops are fodder crops, wheat, barley, and cotton. Other agricultural products are sugar beets, tobacco, fruit, vegetables, and silk (see table 5). In 1994 the largest crop harvests were of wheat (611,000 tons), barley (300,000 tons), potatoes (288,000 tons), and tomatoes (160,000 tons).

Table 5. Kyrgyzstan: Production of Principal Agricultural Crops, 1992-94 (in thousands of tons)

Crop	1992	1993	1994
Wheat	634	863	611
Barley	582	539	300
Potatoes	362	291	288
Tomatoes	201	150	160
Corn	281	184	120
Sugar beets	135	207	110
Apples	75	69	65
Tobacco, leaf	56	60	58
Cotton seed	34	38	40
Cabbage	61	32	35
Grapes	31	30	28

Source: Based on information from *The Europa World Year Book 1996*, 2, London, 1996, 1900.

The chief agricultural use of land is pasturage for livestock, mainly sheep, goats, and cattle, the tending of which is the traditional vocation of the Kyrgyz people. An estimated 83 percent of land in agricultural use is mountainous pastureland. In the 1980s, livestock production accounted for about 60 percent of the value of the country's agricultural output; such production included mutton, beef, eggs, milk, wool, and thoroughbred horses. In 1987, when herds reached their largest numbers, about twice as much grain was used for animal feed as for human consumption. However, the prices of and demand for livestock products have dropped significantly in the 1990s relative to those of crops. For this reason and because Soviet-era herds had been supported largely by cheap imported grain, in 1994 livestock contributed less than half the total value of Kyrgyzstan's agricultural earnings. In 1994 the most important livestock products were cow's milk (750,000 tons), beef and veal (70,000 tons), mutton and lamb (50,000 tons), eggs (30,600 tons), wool (56,300 tons), pork products (30,000 tons), and poultry meat (25,000 tons). All of those figures were below the totals for the previous two years.

Agricultural Trends and Problems

The early 1990s saw many farmers turn from commercial production to subsistence crops, a trend that hurt the country's export activities (roughly half of its exports were agricultural in 1990) as well as the availability of foods within Kyrgyzstan. Experts believe that Kyrgyzstan's main agricultural problems are inappropriate and slow-moving reforms (especially land redistribution), intrusive bureaucratic regulations, poor availability of credit, and delayed payments to farmers for their crops. More immediately, both water and fertilizers have been in short supply since the end of the Soviet Union. In addition, Kyrgyzstan's agriculture uses an average of less than 50 percent of the amount of pesticides used by agriculture in the Western nations.

In 1994 the agriculture sector was in the fourth and most difficult year of a major decline that included reduced output, isolation from commercial markets, decreased earnings, and a deteriorating natural resource base (see table 6). In 1994 total agricultural output dropped by 17 percent, and the decline in marketed and processed output was substantially greater because of the trend toward subsistence farming. Production ceased to increase at about the time of the collapse of the Soviet system, an event that initiated the loss of markets and trading partners, the loss of transfer payments from Moscow, and a condition of general monetary instability. The national government did not address these problems effectively in the first years of independence; in fact, government marketing quotas, price controls, and trade restrictions exacerbated the decline. By restricting farmers' marketing and pricing practices, the government in effect levied a tax on agriculture that redistributed income to other sectors of society. National reforms in land tenure, farm organization, and the financial system, together with privatization of services, were eroded by the continued authority of local officials to interfere in administration of those reforms.

Table 6. Central Asia: Percentage Change in Major Economic Indicators, 1992-93 and 1993-94

	GDP		Industrial Output		Agricultural Output	
Country	**1992-93**	**1993-94**	**1992-93**	**1993-94**	**1992-93**	**1993-94**
Kazakhstan	-12	-26	-17	-28	-3	-23
Kyrgyzstan	-13	-25	-24	-25	-8	-17
Tajikistan	-21	-12	-20	-31	-4	-26
Turkmenistan	8	-24	6	-24	9	-2
Uzbekistan	-3	-4	-4	1	0	13

Source: Based on information from United States, Central Intelligence Agency, *Handbook of International Economic Statistics 1995*, Washington, 1995, 52.

A key agricultural resource, pastureland, was degraded severely by the Soviet-era practice of mandating livestock populations too large for available pasturage on state farms and by post-Soviet transfer of livestock from inefficient collective and state farms to private ownership without limiting grazing rights on common pastures. By 1994 over-grazing had led to serious erosion of much pasture land (see Environmental Problems).

In 1994 a continuing controversy over granting central bank credits to support farmers during the growing season again made financial support a dubious proposition. Without such support, planting and fertilization would be severely limited because farmers in many rural areas lack financial resources to buy seed and fertilizer. On the other hand, such credits have always been a threat to the government's overall economic program. For several reasons, including the state's failure to pay farmers on time for their crops, the agricultural sector's bank debts increased rapidly in the early 1990s. This situation was the basis of arguments that the government could not afford to pay agricultural credits.

Industry

Industrial production in Kyrgyzstan declined significantly in 1992 and 1993, especially in comparison to the average annual growth rate from 1985 to 1990, which was 3.3 percent. Important factors in this decline were the energy crisis caused by the loss of Soviet-era fuel supply agreements and the outflow of skilled Russian industrial and management personnel. By 1994, when output had fallen by another 25 percent, Kyrgyzstan's production was only 42 percent of its 1990 level. Only four of the country's 200 most important industrial products--oil, electrical power, household electric appliances, and alcoholic beverages--showed an increased output in 1994. By the first quarter of 1995, some 120 enterprises, more than one-third of the national total, were idle. The decline was caused by problems in obtaining raw materials, components, and other inputs; a drop in effective demand; the economic weakness of trading partners; and problems in arranging for payments. An important additional problem, however, is the nature of Kyrgyzstan's Soviet-era industrial structure, which was specialized for defense-related manufacturing. Many defense-related industries closed in the early 1990s because they could not find alternative types of production once Soviet defense contracts ended. The government's initial policy was to avoid supporting unprofitable state enterprises, but intense political pressure has kept many such firms open.

Including mining, the electric power industries, and construction, industry contributed about 45 percent of GDP in 1991, but that percentage dropped significantly in the following years, even with a parallel agricultural decline. For example, between 1991 and 1993 production of crude steel decreased 45 percent, cement production decreased by 49 percent, and production of metal cutting machines dropped by 77 percent. Gross capital formation decreased an estimated 55 percent in 1994, and investment for that year was below 25 percent of the rate at the end of the Soviet period. Private investment, however, rose slightly to nearly half of total investment for 1994.

None of the major industrial projects planned for 1993-94 was completed on time. Included in major construction postponements was a cigarette factory in Osh, which could have taken advantage of southern Kyrgyzstan's favorable tobacco-growing conditions. Many other projects were completed on a much smaller scale than originally planned. As conversion to useful new lines of manufacture was delayed, the national economy shrank. In addition, unemployment grew rapidly as state-owned enterprises were phased out but not replaced.

In the mid-1990s, the most valuable industrial components of Kyrgyzstan's economy were machine building, textiles, and food processing, which are centered in Bishkek, Osh, and Jalal-Abad (table 7). Some electronics and instruments are produced in former defense plants, and a limited metallurgical industry also exists. The most productive "industry" is electric power, which is produced in the country's numerous hydroelectric plants.

Table 7. Kyrgyzstan: Production of Principal Industrial Products, 1991-94

Product	1991	1992	1993	1994
Carpets (in thousands of square meters)	1,661	1,701	1,609	1,083
Cement (in thousands of tons)	1,320	1,095	672	426
Electric power (in millions of kilowatt-hours)	14,170	11,890	11,200	12,900
Fabric (in thousands of square meters)	142,778	123,781	89,138	62,144
Footwear (in thousands of pairs)	9,504	5,343	3,528	1,631
Trucks	23,600	14,800	5,000	200
Washing machines	209,400	94,000	76,800	17,100

Source: Based on information from *The Europa World Year Book 1995*, 2, London, 1995, 1824; and *The Europa World Yearbook 1996*, 2, London, 1996, 1900.

Energy

Unlike its neighbors Kazakhstan and Uzbekistan, Kyrgyzstan has no significant exploited reserves of oil or natural gas; in 1994 petroleum production was 88,000 tons, and natural gas production was 39 million cubic meters. Although substantial coal deposits are present, in the mid-1990s experts described Kyrgyzstan's coal industry as in a state of collapse. In the early 1990s, only four of the fourteen state-owned coal mines were considered economically viable, and little coal came from privately owned mines. Between 1991 and 1993, brown coal production decreased by 50 percent (to 959,000 tons), and black coal production decreased by 53 percent (to 712,000 tons). The domestic price of conventional fuels rose slightly above world levels after the much cheaper energy-sharing arrangements of the Soviet era ended. (In 1992 oil and gas import costs were 50 percent of the total state budget, compared with 10 percent in 1991.) In 1994 some 39 percent of Kyrgyzstan's total import expenditures went for the purchase of conventional fuels, contributing an estimated US$100 million to the country's trade imbalance (see Foreign Trade). Energy consumption, meanwhile, has declined sharply since 1991, and experts do not expect it to return to its 1990 level.

Management of national energy and fuel policy is distributed among several ministries and other state agencies--an arrangement that has hindered efficient acquisition and distribution. Distribution of heat and electricity is the responsibility of the state-run Kyrgyzstan National Energy Holding Company, and natural gas purchases are managed by the Kyrgyzstan Natural Gas Administration (Kyrgyzgas). Oil, gas, and coal exploration is the responsibility of the State Geological Commission (Goskomgeologiya). Natural gas, provided by the Republic of Turkmenistan in the Soviet era, now comes mainly from neighboring Uzbekistan. Coal, used to heat households and to fuel some thermoelectric plants, is mainly received from Kazakhstan in a barter arrangement for electrical power. Kazakhstan's coal is preferred because the heaviest demand in Kyrgyzstan is concentrated in the north, and Kyrgyzstan's remaining coal mines are in the south, from which transportation is problematic.

For these reasons, existing thermoelectric stations have been deemphasized in the 1990s in favor of expanded hydroelectric production. Thus, in 1994 thermoelectric power production dropped by 46 percent while hydroelectric production rose by 30 percent. These statistics enabled the national energy sector to show a modest drop of 4 percent in total power generation in 1994, but district heating, which comes from coal- and gas-powered combined heat and power plants, suffered heavily from the transition. Meanwhile, government promotion of electricity brought an increase of 117 percent in household power use between 1991 and 1994, although overall household energy consumption declined by 36 percent during that period. Some aspects of the promotion plan have been criticized, including the large-scale promotion of electric heat in a country with poorly insulated houses.

Emphasis on electricity is backed by abundant water power, mainly from the country's location at the mountain headwaters of the Syrdariya, one of the two largest rivers in Central Asia. On the Naryn River, chief tributary of the Syrdariya, a series of hydroelectric stations has been built, the largest of which is the Kürp-Say Hydroelectric Plant, fed by the Toktogol Reservoir in central Kyrgyzstan. Other major hydroelectric plants are located at Atabashin, Alamedin, and Uchkorgon. Such stations have made possible the net export of electric power, worth an estimated US$100 million in 1994. That figure was only about half the value of Kyrgyzstan's 1990 export, however, because demand in neighboring republics dropped considerably in the early 1990s. The main customer is Kazakhstan, with which power is exchanged through the Central Asian Integrated System.

Only about 10 percent of Kyrgyzstan's hydroelectric power potential and only about 3 percent of the potential of its smaller streams are currently being exploited; the Naryn River is estimated to afford an additional 2,200 megawatts of easily accessible rated capacity. Meanwhile, the Fergana Valley, the only working oil field in the country, has remaining reserves of 14 million tons of oil that require expensive recovery technolgy. No serious oil exploration has been done elsewhere, although the Chu and Ak-Say valleys are believed to be promising.

Economic Reform

Since independence, Kyrgyzstan has undertaken significant structural reforms of its economy; in 1994 the International Monetary Fund (IMF--see Glossary) ranked Kyrgyzstan fourth among former Soviet republics (behind the three Baltic states) in the pace of economic reform, but positive results have not been forthcoming. As elsewhere in the former Soviet Union, one of the most significant reforms is privatization. The goal of privatization, a high priority in the early 1990s, has been to create new productive enterprises with efficient management systems while involving the population in the reform program at a fundamental level. The process began in December 1991 with the adoption of the Privatization and Denationalization Law and the creation of the State Property Fund as the agency to design and implement the program. In late 1992, a new parliamentary "Concept Note" reoriented the program toward rapid sale of small enterprises and ownership transition in larger enterprises by vouchers and other special payments. By the end of 1993, about 4,450 state enterprises, including 33 percent of total fixed enterprise assets, were fully or partially privatized. By mid-1994, nearly all services and 82 percent of assets in trade enterprises, 40 percent of assets in industry, and 68 percent of construction assets were in private hands.

However, the practical results of those statistics have not been nearly so positive. Most privatization (and almost all privatization in industry) was accomplished by creation of joint-stock companies, transferring enterprise shares to labor groups within them. Almost no public bidding for enterprise shares occurred, and the state maintained significant shares in enterprises after their conversion to joint-stock companies. Also, because the sale of shares was prohibited, shareholders wishing to leave the company had to return their holdings to the labor collective. The 1994 Law on Privatization remedied this situation by providing for competitive bidding for shares in small enterprises (with fewer than 100 employees) as well as long-term privatization of medium-sized (with 100 to 1,000 employees) and large enterprises by competitive cash bidding among individuals. The new law also provided for the auctioning of all enterprise shares remaining in state hands, over an undetermined period of time. In 1994 and early 1995, voucher privatization moved toward its goals quickly; by the end of 1994, an estimated 65 percent of industrial output came from non-state enterprises.

Privatization was not the final step in economic success, however. After that step, many firms needed drastic restructuring--most notably in management and technology--to function in a market environment. Because the commercial banking system had not been reformed substantially, enterprises found little financial or technical support for such upgrading (see Financial System). On the other hand, enterprises (especially state enterprises) have not been discouraged from defaulting on loans because they often are closely associated with banks, whose pliable loan policy is backed by the National Bank of Kyrgyzstan. Plans called for establishment of an intermediary agency to distribute foreign and international funds to privatized enterprises until the banking system is able to take over lending activities. A stock exchange opened in Bishkek in May 1995 and was considered an important step in expediting this process.

In the early years of independence, a major cause of Kyrgyzstan's economic distress has been corruption and malfeasance. In a January 1993 speech, President Akayev reported that as much as 70 percent of the money that the country had invested in its economy had been diverted into private hands. Meanwhile, a poll of the country's few entrepreneurs found that 85 percent of them reported having to offer bribes to stay in business. The truth of Akayev's statement was difficult to verify, but reports in newspapers and elsewhere suggest that it could be correct. Official data indicated that since independence at least 100,000 tons of cast iron, steel, aluminum, and zinc had been sold abroad without legal permission, and that a credit for 1.7 billion rubles for the purchase of grain had vanished. Other anecdotal evidence of corruption, often connected with local centers of political power, was plentiful (see Structure of Government).

Financial System

In mid-1995, the banking system continued to be dominated by the central savings bank (the National Bank of Kyrgyzstan, created in 1991) and by the three major commercial banks that succeeded the sectoral banks of the Soviet era and remained under state control. Those banks--the Agricultural and Industrial Bank (Agroprombank), the Industrial and Construction Bank (Promstroybank), and the Commercial Bank of Kyrgyzstan--owned 85 percent of banking assets in 1994. New commercial banks, of which fifteen were established in 1993 and 1994, were owned by individuals or enterprises and had much less financial power than the state-owned banks. The new commercial banks have the right to buy and sell foreign currency and open deposit accounts. The National Bank is the official center of currency exchange, but in the mid-1990s it did not adhere to official exchange rates. In mid-1994, the government established the Bank for Reconstruction and Development, which uses state funds, foreign currency assets, and loans from abroad to aid small and medium-sized enterprises and to invest in targeted spheres of the economy, especially housing, construction, power generation, and agriculture.

The banking system has remained concentrated in the same areas as in the Soviet period. Although some diversification has occurred, loans tend to go to traditional clients. Because new commercial banks are small and initially were owned by state ministries and state-owned enterprises, competition has developed slowly. Through 1994 Soviet-style accounting and reporting systems remained in use, and banking services such as domestic and international payments have remained at the same noncompetitive level as they were prior to 1991. Capabilities vital to a market-type economy, such as credit risk assessment and project appraisal, are lacking. Post-Soviet regulations on capital funds, exposure limits, and lending practices have not been enforced. The technical infrastructure of the banks also requires substantial overhaul. In addition, the National Bank has been plagued by scandal; the first director, an Akayev protégé, was linked to several illegal financial operations in 1993 and 1994.

The limitations of the banking system have made it unable to efficiently mobilize and allocate financial resources into the national economy. This failure has hindered privatization and other types of economic reform that require substantial amounts of risk capital upon which borrowers can rely. Especially critical are the bad loans held by the three state-owned banks (influenced by government interference in loan decisions, together with poor financial discipline on the part of major enterprises) and eroded capital base. In 1995 the National Bank's outstanding loans to agricultural and industrial enterprises totaled 1 billion som each.

Prices, Monetary Policy, and Debt

Kyrgyzstan paid dearly for its designated role as an exporter of raw materials when the Soviet Union unraveled and retail prices began to be freed: the prices paid for raw materials rose much more slowly than did prices of finished goods. Thus, in 1992, for example, the cost of what Kyrgyzstan imported rose by fifty to 100 times, while the amounts received for exports rose by fifteen to twenty times. This explains in part why the GNP for 1992 was valued at 250 billion rubles (for value of the ruble--see Glossary), while the cost of Kyrgyzstan's imports was put at 400 billion rubles. In 1992 Russia began discounting the paper value of the Kyrgyzstan ruble, effectively devaluing the goods that Kyrgyzstan was supplying. Moscow then required that the country assume the imposed "difference" as a loan, which had the effect of increasing Kyrgyzstan's debt burden.

To escape the disparities inherent in dependence on the ruble, in May 1993 Kyrgyzstan was the first former Soviet republic to leave the ruble zone (see Glossary) and introduce its own currency, the som. This new policy earned Kyrgyzstan the hostility of neighboring Kazakhstan and Uzbekistan, which had declared loyalty to the ruble and feared an avalanche of devalued Kyrgyzstani rubles entering their countries. The som, which is fully convertible to foreign currency and has a floating exchange rate, has been underwritten largely by the IMF, which has provided a large measure of stability. After introduction at a rate of two som to the United States dollar, the som traded at eleven to the dollar at the end of 1995. According to President Akayev, about half the som in circulation are backed by gold or by international loans. Although the som has received strong international backing, experts questioned the likelihood that such support would continue once other new national currencies emerged in former Soviet republics, eliminating the som's status as a unique experiment. Such doubt grew clear as Kyrgyzstan's first international loans came due in 1995, with scheduled payments of approximately US$58 million that year, rising to nearly US$100 million the next year. The republic's collapsed economy made it possible that Kyrgyzstan would become a permanent international client state.

Especially in the first year of independence, hyperinflation seriously eroded buying power (see table 8). At the end of 1992, wholesale prices were more than eighteen times higher than in 1991. Retail prices rose 40 percent in December 1992 alone, explaining in part why retail sales declined by 64 percent from 1991, the greatest decline in all of Central Asia. Between 1990 and 1992, meat consumption dropped 20 percent, milk product consumption by 30 percent, and fats consumption by 40 percent. Beginning in 1993, however, international support for the som and for Kyrgyzstan's economy in general has kept inflation much lower than it is elsewhere in the CIS. From a high of about 1,400 percent annually in 1992 and 1993 (caused mainly by large increases in fuel costs), inflation dropped to about 180 percent for 1994 (mainly because of tighter credit and the government's reduced expenditures); the government's inflation target for 1995, set in cooperation with the IMF, was 55 percent, with monthly declines throughout the year. Prices rose by 16 percent in the first quarter of 1995, slightly above target, but budgetary expenditures for the first half of the year were far above the IMF target of 5 percent of GDP.

Table 8. Central Asia: Cost of Living, 1990-93

Country and Category	1990	1991	1992	1993
Kazakhstan				
Food	n.a.	4.7	100	2,297
Clothing	n.a.	4.7	100	1,606
Rent	n.a.	n.a.	100	16,258
Average for all items	n.a.	3.3	100	2,265
Kyrgyzstan (all items)	100	185.0	954.0	n.a.
Tajikistan				
Food	101.8	194.4	1,450.5	n.a.
Alcoholic beverages	100.6	163.4	1,152.1	n.a.
Average for all items	104.0	193.0	1,153.9	n.a.
Turkmenistan (all items)[2]	104.2	202.5	592.9	n.a.
Uzbekistan (all items)[1]	100	205.0	627.7	951.1

Source: Based on information from *The Europa World Year Book 1995*, 2, London, 1995, 1737, 1825, 2952, 3071, 3364.

Notes: [1] All figures 1993 except life expectancy (1989).
[2] All figures 1989.

In the spring of 1995, average monthly pay in Kyrgyzstan was 508 som, compared with a government-estimated minimum family budget of 487 som. Earning statistics are not considered totally reliable, however. In 1995 food required an average of 61 percent of the family budget. To eliminate price distortions inherited from price support policies of the Soviet regime, the Akayev government decontrolled most prices in 1992, which had the immediate result of fueling inflation and reducing individual purchasing power. The economic decline of 1993 caused reintroduction of price controls, notably on agricultural products, and ceilings of 10 to 25 percent were placed on price increases for a wide range of retail commodities. The state Anti-Monopoly and Pricing Committee restricted pricing decisions in most of Kyrgyzstan's large enterprises. Although such institutional mechanisms did not work consistently, they encouraged development of unofficial economic arrangements and barter arrangements, which further undermined the national economy. In 1994 the government again reversed its policy, ending obligatory sale and price controls on agricultural goods that had depressed the agricultural market. The reform would nominally free farmers to negotiate commodity prices with government agencies and other buyers. However, because the government remained the only large-scale purchaser of many products, liberalizing the procurement process was not expected to have immediate effects.

Foreign Investment

Domestic economic investment declined precipitously in the early 1990s, with government investment falling 55 percent in 1994 alone. In the first quarter of 1995, total public and private investment was reported to be 391 million som, of which about 75 percent went to the Kumtor joint-venture gold field. To stimulate foreign investment, the Kyrgyz government has adopted a series of measures to improve the republic's deteriorating economic environment. In the late 1980s, the republic already had begun creating a legal infrastructure to support private investment. The Basic Foreign Investment Law, adopted in June 1991, has been amended several times since that time. In general, this law allows foreign investors full use of their profits, including unlimited export of profits in the form of foreign currency or merchandise.

Foreign firms also enjoy considerable tax advantages, which extend to Kyrgyzstani partners in joint ventures. Investors are granted relief from import duties on materials needed to establish a business, and they continue receiving tax relief for up to five years, depending on their type of business. After that time, several other types of tax relief are available, including various forms of reinvestment in Kyrgyzstan's economy.

As of April 1995, some 328 joint ventures were registered, but only 128 were actually in operation, the vast majority in trade. Only thirty-eight joint ventures were active in manufacturing or mining. At that time, sixty-eight foreign firms (outside the CIS) were registered, the majority of which were Chinese, Afghan, and Turkish. Some fifty-two Russian and thirty-six United States firms were present in some capacity. Kyrgyzstan was among the first of the former Soviet republics to create free economic zones, on the Chinese model, where taxes would be abated and duties waived. The government initially created two such zones, in Naryn and Osh, with another under consideration in Bishkek. The zones became the object of heated debate, however, and by 1995 only the Naryn zone had taken form as planned. The only large-scale foreign investment has been in the gold industry, where the Cameco and the United States Morrison-Knudson Corporation are participating in joint ventures.

Foreign Trade

Kyrgyzstan's principal exports include wool, hides, and cotton (which combined to provide nearly 80 percent of total exports in 1994), together with electric power, electronic products, ferrous and nonferrous metals, food products, and shoes. Besides fuels, the largest volume of imports is in construction materials, ferrous metals, pharmaceuticals, chemicals, and machinery. The largest CIS trading partners are Russia, Kazakhstan, and Uzbekistan, and the largest non-CIS partner is China (see table 9). The predominance of barter agreements makes quantification of the latter relationship approximate, however. Of the estimated US$44 million of trade with China in 1994, less than one-quarter was in cash. During the late 1980s and early 1990s, Kyrgyzstan's economy was highly dependent on external trade. Total exports and imports in 1991 amounted to nearly 80 percent of the country's GDP, but by 1993 that total had shrunk to 52.5 percent. External trade, which in the early 1990s was conducted principally with the other republics of the former Soviet Union, resulted in a large trade deficit, mainly because of the need to obtain petroleum products and natural gas at the much higher prices of post-Soviet markets. During the first years of independence, the deficit from interrepublic and hard-currency (see Glossary) trade was about 20 percent of GDP.

Table 9. Kyrgyzstan: Foreign Trade with Selected Countries, 1992-94

	1992	1993	1994
Imports			
Former Soviet Union			
Armenia	0.1	0.1	0.0
Azerbaijan	0.5	0.6	0.3
Belarus	1.5	0.9	1.2
Estonia	0.0	n.a.	n.a.
Georgia	0.4	0.2	0.1
Kazakhstan	23.3	28.9	28.0
Latvia	0.2	n.a.	n.a.
Lithuania	0.3	n.a.	n.a.
Moldova	0.5	0.1	0.0
Russia	49.0	47.1	33.4
Tajikistan	0.7	0.4	0.5
Turkmenistan	6.1	2.1	4.8
Ukraine	8.1	2.0	1.4
Uzbekistan	9.1	17.3	30.2
Exports			
Former Soviet Union[1]			
Armenia	0.2	0.0	0.0
Azerbaijan	0.9	1.4	0.7
Belarus	3.0	2.0	1.7
Estonia	0.2	n.a.	n.a.
Georgia	0.4	0.1	0.1
Kazakhstan	22.4	29.0	42.9
Latvia	0.3	n.a.	n.a.
Lithuania	1.5	n.a.	n.a.
Moldova	0.6	0.4	0.2
Russia	39.1	45.8	26.0
Tajikistan	1.4	2.5	1.4
Turkmenistan	2.4	3.5	3.4
Ukraine	17.3	5.7	4.0
Uzbekistan	10.4	9.6	19.6

Imports			
Other countries			
Belgium	n.a.	4.8	n.a.
China	16.3	18.6	11.0
Czech Republic	3.3	5.4	0.0
France	6.3	3.0	1.8
Germany	n.a.	3.0	6.8
Hungary	3.7	n.a.	n.a.
Italy	1.8	0.7	0.9
Japan	0.2	0.1	2.7
Korea, Republic of	0.7	0.2	4.0
Netherlands	n.a.	0.1	1.8
Poland	0.2	8.8	15.0
Slovakia[2]	3.3	2.7	1.0
Sweden	0.0	0.1	2.6
Switzerland	n.a.	0.3	2.5
Turkey	3.4	4.5	2.0
Exports			
Other countries[3]			
Austria	1.0	3.1	0.2
China	28.0	59.1	56.1
France	6.8	0.0	2.2
Italy	0.5	0.4	1.8
Japan	2.7	0.0	0.0
Korea, Democratic People's Republic of	3.4	0.2	0.6
Poland	0.3	2.6	3.9
Sweden	1.5	1.1	n.a.
Turkey	1.8	1.1	2.4
United Kingdom	11.6	30.0	29.5

Source: Based on information from World Bank, *Statistical Handbook 1995: States of the Former USSR*, Washington, 1995, 288-90.

Notes: [1] All figures 1993 except life expectancy (1990).
[2] All figures 1989.
[3] All figures 1993 except life expectancy (1989).

In 1994 Kyrgyzstan substantially liberalized state regulation of trade. All export and import license requirements, the issuance of which was the center of recurring corruption rumors in the early 1990s, were eliminated excepting some hazardous materials. Export taxes, which had been levied mainly in retaliation for Russian export taxes, were reduced or eliminated, and plans called for their complete elimination by the end of 1995. Import duties on goods from non-CIS countries were fixed at 5 to 15 percent; there are no duties on goods from within the CIS.

The Ministry for Industry, Trade, and Material Resources is the chief agency for obtaining goods for export and distributing imports. Until the liberalization of 1994, a number of government-signed clearing agreements with former Soviet republics set terms for barter agreements that often avoided the problems caused by late payments. In 1993 such an agreement with Russia exchanged raw cotton, wool, and tobacco and scrap metal for petroleum products, wood, and metal products. Another agreement with Uzbekistan brought natural gas and fertilizers in exchange for nonferrous metals, electrical products, and butter. A third example is the coal-for-electricity arrangement with Kazakhstan (see Energy). Commodity values for such agreements usually were close to world levels, but the rigid procurement methods required for such bilateral trades have distorted the rest of the national economy.

In 1994 Kyrgyzstan's foreign trade decreased by 16.6 percent (to US$93.4 million, after a drop of 65 percent in the 1992-93 period) for exports and by more than 50 percent (to US$52.6 million) for imports. Trade with non-CIS partners showed a surplus, but more than 85 percent of trade still was transacted with CIS nations. Although the condition of the domestic economy did not seem to favor an upturn in foreign trade for 1995, Kyrgyz policy makers expected that increased foreign assistance would improve the trade situation somewhat.

In February 1994, Kyrgyzstan joined with Kazakhstan and Uzbekistan in creating the Central Asian Free Trade Zone in reaction to the collapse of the new ruble zone proposed by Russia in late 1993. Although not the full organization of Central Asian nations that had been envisioned by intellectuals since before independence, this exclusively economic agreement was able to abolish trade barriers among the partners immediately, and trade between Kyrgyzstan and Kazakhstan increased in 1994. But further conditions on credit, prices, taxes, customs, currency convertibility, and creation of a common economic zone in the Fergana Valley, the vital economic region shared by the three partners and Tajikistan, were delayed throughout 1994 and the first half of 1995. Kyrgyzstan has announced its intention to join the World Trade Organization (WTO--see Glossary), successor to the General Agreement on Tariffs and Trade (GATT).

TRANSPORTATION AND TELECOMMUNICATIONS

For reasons of commerce and national unity, Kyrgyzstan urgently needs improved systems of transportation and telecommunications, neither of which has received adequate attention since the 1980s. Some projects did, however, benefit from substantial foreign investment in the early and mid-1990s.

Transportation

The failure to develop Kyrgyzstan's internal communications has exacerbated the republic's tendencies toward regional division between the north (dominated by the population center of Bishkek) and the south (dominated by the population center of Osh). The two regions are separated by sparsely populated, mountainous terrain (see fig. 2; Topography and Drainage). Transportation problems have been exacerbated by the country's energy dependence, which includes the import of 100 percent of its gasoline supply. The republic's road and railroad systems are divided into two parts. The northern part is integrated with the transportation networks of Kazakhstan, and the southern part is integrated with the networks of Uzbekistan. Three government agencies are responsible for transportation: the Ministry of Transportation, the State Civil Aviation Agency, and the Bishkek Railway Department. Kyrgyzstan is part of a large-scale project to coordinate development of the transportation infrastructure in the heartland of Asia, sponsored by the UN Economic and Social Commission for Asia and the Pacific. The agency plans to spend as much as US$1.5 trillion between 1993 and 2000 to facilitate trans-Asian railroad and highway connections.

In 1990 Kyrgyzstan had 28,400 kilometers of roads, of which 22,400 were hard-surfaced. Some 371 million passengers and 43.9 million tons of freight traveled by road in 1992, accounting for 95 percent and 72 percent of total passengers and freight, respectively. The Karakorum Highway, a Chinese-built road from Ürümqi, at the eastern end of the Tian Shan in China's Xinjiang Uygur Autonomous Region, to Islamabad in northern Pakistan, has a connector to Bishkek, which is 1,900 kilometers from Islamabad (and 3,500 kilometers from Karachi on the Arabian Sea) by that route. A planned connector from Osh via Sary-Tash would cut 200 kilometers from those distances. In 1994 the condition of the country's roads was made a state secret.

Although Kyrgyzstan imports 100 percent of the gasoline it uses, government subsidies have kept gasoline prices relatively low because of the economic role of the nation's roads; in early 1995, tariff increases pushed the average price to roughly US$.30 per liter. The subsidy system has meant that supply is quite erratic and unpredictable; an acute shortage occurred in April 1995, raising the black-market gasoline price above US$.50 per liter.

In a country where 95 percent of freight moves by truck, the gasoline shortage has largely isolated the more remote provinces, and it has made ambulance, fire, and police services difficult to maintain. In at least one town in Osh Province, officials responded to the fuel shortage simply by shutting off all services, leaving the people without light, heat, or power. Public transportation has been doubly burdened because the gasoline shortage has restricted use of private cars and crowded an increased number of riders onto a reduced number of buses. In some cities, such as Kant and Naryn, the city bus services simply stopped running, making it almost impossible for people to get to work. Naryn's solution was to replace the municipal buses with horse-drawn omnibuses.

Rail transport plays a minor role, with a total of 370 kilometers of track, mostly in the north, providing links to Russia via Kazakhstan. In the Soviet system, all rail freight moved along this corridor. Short lines in the south connect towns with the Ursatevskaya-Andijon Line in Uzbekistan. In 1992 some 1.7 million passengers and 5.5 million tons of freight were transported by rail. A rail link from Ürümqi to Ashgabat, Turkmenistan, was opened in 1994, widening Kyrgyzstan's export possibilities. In 1995 a spur of that line opened from Ashgabat to Bandar-Abbas on the Strait of Hormuz in southern Iran. Although a proposal has been made to build a north-south rail link connecting Balychki with Kara-Keche, the money for such a project is not expected to be available in the foreseeable future.

In the early 1990s, available air transport facilities were inadequate. The national airline was formed from a share of the aircraft and personnel allocated from the Soviet airline Aeroflot. Manas, the international airport at Bishkek (named after the mythical national hero), was modernized in 1988 to make it the most modern commercial airport in Central Asia. A second international facility is located at Osh, and about twenty-five usable local fields supplement air service. Manas Airport originally offered flights to fifty cities in the CIS, including regular service to Moscow and Tashkent, and charter flights to China, Turkey, and Saudi Arabia. However, that facility has been almost unused since 1991. The shortage of jet fuel has forced Kyrgyzstan to rely almost completely on the Almaty international airport, four hours by road from Bishkek, for international connections, and the availability of air transport greatly decreased in the early 1990s. The loss of air services has exacerbated the country's tendency toward a north-south split.

Telecommunications

Telecommunications in Kyrgyzstan, generally inadequate, suffer from the historically low priority accorded by Soviet authorities to development of that type of infrastructure. In 1994 only 364,000 main telephone lines, or one per twelve Kyrgyzstanis, were in service. Since independence a thriving black market has developed in cable stolen from existing telephone installations, removing many portions of the telephone system from operation. The average age of system components is about fifteen years. Because much existing equipment is operating at capacity, heavier service loads (which experts judge an absolutely necessary element of economic expansion) require large-scale equipment replacement. In 1991 about 600 lines connected Kyrgyzstan to the rest of the Soviet Union; sixty channels connected the republic to international lines via Moscow. In 1995 international calls still were connected through Moscow, allowing Kyrgyzstan to benefit indirectly from the general upgrading of services that has occurred in Russia in the early 1990s. In 1994 Kyrgyzstan received a loan of US$8 million and US$1.5 million in technical assistance from the European Bank for Recovery and Development (EBRD) to upgrade its telecommunications services, especially in the mountainous regions. The Ministry of Communications is responsible for local, national, and international telephone, telex, telegraph, and data communications. The ministry also is charged with postal services, radio and television broadcasting, and management of subscriptions and deliveries of news publications. Telecommunications, despite low tariffs, have been profitable enough to operate independently of the state budget since 1986. But without a revision of the tariff structure and institutional and regulatory restructuring, the state of telecommunications places a major constraint on the development of a market-oriented economy.

Kyrgyzstan Radio and Kyrgyzstan Television are state broadcasting companies. The two state-run national radio stations broadcast some English and German programming. One commercial radio station is in operation. In 1993 three hours of television programming were available per day; Kyrgyzstan Television receives its color broadcasts from the Secam network.

Government and Politics

As independence has progressed, politics have grown increasingly tangled in Kyrgyzstan. President Akayev, who took office amid a chain of events that lent credence to an idealistic promise of democratic reform and stability, has proven more able to formulate goals than to carry them out. Although a constitution was ratified in 1993, many terms of that document have not yet gone into force.

Background

In March 1990, while still part of the Soviet Union, the republic elected a 350-member Jogorku Kenesh (parliament), which remained in power until it dissolved itself in September 1994. This body was elected under the rules prescribed by the *perestroika* (see Glossary) policy of Soviet President Mikhail S. Gorbachev, which mandated that at least 80 percent of legislative seats be contested even though communists likely would win most seats. In the case of Kyrgyzstan, five seats went to the initial opposition movement, the Democratic Movement of Kyrgyzstan (DDK).

Over time it has become apparent that President Akayev prefers dealing with administrators subordinate to him rather than with legislators. The initial harmony between Akayev and the parliament began to sour in 1993. A number of specific points of contention arose, most of them related to growing legislative resistance to what was widely viewed to be government corruption and mismanagement. Throughout 1993 the parliament sought aggressively to extend control over the executive branch. The allotment of development concessions for two of the republic's largest gold deposits was a particular rallying point (see Natural Resources). The chief representative of Cameco, Boris Birshtein, was a Swiss citizen who had been named in a number of financial scandals in Russia and elsewhere in the CIS. When it was discovered that the Kyrgyzstani negotiating team that had sealed the Cameco transaction had financial interests in the deal, the agreement nearly was cancelled entirely. In December 1993, public protest about this gold concession brought down the government of Prime Minister Tursunbek Chyngyshev and badly damaged Akayev's popularity and credibility.

Chyngyshev was replaced by Apas Jumagulov, who had been prime minister during the late Soviet period. Jumagulov was reappointed in March 1995 and again in March 1996. Akayev was not publicly accused of being involved in the gold scandals, but numerous rumors have mentioned corruption and influence-peddling in the Akayev family, especially in the entourage of his wife. As these rumors circulated more widely, President Akayev held a public referendum of approval for his presidency in January 1994. Most impartial observers regarded the 96 percent approval that Akayev claimed after the referendum as a political fiction.

Constitution

Besides electing Akayev, the 1990 parliament fashioned the legislative foundation for the political transformation of the republic, in concert with the president. Perhaps the biggest accomplishment in this phase was the drafting and passage, in May 1993, of the country's constitution. The constitution mandates three branches of government: a unicameral parliament; an executive branch, consisting of government and local officials appointed by the president; and a judiciary, with a presidentially appointed Supreme Court and lower courts.

In many ways, however, the constitution has not been put into force. Akayev is still president under a popular mandate gained in an uncontested election in 1991, and most of the judicial system has not been appointed. The existing bicameral parliament, which was elected early in 1995, does not match the unicameral body prescribed by the constitution. This structural change was attained through popular referendum, for which the constitution does not provide, although the same referendum simultaneously gave popular (and retroactive) permission for this abrogation of the constitution. In February 1996, Akayev's proposed constitutional amendments strengthening the office of president were approved by 94 percent of voters in a national referendum.

Structure of Government

Although the constitution calls for a government of three branches, in practice the presidency has been the strongest government office. As economic and social conditions deteriorated in the early 1990s, President Akayev sought extraconstitutional authority in dealing with a series of crises. Under these conditions, Akayev faced occasional opposition from parliament, and pockets of local resistance grew stronger in the southern provinces.

President and Council of Ministers

Akayev is able to act as he does because under the constitution the president stands outside the three-branch system in the capacity of guarantor of the constitutional functioning of all three branches. The president names the prime minister and the Council of Ministers, subject to legislative confirmation.

According to the constitution, the president is to be elected once every five years, for no more than two terms, from among citizens who are between thirty-five and sixty-five years of age, who have lived at least fifteen years in the republic, and who are fluent in the state language, which is Kyrgyz. There is no vice president. Akayev defied predictions that he would seek referendum approval of an extension of his term rather than stand for reelection in 1996 as mandated in the constitution. (The presidents of Kazakhstan, Turkmenistan, and Uzbekistan had followed the former course in 1994 and 1995.) In the presidential election of December 1995, Akayev gained 71.6 percent of the vote against two communist challengers. Several other political figures protested that they had been prevented illegally from participating. International observers found the election free and fair. Earlier, newly elected deputies of the 1995 parliament had proposed that presidential elections be postponed until at least the year 2000, with Akayev to remain president in the interim. According to rumors, Akayev favored using a referendum to extend his own term of office, but he found acceptance of parliament's proposal unwise. Kyrgyzstan depends heavily on the loans of Western banks and governments, who objected strenuously to the cancellation of elections as a "step back from democracy."

The Council of Ministers nominally is entrusted with day-to-day administration of the government. In general, however, the office of the presidency has dominated policy making; in most cases, Akayev's prerogative of appointing the prime minister and all cabinet positions has not been effectively balanced by the nominal veto power of parliament over such appointments. The new parliament of 1995 showed considerably more independence by vetoing several key Akayev administrative appointments. In February 1996, the government resigned following the approval of Akayev's constitutional amendments. The new government that Akayev appointed in March 1996 included fifteen ministries: agriculture, communications, culture, defense, economy, education and science, finance, foreign affairs, health, industry and trade, internal affairs, justice, labor and social welfare, transportation, and water resources, plus deputy prime ministers for agrarian policy, sociocultural policy, and industrial policy and the chairmen of nine committees and agencies. Many individuals retained their positions from the preceding government; changes occurred mainly in agencies dealing with social affairs and the economy.

Legislature

In October 1994, Akayev took the legally questionable step of holding a referendum to ask public approval for bypassing legal requirements to amend the constitution. The referendum asked permission to amend the constitution to establish a bicameral legislature that would include an upper chamber, called the Legislative House, which would have only thirty-five members. Those deputies would receive government salaries and would sit in permanent session. A lower chamber, the House of National Representatives, would have seventy members and would convene more irregularly. Akayev's plan also provided that deputies in this new parliament would not be able to hold other government positions, a clause that caused most of the republic's prominent politicians to drop out of consideration for election to parliament.

In the elections to the new parliament that began in February 1995, only sixteen deputies managed to get clear mandates on the first round of balloting. Second-round voting also proved indecisive. When the parliament was convened for the first time, in March 1995, fifteen seats remained unfilled; two important provinces (Naryn and Talas) had no deputies in the upper house at all, prompting angry cries that regional interests were not being properly represented when the two houses elected their respective speakers. A later round of elections, which extended into May, was marked by widespread accusations of fraud, ballot-stuffing, and government manipulation.

Such circumstances aroused strong doubts about the legislative competency of the parliament. Only six of the deputies have previous parliamentary experience, and a number of prominent political figures, including Medetkan Sherymkulov, speaker of the 1990-94 parliament, failed to win what had been assumed were "safe" seats. Even more serious were concerns about the incomplete mandate of the new legislative system. The constitutional modifications voted on by referendum did not specify what the duties and limitations of the two houses would be. Thus, the early sessions of 1995 were preoccupied by procedural wranglings over the respective rights and responsibilities of the legislative, executive, and judicial branches. Because little business of substance was conducted in that session, several deputies threatened that this parliament, like the previous one, might "self-dissolve." However, the body remained intact as of mid-1996.

Judiciary

According to the constitution, judges are to be chosen by the president, subject to parliamentary confirmation. Potential judges must be Kyrgyzstani citizens between thirty-five and sixty-five years of age who have legal training and at least ten years of legal experience. The length of judges' tenure is unlimited, but judges are subject to dismissal for cause by parliament. In the mid-1990s, the judicial system remained incomplete both in the filling of prescribed positions and in the establishment of judicial procedures and precedents. A Supreme Court was appointed, but its functioning was delayed in 1995 by parliament's refusal to approve Akayev's nominee as chief justice. Although the parliament of 1991-94 also mandated a national constitutional court (over the objections of Akayev), that body never has been established.

In general, the rule of law is not well established in the republic. The one area of the law that has flourished in Kyrgyzstan is libel law, which public figures have used widely to control the republic's press. By contrast, the observance of laws designed for the regulation of the economy is not uniform or consistent, even by government officials. The functioning of the State Arbitration Court, which has responsibility for financial and jurisdictional disputes within government agencies and between government agencies and private enterprises, has been extremely irregular and lacking in oversight by any other government institution.

Local Government

The republic is divided into seven administrative regions: six provinces and the capital city of Bishkek. The so-called northern provinces are Naryn, Ysyk-Köl, Chu, and Talas, and the southern provinces are Osh and Jalal-Abad. Jalal-Abad was formed out of Osh Province in 1991, largely to disperse the political strength of the south that had become centered in Osh. Each province has a local legislature, but real power is wielded by the province governor (until 1996 called the *akim*), who is a presidential appointee. In some cases, the *akim* became a powerful spokesman for regional interests, running the district with considerable autonomy. Particularly notable in this regard was Jumagul Saadanbekov, the *akim* of Ysyk-Köl Province. The government reorganization of early 1996 widened the governors' responsibilities for tax collection, pensions, and a variety of other economic and social functions.

Akayev has had difficulty establishing control over the two southern provinces. Several southern politicians (the most important of whom was Sheraly Sydykov, scion of an old Osh family that enjoyed great prominence in the Soviet era) have taken the lead in national opposition against Akayev. Sydykov headed the parliamentary corruption commission in 1994, and he headed the influential banking and ethics committees of the parliament elected in 1995.

When the *akim* of Osh resigned to run for the new parliament, Akayev appointed as his replacement Janysh Rustambekov, an Akayev protégé who had been state secretary. Rustambekov, the first northerner to head this southern province and a highly controversial appointment, was considered to be a direct surrogate of Akayev in improving control over the south. Rustambekov, who has fired large numbers of local administrators, is opposed chiefly by Osh Province Council head Bekamat Osmonov, who is one of the most skilled and influential politicians in the south. Osmonov, who also was a deputy in the lower house of the new legislature, emerged as a powerful critic of Akayev and a possible presidential rival if Akayev could not prevent the next election.

Political Parties

The period immediately preceding and following independence saw a proliferation of political groups of various sizes and platforms. Although President Akayev emerged from the strongest of those groups, in the early 1990s no organized party system developed either around Akayev or in opposition to him.

Communist Parties

The Communist Party of Kyrgyzstan (CPK), which was the only legal political party during the Soviet years, was abolished in 1991 in the aftermath of the failed coup against the Gorbachev government of the Soviet Union. A successor, the Kyrgyzstan Communist Party, was allowed to register in September 1992. It elected two deputies to the lower house of parliament in 1995. In that party, significant oppositionists include past republic leader Absamat Masaliyev, a former first secretary of the CPK. The 1995 election also gave a deputy's mandate to T. Usubaliyev, who had been head of the CPK and leader of the republic between 1964 and 1982. Another party with many former communist officials is the Republican People's Party. Two other, smaller neocommunist parties are the Social Democrats of Kyrgyzstan, which gained three seats in the upper house and eight seats in the lower house of the 1995 parliament, and the People's Party of Kyrgyzstan, which holds three seats in the lower house.

Other Parties

All of the other parties in existence in 1995 began as unsanctioned civic movements. The first is Ashar (Help), which was founded in 1989 as a movement to take over unused land for housing; Ashar took one seat in the upper house in the 1995 elections. A fluctuating number of parties and groups are joined under the umbrella of the Democratic Movement of Kyrgyzstan (DDK); the most influential is Erkin Kyrgyzstan (Freedom for Kyrgyzstan), which in late 1992 split into two parties, one retaining the name Erkin Kyrgyzstan, and the other called Ata-meken (Fatherland). In the 1995 elections, Erkin Kyrgyzstan took one seat and Ata-meken two seats in the upper house. In the spring of 1995, the head of Erkin Kyrgyzstan was indicted for embezzling funds from the university of which he is a rector; it is unclear whether or not this accusation was politically motivated.

Another democratically inclined party, Asaba (Banner) also took one seat in the upper house. Registration was denied to another group, the Freedom Party, because its platform includes the creation of an Uygur autonomous district extending into the Chinese Xinjiang Uygur Autonomous Region, which the Chinese government opposes. The Union of Germans took one seat in the lower house, and a Russian nationalist group, Concord, also took one seat.

For all their proliferation, parties have not yet played a large part in independent Kyrgyzstan. In the mid-1990s, early enthusiasm for the democratic parties faded as the republic's economy grew worse and party officials were implicated in the republic's proliferating political corruption. The communist successor parties, on the other hand, appeared to gain influence in this period. In the absence of elections, and with President Akayev belonging to no party, it is difficult to predict the future significance of any of these parties.

The Media

For the first two years of independence, Kyrgyzstan's newspapers were a remarkable phenomenon, with real political significance and power. Save that Kyrgyzstan's newspapers had not yet developed a Western-style code of journalistic scrupulousness and restraint, it would have been possible to say that the press was beginning to become the fourth estate that the media represent in developed democracies. Through late 1993, Kyrgyzstan's newspapers enjoyed the greatest freedom of publication in any of the Central Asian nations, rivaling the freedom of the post-1991 Moscow press. Although a state secrecy committee had the power to require submission of materials in advance of publication, in fact the newspapers were able to discuss issues of public interest closely and dispassionately. During the gold scandals, for example, the newspapers played a crucial role in airing both opposition attacks on Akayev and his government, and the government's defense against those attacks.

Since 1993, however, the government has moved increasingly to impose control. In August 1993, formal censorship was briefly reimposed, but then a spirited outcry from the press brought a reversal of that move. More subtle methods of censorship were applied in January 1994, during the run-up to the public referendum on Akayev's performance. Although there are several independent or quasi-independent newspapers in the republic, all printing presses remain in government hands, which gives the state the option of simply refusing to print opposition newspapers.

In 1994 the Akayev government stepped up pressure on the local press, closing three newspapers entirely, including the popular Russian-language *Svobodnye gory*, the official organ of the parliament. Government officials also began to bring suits against newspapers as private individuals, claiming defamation and slander. One such case resulted in a costly judgement against the editor of *Delo No*, a tabloid-style scandal sheet that is perhaps the most widely read newspaper in the country. In the spring of 1995, Akayev used the same tactic against the editor of *Respublika*, long one of the most persistent and successful critics of the regime; the president succeeded in getting a judgement that forbids the editor from working for eighteen months.

Beginning in 1994, the Kyrgyz populace began to feel threatened by the government and other forces in the republic. The atmosphere has not been helped by a series of unexplained attacks on journalists, including one popular commentator, a persistent investigator of the gold scandals, who died after being struck on the head. Although the newsman's grave also was desecrated shortly after his burial, no government investigation was conducted. The government has shown reluctance to impose direct Soviet-style censorship, but Akayev warned in January 1995 that the press would be wise to begin practicing self-censorship and to print more positive news.

The economic conditions of journalism prevent any Kyrgyzstani newspaper from being totally free. None of the republic's papers has yet developed a sustaining readership, and because the economy is insufficiently developed to provide advertising revenue, all newspapers must depend on sponsors. For many papers, including *Slovo Kyrgyzstana*, which has the largest circulation, the sponsor is the government. Others such as *Asaba* have political sponsors, and at least one is sponsored by Turkish investors. Even the most independent of the papers, *Respublika*, has been forced to turn to commercial sponsors, which, according to rumor, include Seabeco-Kyrgyzstan, the scandal-tainted intermediary in the Kumtor gold deal.

The most important Russian-language newspapers are *Slovo Kyrgyzstana*, the official government paper (circulation about 15,000 in 1994); *Vechernii Bishkek*, a more domestic city paper (reaching 75,000 readers on Fridays); the tabloid scandal sheet *Delo No* (30,000 copies); *Asaba*, the organ of the party of the same name (20,000 copies); and *Respublika*, the most prominent surviving opposition paper (7,000 copies). The major Kyrgyz language newspapers are *Kyrgyz guusu* and *Kut Bilim*. A bilingual newspaper, *Erkin Too/Svobodnye gory*, has appeared, but, unlike its earlier namesake, it is not an opposition paper. One English-language paper, *Kyrgyzstan Chronicle*, mostly reproduces articles from foreign English-language sources.

The electronic media are unevenly developed in the republic, both because of the physical constraints imposed by the country's mountainous terrain and because of financial difficulties. Resources are concentrated in Bishkek, which is well supplied with television and with radio. Penetration of more remote areas, however, is incomplete.

The government retains ownership of all but one broadcast facility, giving it a strong voice in the development of independent programming. There is at least one independent radio company, called Piramida, and several independent television production companies. In June 1995, the government proposed reinstitution of formal state control over all broadcasting in the republic.

Financial problems have caused Kyrgyzstan to cut back on the number of hours of Russian television that it relays from Moscow, although the Russian government has shown an inclination to work with Kyrgyzstan to keep Russian-language programming on the air in the republic. In the south, most programming originates in Uzbekistan, a situation that tends to exacerbate the north-south split within Kyrgyzstan.

Human Rights

In its early days, Kyrgyzstan demonstrated a strong commitment to observation of human rights, from which it has subsequently stepped back. Nevertheless, the republic remains generally more sensitive to human rights than are the states in its immediate environment.

The republic's constitution provides very strong guarantees of personal liberty, protection of privacy, freedom of assembly and expression, and other hallmarks of democratic societies. On several occasions, the government has violated or abrogated the constitution, raising the possibility of abuse of human rights.

In practice, however, the Akayev government has proven itself generally responsive on issues of human rights, at least in part because of the republic's dependence upon the approval of Western financial supporters. The present legal system, which remains based almost entirely upon Soviet-era practices, does permit pre-trial detention of up to one year (there is no bail), which in one or two celebrated cases has appeared abusive. However, international monitoring organizations have found no evidence of political arrests, detentions, disappearances, or extrajudicial punishments. There have been some unsubstantiated complaints by political activists of wiretapping and other illegal surveillance.

In a celebrated case in 1992, Uzbekistani security forces arrested two Uzbek delegates to a human rights conference held in Bishkek. Although this arrest was subsequently found to be in technical agreement with Kyrgyzstani law, the public manner in which the arrest was conducted demonstrated Kyrgyzstan's lack of resources to defend human rights activists.

Foreign Relations

Kyrgyzstan's foreign policy has been controlled by two considerations--first, that the country is too small and too poor to be economically viable without considerable outside assistance, and second, that it lies in a volatile corner of the globe, vulnerable to a number of unpleasant possibilities. These two considerations have influenced substantially the international position taken by Kyrgyzstan, especially toward the developed nations and its immediate neighbors.

Akayev and his ministers have traveled the globe tirelessly since independence, seeking relations and partners. In the first four years of independence, Akayev visited the United States, Turkey, Switzerland, Japan, Singapore, and Israel. His emissaries have also been to Iran, Lebanon, and South Africa, and his prime minister made a trip through most of Europe. One consequence of these travels is that Kyrgyzstan is recognized by 120 nations and has diplomatic relations with sixty-one of them. The United States embassy opened in Bishkek in February 1992, and a Kyrgyzstani embassy was established in Washington later that year. Kyrgyzstan is a member of most major international bodies, including the UN, the Organization for Security and Cooperation in Europe (OSCE--see Glossary), the World Bank, the IMF, and the EBRD. It has also joined the Asian Development Bank, the Economic Cooperation Organization (ECO--see Glossary), and the Islamic Bank.

Akayev has stressed repeatedly that the principle behind his search for contacts is strict neutrality; Kyrgyzstan is a small, relatively resource-poor, remote nation more likely to seek help from the world community than to contribute to it. Especially in the first months of independence, Akayev stressed Kyrgyzstan's intellectual and political potential, hoping to attract the world community to take risks in an isolated experiment in democracy. Akayev referred to making his nation an Asian Switzerland, transformed by a combination of international finance and the light, clean industry, mostly electronic, that he expected to spring up from conversion of the Soviet-era defense industries. Largely because of Akayev's reputation and personality, Kyrgyzstan has become the largest per capita recipient of foreign aid in the CIS (see Foreign Investment).

However, the decay of the domestic economy and increasing dissatisfaction among constituents have made the Akayev government distinctly less optimistic about the degree to which it can rely upon the distant world community. At the same time, political and social developments in the republic's immediate area have directed the republic's attention increasingly to foreign policy concerns much closer to home.

Central Asian Neighbors

Kyrgyzstan is bordered by four nations, three of which--Kazakhstan, Uzbekistan, and Tajikistan--are former Soviet republics. China's Xinjiang Uygur Autonomous Region, where a substantial separatist movement has been active, also adjoins the republic. Although Kazakhstan and Uzbekistan have recognized their existing borders with Kyrgyzstan, as of 1996 Tajikistan had not done so. China recognizes the old Soviet Union border but is said to have objections to twelve specific points of its common border with Kyrgyzstan. The objections have been referred to a Chinese-CIS border committee for resolution.

Undoubtedly the most immediate concern is neighboring Uzbekistan, which, under the leadership of President Islam Karimov, is emerging as the strongest state in post-Soviet Central Asia. Although Uzbekistan faces serious economic problems of its own, it has a homogeneous and well-educated population of more than 20 million, a diversified and developed economy, and sufficient natural resources to allow the country to become self-sufficient in energy and a major exporter of gold, cotton, and natural gas.

Uzbekistan has the best organized and best disciplined security forces in all of Central Asia, as well as a relatively large and experienced army and air force. Uzbekistan dominates southern Kyrgyzstan both economically and politically, based on the large Uzbek population in that region of Kyrgyzstan and on economic and geographic conditions (see Ethnic Groups). Much of Kyrgyzstan depends entirely on Uzbekistan for natural gas; on several occasions, Karimov has achieved political ends by shutting pipelines or by adjusting terms of delivery. In a number of television appearances broadcast in the Osh and Jalal-Abad provinces of Kyrgyzstan, Karimov has addressed Akayev with considerable condescension; Akayev, in turn, has been highly deferential to his much stronger neighbor. Although Uzbekistan has not shown overt expansionist tendencies, the Kyrgyz government is acutely aware of the implications of Karimov's assertions that he is responsible for the well-being of all Uzbeks, regardless of their nation of residence.

Although it presents no such expansionist threat, Kazakhstan is as important to northern Kyrgyzstan as Uzbekistan is to the south. The virtual closure of Manas Airport at Bishkek makes Kazakhstan's capital, Almaty, the principal point of entry to Kyrgyzstan. The northwestern city of Talas receives nearly all of its services through the city of Dzhambyl, across the border in Kazakhstan. Although Kazakhstan's president Nursultan Nazarbayev has cooperated in economic agreements, in May 1993 Kyrgyzstan's introduction of the som caused Nazarbayev to close his country's border with Kyrgyzstan to avoid a flood of worthless Kyrgyzstani rubles.

Kyrgyzstan's relations with Tajikistan have been tense. Refugees and antigovernment fighters in Tajikistan have crossed into Kyrgyzstan several times, even taking hostages. Kyrgyzstan attempted to assist in brokering an agreement between contesting Tajikistani forces in October 1992 but without success. Akayev later joined presidents Karimov and Nazarbayev in sending a joint intervention force to support Tajikistan's president Emomali Rakhmanov against insurgents, but the Kyrgyzstani parliament delayed the mission of its small contingent for several months until late spring 1993. In mid-1995 Kyrgyzstani forces had the responsibility of sealing a small portion of the Tajikistan border near Panj from Tajikistani rebel forces.

The greater risk to Kyrgyzstan from Tajikistan is the general destabilization that the protracted civil war has brought to the region. In particular, the Khorugh-Osh road, the so-called "highway above the clouds," has become a major conduit of contraband of all sorts, including weapons and drugs (see Internal Security). A meeting of the heads of the state security agencies of Tajikistan, Kyrgyzstan, Kazakhstan, and Uzbekistan, held in Osh in the spring of 1995, also drew the conclusion that ethnic, social, and economic conditions in Osh were increasingly similar to those in Tajikistan in the late 1980s, thus recognizing the contagion of Tajikistan's instability.

Chinese-Kyrgyzstani relations are an area of substantial uncertainty for the government in Bishkek. China has become Kyrgyzstan's largest non-CIS trade partner, but China's influence is stronger in the north of Kyrgyzstan than in the south. This limitation could change if efforts to join the Karakorum Highway to Osh through Sary-Tash are successful. The free-trade zone in Naryn has attracted large numbers of Chinese businesspeople, who have come to dominate most of the republic's import and export of small goods. Most of this trade is in barter conducted by ethnic Kyrgyz or Kazaks who are Chinese citizens. The Kyrgyzstani government has expressed alarm over the numbers of Chinese who are moving into Naryn and other parts of Kyrgyzstan, but no preventive measures have been taken.

The Akayev government also must be solicitous of Chinese sensibilities on questions of nationalism because the Chinese do not want the independence of the Central Asian states to stimulate dreams of statehood among their own Turkic Muslim peoples. Although the Kyrgyz in China have been historically quiescent, China's Uygurs (of whom there is a small exile community in Kyrgyzstan) have been militant in their desire to attain independence. This is the major reason that Kyrgyzstan has refused to permit the formation of an Uygur party (see Political Parties).

In the 1990s, trade with China has grown to such a volume that some officials in Kyrgyzstan fear that by the late 1990s Kyrgyzstan's economy will be entirely dominated by China. In some political quarters, the prospect of Chinese domination has stimulated nostalgia for the days of Moscow's control.

Russia

In fact, whereas the other Central Asian republics have sometimes complained of Russian interference, Kyrgyzstan has more often wished for more attention and support from Moscow than it has been able to obtain. For all the financial support that the world community has offered, Kyrgyzstan remains economically dependent on Russia, both directly and through Kazakhstan. In early 1995, Akayev attempted to sell Russian companies controlling shares in the republic's twenty-nine largest industrial plants, an offer that Russia refused.

Akayev has been equally enthusiastic about more direct forms of reintegration, such as the Euro-Asian Union that Nazarbayev proposed in June 1994. Because Kyrgyzstan presumably would receive much more from such a union than it would contribute, Akayev's enthusiasm has met with little response from Russia and the other, larger states that would be involved in such an arrangement. Akayev's invitation for Russian border guards to take charge of Kyrgyzstan's Chinese border, a major revision of his policy of neutrality, was another move toward reintegration (see Armed Forces).

The Kyrgyzstani government also has felt compelled to request Russia's economic protection. The harsh reality of Kyrgyzstan's economic situation means that the nation is an inevitable international client state, at least for the foreseeable future. Despite concerted efforts to seek international "sponsors," Akayev has not received much more than a great deal of international good will. Even if the president had not lived seventeen years in Russia himself and even if his advisers, family, and friends were not all Soviet-era intellectuals with a high degree of familiarity with Russia, economic necessity probably would push Kyrgyzstan further toward Russia.

On his February 1994 visit to Moscow, Akayev signed several economic agreements. Having promised the republic a 75-billion-ruble line of credit (presumably for use in 1994) and some US$65 million in trade agreements, Russia also promised to extend to Kyrgyzstan most-favored-nation status for the purchase of oil and other fuels. For its part, Kyrgyzstan agreed to the creation of a Kyrgyzstani-Russian investment company, which would purchase idle defense-related factories in the republic to provide employment for the increasingly dissatisfied Russian population of Kyrgyzstan. In early 1995, prime ministers Jumagulov of Kyrgyzstan and Viktor Chernomyrdin of Russia signed a series of agreements establishing bilateral coordination of economic reform in the two states, further binding Kyrgyzstan to

Russia. After lobbying hard for inclusion, Kyrgyzstan became a member of the customs union that Russia, Belarus, and Kazakhstan established in February 1996.

For its part, Russia sees aid to Kyrgyzstan as a successful precedent in its new policy of gaining influence in its "near abroad," the states that once were Soviet republics. Russia does not want a massive in-migration of Russians from the new republics; some 2 million ethnic Russians moved back to Russia between 1992 and 1995, with at least that many again expected by the end of the century. Akayev, on the other hand, must find a way to stem the loss of his Russian population, which already has caused an enormous deficit of doctors, teachers, and engineers.

For these reasons, despite opposition from Kyrgyz nationalists and other independence-minded politicians, in 1995 Akayev granted the request of Russian president Boris N. Yeltsin to review the constitutional provision making Kyrgyz the sole official language. Early in 1996, Kyrgyzstan took legal steps toward making Russian the republic's second official language, subject to amendment of the constitution. That initiative coincided with the customs union signed with Russia, Kazakhstan, and Belarus in February 1996. The long-term success of Akayev's search for reintegration is questionable because of Kyrgyzstan's minimal strategic importance and the potential cost to an outside country supporting the republic's shaky economy.

NATIONAL SECURITY

Located in a region of low strategic importance and surrounded by nations with major concerns in other directions, Kyrgyzstan did not make developing its own armed forces a high priority after separation from the Soviet Union. The long-standing civil war in nearby Tajikistan, however, has forced reevaluation of that conservative position. Internal security has been a major concern because of rampant crime and a well-developed narcotics industry.

Armed Forces

In the early 1990s, Kyrgyzstan began to build a small armed force based on the military doctrine that Russia will remain chief guarantor of Kyrgyzstan's national security interests. The only operational branch of the armed forces is the ground forces.

Development of Military Policy

Kyrgyzstan made its first moves toward a national military force in September 1991, immediately after declaring independence, by drawing up plans to create a national guard. However, events overtook that plan, which was never realized. In the early months of independence, President Akayev was an avid supporter of a proposed "unified army" of the CIS, which would replace the former Soviet army. Those plans collapsed when Russia announced that it would not finance CIS troops. In April 1992, Kyrgyzstan formed a State Committee for Defense Affairs, and in June the republic took control of all troops on its soil (meaning remaining units of the former Soviet army). At that time, about 15,000 former Soviet soldiers of unknown ethnic identity remained in Kyrgyzstan.

Although the Kyrgyzstani government did not demand a new oath of service until after adoption of the Law on Military Service (the first draft of which in 1992 was copied so hastily from Soviet law that it included provisions for a navy), the majority of the officer corps (mostly Russian) refused to serve in a Kyrgyzstani army, and since that time many Russian officers have sought repatriation to Russia. A more informal outflow of draftees already had been underway before Kyrgyzstan's independence. According to one estimate, as many as 6,000 Russians deserted from duty in Kyrgyzstan, although that loss was partially offset by the return of almost 2,000 Kyrgyz who had been serving in the Soviet army outside their republic. According to reports, in 1993 between 3,000 and 4,000 non-Kyr gyz soldiers, mostly Russians, remained in the republic.

In the early days of independence, Kyrgyzstani authorities spoke of doing without an army entirely. That idea since has been replaced by plans to create a standing conscripted army of about 5,000 troops, with reserves of two to three times that number. The question of who would command these troops has been very troublesome. Russian officers continued leaving Kyrgyzstan through 1993 because of low pay and poor living conditions, and in 1994 Moscow was officially encouraging this exodus. To stem the out-migration, agreements signed in 1994 by Bishkek and Moscow obligate Kyrgyzstan to pay housing and relocation costs for Russian officers who agree to serve in the Kyrgyzstani army until 1999.

In 1994 Kyrgyzstan agreed to permit border troops of the Russian Army to assume the task of guarding Kyrgyzstan's border with China. This agreement followed Russia's complaints that continuing desertions by Kyrgyzstani border troops were leaving the former Soviet border--which Russia continues to argue is its proper border--essentially unguarded. Akayev has periodically pushed for even more Russian military presence in the republic, hinting broadly that if Russia is not interested in resuming control of the Soviet airbases in the republic, perhaps other powers, such as the United States or the North Atlantic Treaty Organization (NATO--see Glossary), might be; however, the fact that Kyrgyzstan in early 1995 gave the last remnants of its Soviet-era air fleet to Uzbekistan in a debt swap suggests that neither Moscow nor Tashkent has taken such offers seriously.

It is not entirely clear what weapons Kyrgyzstan's army will possess. The republic lost twelve IL-39 jets in March 1992, when they were "repatriated" to Russia from a training field near the capital, and the 1995 swap with Uzbekistan lost an unknown number of MiG-21 fighters and L-39C close-support aircraft. Available information suggests strongly that Kyrgyzstan, as the least militarized of the Central Asian republics, is incapable of defending itself against a military threat from any quarter.

Command Structure

Formally, the army is under the command of the president, in his role as commander in chief; the National Security Council is the chief agency of defense policy. Established in 1994, the National Security Council has seven members, not including the president, who is the chairman: the prime minister, the deputy prime minister, the state secretary, the minister of internal affairs, the minister of defense, the chairman of the State Committee for National Security (successor to the Kyrgyzstan branch of the Committee for State Security--KGB), and the commander of the National Guard. The president appoints and dismisses senior military officers. President Akayev also has followed the formulation of defense policy quite closely. The Ministry of Defense has operational command of military units; General Myrzakan Subanov has been minister of defense since the agency was founded in 1992. The Ministry of Defense and the National Security Council are advised by the Center for Analysis, a research institution established in 1992.

The chief of the General Staff, the second-ranking officer in the armed forces, is responsible for coordinating the National Security Council, the State Committee for National Security, the border troops, and civil defense. Since 1993 that position has been occupied by General Feliks Kulov, a Kyrgyz. The General Staff, modeled after the Russian structure, includes the commanders of the National Guard, the ground forces, the air and air defense forces, and the internal forces.

Ground Forces

In 1996 the Kyrgyzstani ground forces included 7,000 troops, which comprise one motorized rifle division with armor and artillery capability. Sapper and signals regiments are attached, as is a mountain infantry brigade. Headquarters is at Bishkek. Plans called for the ground forces to be restructured in 1995 into a corps of two motorized rifle brigades and for an airborne battalion to be added. In 1994 about 30 percent of the officer corps was Russian; the commander was General Valentin Luk'yanov, a Ukrainian.

Air and Air Defense Forces

Because of expense and military doctrine, Kyrgyzstan has not developed its air capability; a large number of the MiG-21 interceptors that it borrowed from Russia were returned in 1993, although a number of former Soviet air bases remain available. In 1996 about 100 decommissioned MiG-21s remained in Kyrgyzstan, along with ninety-six L-39 trainers and sixty-five helicopters.

The air defense forces have received aid from Russia, which has sent military advisory units to establish a defense system. Presently Kyrgyzstan has twenty-six SA-2 and SA-3 surface-to-air missiles in its air defense arsenal.

Border Troops

In 1992 a Kyrgyzstani command took over the republic's directorate of the KGB's Central Asian Border Troops District, which had about 2,000 mostly Russian troops. In late 1992, alarmed by the possibility of penetration of the border from Tajikistan and China, Russia established a joint Kyrgyzstani-Russian Border Troop Command, under Russian command. However, that force has been plagued with desertions by Kyrgyz troops, about 200 of whom fled to China in 1993. Border troop bases are located at Isfara, Naryn, and Karakol.

Training

Cadets and noncommissioned officers (NCOs) in the ground forces are trained at the Bishkek Military School, which played the same role in the Soviet era. Under a 1993 agreement, a small number of ground forces cadets study at Russian military schools, with the specific goal of bolstering the ethnic Kyrgyz officer corps. Small groups of Kyrgyz cadets also attend military schools in Uzbekistan and Turkey. Officers selected for higher commands attend a three-year course at Frunze Military Academy in Moscow and other Russian military academies.

For the air force, the main training site is the Bishkek Aviation School, once a major center for training foreign air cadets but reduced in 1992 to a small contingent of mostly

Kyrgyz cadets. In 1992 Kyrgyzstan had five training regiments using 430 aircraft, but that number was depleted by the mid-1990s. A 1994 agreement calls for some Kyrgyz pilots to attend air force schools in Russia.

Internal Security

In the early and mid-1990s, preservation of internal security against a variety of crimes, and especially against growing commerce in narcotics, became an extremely difficult task. White-collar crime and government corruption have added to the atmosphere of social disorder.

Security Troops

In 1991 President Akayev abolished the Kyrgyzstan branch of the KGB and replaced it with the State Committee for National Security, whose role subsequently was prescribed in a 1992 law. In 1996 the armed force of the committee, the National Guard, was an elite force of 1,000 recruited from all national groups in Kyrgyzstan. Organized in two battalions, the National Guard has been commanded since its inception by a Kyrgyz general; the chief of the border troops also is under that commander. The National Guard has the prescribed function of protecting the president and government property and assisting in natural disasters; except under exceptional circumstances, its role does not include maintenance of domestic order.

Police

The republic's police system is largely unchanged from the Soviet era. Still called "militia," the police are under the jurisdiction of the Ministry of Internal Affairs. A force estimated at 25,000 individuals, the militia is commanded by the Central Police Force in Bishkek. The republic's police have suffered the same large-scale resignations because of low pay and bad working conditions as have other former Soviet republics lacking resources to support internal security. In April 1995, the national power company shut off power to the Central Police Force headquarters for nonpayment of electric bills, leaving the capital without even emergency police service for five hours. The poor equipment of the police further hampers their ability to respond to crimes. Police personnel frequently have been implicated in crime. Nearly 700 police were caught in the commission of crimes in the two months after President Akayev replaced the entire administration of the Ministry of Internal Affairs in 1995.

Crime

Kyrgyzstan's crime problem is generally regarded as out of control. In 1994 more than 40,000 crimes were reported, or more than one crime per 100 citizens, and a high percentage of those crimes were classified as serious.

Petty crime touches every sector of the economy. For example, although cellular telephone networks and satellite linkups have been established in Bishkek, telecommunications elsewhere have grown much worse because the theft and resale of cable has become common. Power outages are frequent for the same reason, and any sort of equipment with salvageable metal is said to be quickly stripped if left unattended.

Foreigners are not exempt from crime, as they were in the Soviet era. In 1994 some 185 crimes against foreigners were registered in Bishkek. Most of these crimes were apartment burglaries, although beatings and armed robberies also have been reported. In April 1995, a small bomb was left in front of a Belgian relief mission's door, and "Foreigners Out of Bishkek" was painted on the wall opposite.

President Akayev vowed to crack down on crime in the mid-1990s, proposing much stiffer penalties for common crimes, including life imprisonment for auto theft. One sign of his seriousness was the replacement in January 1995 of the entire senior staff of the Ministry of Internal Affairs. The new minister, the Kyrgyz Modolbek Moldashev, served in the Soviet KGB and lived most of his life outside the republic. When he took office, Moldashev brought in his own people from the State Committee for National Security and the Ministry of Defense. However, it is far from clear that Kyrgyzstan's security organizations are capable of cracking down on the drug-driven sector of the economy, and experts predict that if narcotics escape control, the spiral of criminal activities will continue to grow.

Government corruption and malfeasance also contribute to an atmosphere of lawlessness. In the mid-1990s, bribery, kickbacks, and influence peddling became increasingly common in government agencies. Law enforcement officials have received little cooperation from legislators in punishing their colleagues who are caught violating the law. In 1993 the Interregional Investigative Unit, established to combat bribery, found itself shut down after twenty successful investigations and replaced by an economic crimes investigation unit, some members of which began taking bribes themselves.

Narcotics Control

Perhaps the most lucrative, and certainly the most problematic, of Kyrgyzstan's exports is narcotics, particularly opium and heroin. Government officials believe that the narcotics industry presents the greatest challenge to the internal security of Kyrgyzstan because of its capacity to destabilize the country.

In the Soviet era, the Kyrgyz Republic was a legal producer of opium, with about 2,000 hectares of land planted to poppies in 1974, the last year before world pressure forced such farms to be closed. At that point, an estimated 16 percent of the world's opium came from Kyrgyzstan. The country's climate is exceptionally well suited to cultivation of opium poppies and wild marijuana, producing unusually pure final products from both types of plant. Kyrgyzstan is said to produce even better poppies than does nearby Afghanistan, which has surpassed Burma as the world's leading supplier of heroin.

In 1992 Kyrgyzstan applied to the World Health Organization for permission to reinstitute the production of medicinal opium as a means of generating desperately needed revenue. The plan was to increase the planting in the northeastern Ysyk-Köl area to about 10,000 hectares and to open plantations in Talas and Naryn as well, yielding a projected annual profit of about US$200 million. Under pressure from the world community, the plan was dropped.

In 1992 republic narcotics police uncovered thirteen drug-refining laboratories and seized two tons of ready narcotics. The police reported that drug-related crime rose 222 percent from 1991 to 1992 and that 830 people had been arrested on drug-distribution charges. Another report indicated that 70 percent of the 44,000 crimes reported in the republic in 1992 had a connection to drugs in one way or another. At that time, the head of the country's narcotics police estimated that only about 20 percent of the narcotics traffic was being interdicted, mainly because resources are very inadequate. Government officials fear that this industry will continue to grow, especially in the absence of large-scale international assistance; in 1994 Russia ceased its cooperation with Kyrgyzstan in narcotics interdiction. An emerging distribution chain moves opium to Moscow, then to Poland, from where it is transferred to Europe and the United States.

Osh is said to have become a major new international point-of-purchase for opium and heroin, which is produced in all of the countries adjoining the Fergana Valley, including Kyrgyzstan. More than 300 kilograms of opium were seized in Osh Province in 1994, an amount estimated to be less than 10 percent of the total moving through Osh. At the end of 1994, the head of the National Security Committee characterized the narcotics trade as the republic's sole growth industry, which he warned was solidifying its grip on the republic's conventional economy.

Court System

The court system remains essentially unchanged from the Soviet era. Nominally there are three levels in the court system: local courts, which handle petty crimes such as pickpocketing and vandalism; province-level courts, which handle crimes such as murder, grand larceny, and organized crime; and the Supreme Court, to which decisions of the lower courts can be appealed. However, there has been persistent conflict between Akayev and the legislature over the composition and authority of the Supreme Court, as well as over Akayev's choice of chief justice. As in the Soviet system, the office of the state procurator, chief civilian legal officer of the state, acts as both prosecuting attorney and chief investigator in each case.

The protections for individuals accused of crimes remain at the primitive level of Soviet law. According to law, the accused can be held for three days before a charge is made, and pretrial detention can last for as long as a year. There is no system of bail; the accused remains incarcerated until tried. Both the police and forces of the State Committee for National Security have the right to violate guarantees of privacy (of the home, telephone, mail, and banks), with the sanction of the state procurator. In theory search warrants and judicial orders for such things as wiretaps only are issued by authority of a judge; in practice this is not always done.

Prisons

Very little current information is known about Kyrgyzstan's prison system. In the Soviet era, at least twelve labor camps and three prisons operated in the republic, including at least one uranium mine-labor camp in which prisoners worked without protective gear. The total prison capacity and present population are not known, but it may be presumed that prisons in Kyrgyzstan are suffering the same overcrowding as are prisons elsewhere in the former Soviet Union. The 1995 purge of the Ministry of Internal Affairs included appointment of a new head of the prison system, a colonel who had been assistant minister of internal affairs prior to the shakeup.

National Security Prospects

Although internal stability has not been a serious problem during the Akayev era, events in the mid-1990s threatened to make it so. By 1995 economic hardship, to which international experts did not predict a rapid end, combined with insufficient internal security forces and the opportunity for profits from organized narcotics activities to threaten the stability of Kyrgyzstan's society, especially in the major urban centers of Bishkek and Osh. The high crime rate also interfered with plans to attract Western tourist trade.

Meanwhile, as of 1995 external security came exclusively from Russia, a situation that Kyrgyzstan officially welcomed in the absence of domestic resources to build a credible military force for its very small and isolated nation. As in the economic field, however, policy makers were not sure how long Russia would view strong support of Kyrgyzstan's national security as an important element of Russian foreign policy. Although no major regional threat loomed in the mid-1990s, major policy questions remained unanswered.

Glossary

Bolshevik Revolution
Coup organized by Vladimir I. Lenin and carried out by the Bolshevik radical group of the Russian Social Democratic Labor Party to overthrow the Provisional Government of Russia in November 1917. Also known as the October Revolution.

Commonwealth of Independent States (CIS)
Official designation of the former republics of the Soviet Union that remained loosely federated in economic and security matters after the Soviet Union disbanded as a unified state in 1991. Members in 1996 were Armenia, Azerbaijan, Belarus, Georgia, Kazakhstan, Kyrgyzstan, Moldova, Russia, Tajikistan, Turkmenistan, Ukraine, and Uzbekistan.

Conventional Forces in Europe (CFE) Treaty
An agreement signed in 1990 by members of the Warsaw Pact and the North Atlantic Treaty Organization (NATO--*q.v.*) to establish parity in conventional weapons between the two organizations from the Atlantic to the Urals. Included a strict system of inspections and information exchange. In 1995 Russia requested exemptions for forces stationed in the Caucasus region, and substantial changes were negotiated by the thirty signatory nations in 1997.

Economic Cooperation Organization (ECO)
Established in 1985, an economic union of Islamic countries to promote regional cooperation in trade, transportation, communications, culture, and overall economic development. Members in 1996 were Afghanistan, Azerbaijan, Iran, Kazakhstan, Kyrgyzstan, Pakistan, Tajikistan, Turkey, the "Turkish Republic of Northern Cyprus," Turkmenistan, and Uzbekistan.

glasnost

Russian term, literally meaning "public voicing." Applied in the Soviet Union beginning in 1987 to official permission for public discussion of issues and public access to information, initially intended as a means for the regime of Mikhail S. Gorbachev to publicize the need for political and economic reform.

gross domestic product (GDP)

The total value of goods and services produced exclusively within a nation's domestic economy, in contrast to the gross national product (GNP--*q.v.*). Normally computed over one-year periods.

gross national product (GNP)

The total value of goods and services produced within a country's borders and the income received from abroad by residents, minus payments remitted abroad by nonresidents. Normally computed over one-year periods.

hard currency

National currencies that are freely convertible and traded on international currency markets.

International Monetary Fund (IMF)

Established with the World Bank (*q.v.*) in 1945, a specialized agency affiliated with the United Nations and responsible for stabilizing international exchange rates and payments. Its main function is to provide loans to its members (including industrialized and developing countries) when they experience balance of payments difficulties. These loans frequently have conditions that require substantial internal economic adjustments by the recipients, most of which are developing countries.

Iranian

Linguistically, a subgroup of the Indo-Iranian branch of Indo-European languages, which in modern times includes Persian (*q.v.*)--the most widely used--Pushtu, Kurdish (*q.v.*) dialects, and Ossetic. In the Middle Iranian stage of the group's development (third century B.C. to tenth century A.D.), the chief languages were Parthian, Pahlavi (middle Persian), and Soghdian.

Kurdish

Term referring to a mainly Muslim people speaking an Indo-European language similar to Persian. Kurds constitute significant minorities in Iran, Iraq, and Turkey, with smaller groups in Armenia and Syria. Despite international proposals in response to minority persecution, never united in a single state.

manat

Beginning in 1993, national currency of Turkmenistan. Inflation rapid in 1994 and 1995. In January 1996, official rate 200 per US$1.

Manichaeism
A dualistic religious movement founded in Persia, third century A.D., incorporating elements of Christianity and Iranian and Indian religions.

net material product (NMP)
In countries having centrally planned economies, the official measure of the value of goods and services produced within the country. Roughly equivalent to the gross national product (*q.v.*), NMP is based on constant prices and does not account for depreciation.

New Economic Policy (Novaya ekonomicheskaya politika--NEP)
Instituted in 1921 by Vladimir I. Lenin, program allowing peasants in the Soviet Union to sell produce on an open market and small enterprises to be privately owned and operated. Officially ended in 1929 with enforcement of national central planning of all economic activities.

North Atlantic Treaty Organization (NATO)
During the postwar period until the dissolution of the Soviet Union in 1991, the primary collective defense agreement of the Western powers against the military presence of the Warsaw Pact nations in Europe. Founded in 1949. Its military and administrative structure remained intact after 1991, but early in 1994 the Partnership for Peace offered partial membership to all former Warsaw Pact nations and former republics of the Soviet Union.

Organization for Security and Cooperation in Europe (OSCE)
Beginning in 1995, the name of the former Conference on Security and Cooperation in Europe (CSCE). Established in 1972 as an international forum for negotiation, the organization consisted of fifty-three member nations in 1996, including all European countries. The Charter of Paris (1990) changed the CSCE from an ad hoc forum to an organization with permanent institutions. In 1992 the CSCE took on new roles in conflict mediation, including crises in the former Yugoslavia, the Caucasus region, and Nagorno-Karabakh. Beginning in 1994, Russia advocated CSCE/OSCE as the chief European peacekeeping agency in preference to possible NATO expansion.

perestroika
Russian term meaning "restructuring." Applied in the late 1980s to an official Soviet program of revitalization of the Communist Party of the Soviet Union (CPSU), the economy, and the society by adjusting economic, social, and political mechanisms in the central planning system. Identified with the tenure of Mikhail S. Gorbachev as leader of the Soviet Union.

Persian
As a language, a member of the Iranian subgroup in the Indo-European language family. The official language of modern Iran and spoken widely in Afghanistan. Middle Persian (Pahlavi) was used between the third century B.C. and the ninth century A.D. and was the official language of the Sassanid Empire that ruled parts of Central Asia from the third century to the sixth century A.D. Modern Persian is called Farsi by native speakers.

ruble
Currency of the Soviet Union; then, beginning in 1992, of Russia. In February 1997, the exchange rate was 5,670 rubles to US$1.

ruble zone
Currency exchange arrangement by which former republics of the Soviet Union continued using the ruble as their national currency, forcing dependence on Russian currency valuations and economic developments elsewhere in the Commonwealth of Independent States (*q.v.*). In 1993 all Central Asian republics except Tajikistan established national currencies independent of the ruble.

Shia
The smaller of the two great divisions of Islam, supporting the claims of Ali to leadership of the Muslim community, in opposition to the Sunni (*q.v.*) view of succession to Muslim leadership--the issue causing the central schism within Islam.

som
Beginning in 1993, currency of Kyrgyzstan and Uzbekistan. In 1996 average exchange rate of Uzbekistani som was thirty-five to US$1; of Kyrgyzstani som, eleven to US$1.

Sunni
The larger of the two fundamental divisions of Islam, opposed to the Shia (*q.v.*) on the issue of succession to Muslim leadership.

Tajikistani ruble
Beginning in 1995, currency of Tajikistan. In January 1996, exchange rate 284 rubles per US$1.

tenge
Beginning in 1993, currency of Kazakhstan. In January 1996, exchange rate sixty-four tenge to US$1.

value-added tax (VAT)
A tax applied to the additional value created at a given stage of production and calculated as a percentage of the difference between the product value at that stage and the cost of all materials and services purchased or introduced as inputs.

World Bank
Informal name for a group of four affiliated international institutions: the International Bank for Reconstruction and Development (IBRD); the International Development Association (IDA); the International Finance Corporation (IFC); and the Multilateral Investment Guaranty Agency (MIGA). The four institutions are owned by the governments of the countries that subscribe their capital for credit and investment in developing countries; each institution has a specialized agenda for aiding economic growth in target countries. To participate in the World Bank group, member states first must belong to the International Monetary Fund (IMF--*q.v.*).

World Trade Organization (WTO)

Established 1995 as successor to the General Agreement on Tariffs and Trade (GATT), aimed at liberalizing and securing international trade. Formed in the Uruguay Round of trade negotiations, the WTO had 115 member nations in 1996, and fifteen others applied WTO rules to their trade policies. Administered by a general council, trade dispute negotiation panel, and secretariat.

Zoroastrianism

Religion founded in the sixth century B.C. by the Iranian prophet Zoroaster. With monotheistic and dualistic aspects, it influenced subsequently founded religions, including Christianity and Islam. Now practiced most widely by Persian immigrants in India.

BIBLIOGRAPHY

"Central Asia," *Current History*, 93, April 1994, 145-86.

"Central Asia: Five-State Commonwealth Set Up," *Current Digest of the Post-Soviet Press*, 45, February 3, 1993, 1-8.

"Central Asia: Patterns of Change, Past, Present, and Future," *Harvard International Report*, 15, Spring 1993, 6-12.

"Konflikt na granitse Kirgizii i Tadzhikistana" (Conflict on the Border of Kyrgyzia and Tajikistan), *Turkestan* [Ashgabat], 1990, No. 1, 5.

"Natsional'nyy vopros i mezhnatsional'nyye otnosheniya v SSSR: Istoriya i sovremennost'" (The National Question and Inter-national Relations in the USSR: History and the Present). *Voprosy istorii*, 1989, No. 5, 3-97.

"Russia: World Drugs Capital?" *The Economist Foreign Report*, April 27, 1995, 3-4.

"Uzbekistan," *Central Asia Monitor*, 1996, No. 3, entire issue.

1995 Britannica Book of the Year. Chicago: 1995.

Abduvakhitov, Abdujabar. "Independent Uzbekistan: A Muslim Community in Development." Pages 293-306 in Michael Bourdeaux, ed., *The Politics of Religion in Russia and the New States of Eurasia*. Armonk, New York: M.E. Sharpe, 1995.

Adshead, Samuel Adrian M. *Central Asia in World History*. New York: St. Martin's Press, 1993.

Ahmed, Akbar, and David Hart, eds. *Islam in Tribal Societies*. London: Routledge and Kegan Paul, 1984.

Akademiya nauk SSSR. Institut etnografii. *Sotsial'no-kul'turnyy oblik sovetskikh natsiy* (The Social-Cultural Aspect of the Soviet Nations). Moscow: Nauka, 1986.

Akademiya nauk Tadzhikskoy SSR. *Istoriya tadzhikskogo naroda* (A History of the Tajik People), 3. Moscow: Nauka, 1965.

Akademiya nauk Tadzhikskoy SSR. *Tadzhikistan: priroda i resursy* (Tajikistan: Nature and Resources). Dushanbe: Donish, 1982.

Akademiya nauk Tadzhikskoy SSR. *Tadzhikskaya Sovetskaya Sotsialisticheskaya Respublika* (The Tajik Soviet Socialist Republic). Ed., M.S. Asimov. Dushanbe: 1974.

Akbarzadeh, Shahram. "Nation Building in Uzbekistan," *Central Asian Survey* [Abingdon, United Kingdom], 15, March 1996, 23-32.

Akchurin, Marat. "Soviet Muslims: Seeking Reform, Not Revolution," *World and I*, 6, October 1991, 86-93.

Akiner, Shirin, ed. *Central Asia: 130 Years of Russian Dominance, an Historical Overview*. Durham: Duke University Press, 1994.

Akiner, Shirin, ed. *Economic and Political Trends in Central Asia*. New York: Routledge & Kegan Paul, 1992.

Akiner, Shirin. *Islamic Peoples of the Soviet Union: An Historical and Statistical Handbook*. New York: Kegan Paul International, 1986.

Akiner, Shirin. *Islamic Peoples of the Soviet Union: An Historical and Statistical Handbook*. New York: Routledge, 1986.

Alikhanov, B. B., and S. S. Tursunov, *Ekonomicheskiye problemy okhrany okruzhayushchey sredy v usloviyakh Uzbekistana* (Economic Problems of Environmental Protection in the Conditions of Uzbekistan). Tashkent: State Committee on Hydrology, 1990.

Allworth, Edward, ed. *Central Asia: 120 Years of Russian Rule*. Durham: Duke University Press, 1989.

Allworth, Edward, ed. *Central Asia: A Century of Russian Rule*. New York: Columbia University Press, 1967.

Allworth, Edward, ed. *Muslim Communities Reemerge: Historical Perspectives*. Durham: Duke University Press, 1994.

Allworth, Edward, ed. *The Nationality Question in Soviet Central Asia*. New York: Praeger, 1973.

Alptekin, Erkin. "Chinese Policy in Eastern Turkestan," *Institute of Muslim Minority Affairs Journal*, 13, January 1992, 185-95.

Amnesty International. *Tadzhikistan*. London: 1993.

Anderson, John. "Authoritarian Political Development in Central Asia: The Case of Turkmenistan," *Central Asian Survey* [Abingdon, United Kingdom], 14, No. 4, 1995, 509-28.

Andreyev, M.S. "Po etnografii tadzhikov: Nekotoryye svedeniya" (On the Ethnography of the Tajiks: Some Information). Pages 151-77 in *Tadzhikistan*. Tashkent: Obshchestvo dlya izucheniya Tadzhikistana i iranskikh narodnostey za yego predelami, 1925.

Andreyev, Nikolai. "Central Asia: From Marx to Mohammed," *New Times International* [Moscow], No. 39, 1992, 19-22.

Andreyev, Nikolai. "What Future for Uzbekistan, Kirgizia, Turkmenia?" *Current Digest of the Post-Soviet Press*, 44, July 22, 1992, 8-11.

Atkin, Muriel. "Islamic Assertiveness and the Waning of the Old Soviet Order," *Nationalities Papers*, 20, No. 1, Spring 1992, 55-72.

Atkin, Muriel. "Religious, National, and Other Identities in Central Asia." Pages 46-72 in Jo Ann Gross, ed., *Muslims in Central Asia*. Durham: Duke University Press, 1992.

Atkin, Muriel. "Tajikistan: Ancient Heritage, New Politics." Pages 361-83 in Ian Bremmer and Ray Taras, eds., *Nation and Politics in the Soviet Successor States*. Cambridge: Cambridge University Press, 1993.

Atkin, Muriel. "The Survival of Islam in Soviet Tajikistan," *Middle East Journal*, 43, No. 4, Autumn 1989, 605-18.

Atkin, Muriel. *The Subtlest Battle: Islam in Soviet Tajikistan*. Philadelphia: Foreign Policy Research Institute, 1989.

Aziz, Sartaj. "The Rediscovery of Central Asia," *Economics Review* [Karachi], 23, June 1992, 15-17.

Azv'yalova, L.V., O.A. Agafonova, and L.A. Semakina. *Zagryazneniye atmosfery Sredney Azii tyazhelymi metallami* (Atmospheric Pollution by Heavy Metals in Central Asia). Tashkent: State Committee on Hydrology, 1991.

Bachmann, Berta. *Memories of Kazakhstan: A Report on the Life Experiences of a German Woman in Russia.* Lincoln, Nebraska: American History Society, 1983.

Bacon, Elizabeth E. *Central Asians under Russian Rule: A Study in Culture Change.* Ithaca: Cornell University Press, 1980.

Bacon, Elizabeth. *Central Asians under Russian Rule.* Ithaca: Cornell University Press, 1980.

Bacon, Elizabeth. *Central Asians under Russian Rule: A Study in Culture Change.* Ithaca: Cornell University Press, 1980.

Baldick, Julian. *Imaginary Muslims: The Uwaysi Sufis of Central Asia.* Irvington: New York University Press, 1994.

Banuazizi, Ali, and Myron Weiner, eds. *The New Geopolitics of Central Asia and Its Borderlands.* Bloomington: Indiana University Press, 1994.

Bartol'd, Vasilii Vladimirovich. "A History of the Turkman People (An Outline)." Pages 73-170 in *Four Studies on the History of Central Asia* III. Trans., V. and T. Minorsky. Leiden: E.J. Brill, 1962.

Bartol'd, Vasilii Vladimirovich. *Histoire des Turcs d'Asie centrale.* Trans., M. Donskis. Philadelphia: Porcupine Press, 1977.

Bartol'd, Vasilii Vladimirovich. *Turkestan Down to the Mongol Invasion.* London: Lazac, 1968.

Barylski, Robert V. "The Caucasus, Central Asia, and the Near-Abroad Syndrome," *Central Asia Monitor,* No. 4, 1993, 31.

Basilov, Vladimir Nikolayevich. "Honor Groups in Traditional Turkmenian Society." Pages 220-43 in Akbar Ahmed and David Hart, eds., *Islam in Tribal Societies.* London: Routledge and Kegan Paul, 1984.

Basilov, Vladimir Nikolayevich. "Popular Islam in Central Asia and Kazakhstan," *Journal of the Institute of Muslim Minority Affairs*, 8, No. 1, 1987, 7-17.

Batalden, Stephen K., and Sandra L. Batalden. *The Newly Independent States of Eurasia: Handbook of Former Soviet Republics.* Phoenix: Oryx, 1993.

Baumann, Robert F. *Russian-Soviet Unconventional Wars in the Caucasus, Central Asia, and Afghanistan.* Fort Leavenworth, Kansas: Combat Studies Institute, 1993.

Becker, Seymour. "National Consciousness and the Politics of the Bukharan People's Counciliar Republic." Pages 159-67 in Edward Allworth, ed., *The Nationality Question in Soviet Central Asia.* New York: Praeger, 1973.

Becker, Seymour. *Russia's Protectorates in Central Asia: Bukhara and Khiva, 1865-1924.* Cambridge: Harvard University Press, 1968.

Bennigsen, Alexandre, and S. Enders Wimbush. *Muslims of the Soviet Empire.* Bloomington: Indiana University Press, 1986.

Bennigsen, Alexandre. *Mystics and Commissars: Sufism in the Soviet Union.* London: Hurst, 1985.

Berdi Murat, Aman. "Turkmenistan and the Turkmen." Pages 262-82 in Zev Katz, ed., *Handbook of Major Soviet Nationalities.* New York: Free Press, 1975.

Bilan du Monde: l'Année économique et sociale 1995. Ed., Jacques-François Simon. Paris: Le Monde, 1996.

Blank, Stephen. "Energy, Economics, and Security in Central Asia: Russia and Its Rivals," *Central Asian Survey*, 14, No. 3, 1995, 373-406.

Bohr, Annette. "Health Catastrophe in Karakalpakstan," *Report on the USSR* [Munich], 1, July 21, 1989, 37-38.

Bourdeaux, Michael, ed. *The Politics of Religion in Russia and the New States of Eurasia*. Armonk, New York: M.E. Sharpe, 1995.

Bradley, Catherine. *Kazakhstan*. Brookfield, Connecticut: Millbrook Press, 1992.

Bregel, Yuriy. "Nomadic and Sedentary Elements among the Turkmens," *Central Asiatic Journal*, 25, Nos. 1-2, 1981, 5-37.

Bregel, Yuriy. "The Peoples of Southern Turkmenistan and Khorasan in the 17th and 18th Centuries," *Central Asian Review*, 8, No. 3, 1960, 264-72.

Bremmer, Ian, and Ray Taras, eds. *Nation and Politics in the Soviet Successor States*. Cambridge: Cambridge University Press, 1993.

Brezhnev, Leonid. *Virgin Lands: Two Years in Kazakhstan, 1954-55*. Tarrytown, New York: Elsevier Science, 1982.

Brown, Bess. "Central Asia: The First Year of Unexpected Statehood," *RFE/RL Research Report* [Munich], 2, No. 1, January 1, 1993, 25-36.

Brown, Bess. "National Security and Military Issues in Central Asia." Pages 234-52 in Bruce Parrott, ed., *State Building and Military Power in Russia and the New States of Eurasia*. Armonk, New York: M.E. Sharpe, 1995.

Brown, Bess. "Three Central Asian States Form Economic Union," *RFE/RL Research Report* [Munich], 3, No. 13, April 1, 1994, 33-35.

Broxup, Marie. "Islam in Central Asia since Gorbachev," *Asian Affairs* [London], 18, October 1987, 283-93.

Canfield, Robert, ed. *Turco-Persia in Historical Perspective*. New York: Cambridge University Press, 1991.

Carlisle, Donald S. "Power and Politics in Soviet Uzbekistan: From Stalin to Gorbachev." Pages 93-130 in William Fierman, *Soviet Central Asia: The Failed Transformation*. Boulder, Colorado: Westview Press, 1991.

Carrère D'Encausse, Hélène. *Islam and the Russian Empire: Reform and Revolution in Central Asia*. Berkeley: University of California Press, 1989.

Carrère d'Encausse, Hélène. *Réforme et révolution chez les Musulmans de l'Empire russe*. Paris: Librarie Armand Colin, 1966.

Chalidze, F. "Aral Sea Crisis: A Legacy of Soviet Rule," *Central Asia Monitor*, 1992, No. 1, 30-34.

Clark, Susan L. "The Central Asian States: Defining Security Priorities and Developing Military Forces." Pages 177-206 in Michael Mandelbaum, ed., *Central Asia and the World: Kazakhstan, Uzbekistan, Tajikistan, Kyrgyzstan, and Turkmenistan*. New York: Council on Foreign Relations Press, 1994.

Clark, Susan L. *Security in Russia and Eurasia: The New National Militaries and Emerging Defense Policies*. Boulder, Colorado: Westview Press, 1995.

Colton, Timothy J., and Robert C. Tucker, eds. *Patterns in Post-Soviet Leadership*. Boulder, Colorado: Westview Press, 1995.

Commonwealth of Independent States. Statistical Committee. *Strany-chleny Sodruzhestva nezavisimykh gosudarstv: Statisticheskiy yezhegodnik* (The Member Nations of the Commonwealth of Independent States: A Statistical Yearbook). Moscow: Finansovyy inzhiniring, 1992.

Corbin, Henry. "Nasir-i Khusrau and Iranian Isma'ilism." Pages 520-42 in Richard N. Frye, ed., *The Cambridge History of Iran*, 4. Cambridge: Cambridge University Press, 1975.

Critchlow, James. *Nationalism in Uzbekistan*. Boulder, Colorado: Westview Press, 1991.

Dannreuther, Roland. *Creating New States in Central Asia*. Adelphi Paper No. 288. London: Brassey's for International Institute for Strategic Studies, 1994.

Dave, Bhavna. "A New Parliament Consolidates Presidential Authority," *Transition*, March 22, 1996, 33-37.

Dave, Bhavna. "Kazakhstan Staggers under Its Nuclear Burden," *Transition*, November 17, 1995, 12-13.

Davis, Christopher M. "Health Care Crisis: The Former Soviet Union," *RFE/RL Research Report* [Munich], 2, No. 40, October 8, 1993, 35-43.

Dawisha, A.I., and Karen Dawisha, eds. *The Foreign Policy Interests of Russia and the New States of Eurasia*. Armonk, New York: M.E. Sharpe, 1995.

Dawisha, Karen, and Bruce Parrott. *Russia and the New States of Eurasia: The Politics of Upheaval*. Port Chester, New York: Cambridge University Press, 1994.

Demidov, Sergey Mikhaylovich. *Istoriya religioznykh verovaniy narodov Turkmenistana* (A History of the Religious Faiths of Turkmenistan). Ashgabat: Ylym, 1990.

Deweese, Devin. *Islamization and Native Religion in the Golden Horde*. University Park: Pennsylvania State University Press, 1994.

Dienes, Leslie. "Economic Geographic Relations in the Post-Soviet Republics," *Post-Soviet Geography*, 34, October 1993, 497-529.

Diller, Daniel C., ed. *Russia and the Independent States*. Washington: Congressional Quarterly, 1993.

Diuk, Nadia, and Adrian Karatnycky. *The Hidden Nations: The People Challenge the Soviet Union*. Fairfield, New Jersey: William Morrow, 1990.

Doolotaliyev, S. "Some Issues in the Development of the Sary-Dzhaz Mining Industrial Center, Kirghiz SSR," *Sovetskaya Geografiya*, 30, May 1989, 371-4.

Dorian, James P. "The Kazakh Oil Industry: A Potential Critical Role in Central Asia," *Energy Policy*, 22, August 1994, 685-98.

Drobizheva, L.M. "Kul'tura i mezhnatsional'yye otnosheniya v SSSR" (Culture and International Relations in the USSR), *Voprosy istorii* [Moscow], 1979, No. 11, 3-15.

Drobizheva, Leokadia, et al., eds. *Ethics Conflict in the Post-Soviet World: Case Studies and Analysis*. Armonk, New York: M. E. Sharpe, 1996.

Durdyyev, Marat, and Shukhrat Kadyrov. *Turkmeny mira* (Turkmen of the World). Ashgabat: Kharp, 1991.

Dzharylgasimova, R.Sh., and L.S. Tolstova, eds. *Etnicheskiye protsessy u natsional'nykh grupp Sredney Azii i Kazakhstana* (Ethnic Processes in the National Groups of Central Asia and Kazakhstan). Moscow: Nauka, 1980.

Dzhikiyev, Ata. *Ocherki proiskhozhdeniya i formirovaniya turkmenskogo naroda v epokhu srednovekov'ya* (Essays on the Origin and Formation of the Turkmen People in the Middle Ages). Ashgabat: Ylym, 1991.

Economist Intelligence Unit. *Country Report: Georgia, Armenia, Azerbaijan, Central Asian Republics*. London: 1994.
Economist Intelligence Unit. *Country Report: Kazakhstan, Kyrgyz Republic, Tajikistan, Turkmenistan, Uzbekistan* [London], No. 1, 1996.
Eickelman, Dale F., ed. *Russia's Muslim Frontiers: New Directions in Cross-Cultural Analysis*. Bloomington: Indiana University Press, 1993.
Elebayeva, Aynur B. "The Osh Incident: Problems for Research," *Post-Soviet Geography*, 33, February 1992, 78-86.
Ellis, C.H. *The Transcaspian Episode, 1918-1919*. London: Hutchinson, 1963.
Encyclopedia Iranica, 5. Costa Mesa, California: Mazda, 1990.
Entsiklopediyai sovetii Tojik (Soviet Tajik Encyclopedia). Dushanbe: Sarredaktsiyai ilmii entsiklopediyai sovetii Tojik, 1978-1987.
Evans, John L. *Russia and the Khanates of Central Asia to 1865*. New York: Associated Faculty Press, 1982.
Fane, Daria. "Ethnicity and Regionalism in Uzbekistan: Maintaining Stability Through Authoritarian Control." Pages 271-302 in Leokadia Drobizheva, et al., eds. *Ethnic Conflict in the Post- Soviet World: Case Studies and Analysis*. Armonk, New York: M.E. Sharpe, 1996.
Farmayan, Hafez. "Turkoman Identity and Presence in Iran," *Iran*, 4, Summer 1981, 45-63.
Fedorova, T.I. *Goroda Tadzhikistana i problemy rosta i razvitiya* (Cities of Tajikistan and Problems of Growth and Development). Dushanbe: Irfon, 1981.
Feldman, Walter. "Interpreting the Poetry of Makhtumquli." Pages 167-89 in Jo-Ann Gross, ed., *Muslims in Central Asia: Expressions of Identity and Change*. Durham: Duke University Press, 1992.
Ferdinand, Peter, ed. *The New States of Central Asia and Their Neighbors*. New York: Council on Foreign Relations Press, 1994.
Feshbach, Murray, and Alfred Friendly, Jr. *Ecocide in the USSR: Health and Nature under Siege*. New York: Basic Books, 1992.
Fierman, William, ed. *Soviet Central Asia: The Failed Transformation*. Boulder, Colorado: Westview Press, 1991.
Fierman, William. "Independence and the Declining Priority of Language Law Implementation in Uzbekistan." Pages 205-30 in Yaacov Ro'i, ed., *Muslim Eurasia: Conflicting Legacies*. London: Frank Cass, 1995.
Forsythe, Rosemarie. "The Politics of Oil in the Caucasus and Central Asia," *Adelphi Papers*, 300, May 1996, whole issue.
Freidin, Gregory. "Coup II," *The New Republic*, 205, No. 16, October 14, 1991, 16-18.
Friedman, L. "Ethnic and National Composition of Population in Newly Independent Countries of the Middle East and Caucasus," *Central Asia Today*, 1993, No. 1, 56-60.
Frye, Richard N. "The Samanids." Pages 136-61 in Richard N. Frye, *The Cambridge History of Iran*. Cambridge: Cambridge University Press, 1975.
Frye, Richard N. *Bukhara: The Medieval Achievement*. Norman: University of Oklahoma Press, 1965.
Frye, Richard N., ed. *The Cambridge History of Iran*. Cambridge: Cambridge University Press, 1975.
Fuller, Graham. "Central Asia: The Quest for Identity," *Current History*, 93, April 1994, 145-49.

Fuller, Graham. "The Emergence of Central Asia," *Foreign Policy*, Spring 1990, 49-67.

Fuller, Graham. *Central Asia: The New Geopolitics*. Santa Monica, California: Rand, 1992.

Furtado, Charles F., and Henry R. Huttenback, eds. "The Ex-Soviet Nationalities Without Gorbachev," *Nationalities Papers*, 20, Fall 1992, 1-124.

Geldiyev, B., S.P. Tokarev, and T. Sakhatliyev. *Razvitiye promyshlennosti Turkmenistana za 50 let* (The Development of Industry in Turkmenistan over 50 Years). Ashgabat: Turkmenistan, 1974.

Ghorban, Narsi. "The Role of the Multinational Oil Companies in the Development of Oil and Gas Resources in Central Asia and the Caucasus," *Iranian Journal of International Affairs*, 5, Spring 1993, 1-15.

Gleason, Gregory. "Central Asia: Land Reform and the Ethnic Factor," *RFE/RL Research Report* [Munich], 2, No. 3, 1993, 28-33.

Gleason, Gregory. "The Political Economy of Dependency under Socialism: The Asian Republics in the USSR," *Studies in Comparative Communism*, 24, December 1991, 335-53.

Gleason, Gregory. "The Struggle for Control over Water in Central Asia: Republican Sovereignty and Collective Action." *RFE/RL Report on the USSR* [Munich], 3, No. 25, June 21, 1991, 11-19.

Gleason, Gregory. *An Introduction to the History of the Turkic Peoples*. Wiesbaden: Otto Harrasowitz, 1992.

Goetz, Roland, and Uwe Halbach. *Informationen über eine unbekannte Republik, I-II*. Berichte des Bundesinstituts für ostwissenschaftliche und internationale Studien. Cologne: 1995.

Goron, Leonard, and Alex Pravda, eds. *Who's Who in Russia and the New States*. London: I.B. Tauris, 1993.

Gretsky, Sergei. "Civil War in Tajikistan and Its International Repercussions," *Critique*, Spring 1995, 3-24.

Gretsky, Sergei. "Qadi Akbar Turajonzoda," *Central Asia Monitor*, 1994, No. 1, 16-24.

Gretsky, Sergei. "Russia and Tajikistan." Pages 231-51 in A.Z. Rubinstein and O.M. Smolansky, eds. *Regional Power Rivalries in the New Eurasia: Russia, Turkey, and Iran*. Armonk, New York: M.E. Sharpe, 1995.

Gross, Jo-Ann, ed. *Muslims in Central Asia: Expressions of Identity and Change*. Durham: Duke University Press, 1992.

Grousset, Rene. *The Empire of the Steppes*. Trans., N. Walford. New Brunswick: Rutgers University Press, 1970.

Haghayeghi, Mehrdad. *Islam and Politics in Central Asia*. New York: St. Martin's Press, 1995.

Hale, Henry. "Islam, State-building, and Uzbekistan Foreign Policy," Pages 136-72 in Ali Banuazizi and Myron Weiner, eds., *The New Geopolitics of Central Asia and Its Borderlands*. Bloomington: Indiana University Press, 1994.

Hambly, Gavin, ed. *Central Asia*. New York: Delacorte Press, 1969.

Helsinki Watch. *Conflict in the Soviet Union*. New York: Human Rights Watch, 1991.

Henley, John S., and George B. Assaf. "Re-Integrating the Central Asian Republics into the World Economy," *Intereconomics*, 30, September-October 1995, 235-45.

Henze, Paul B. *Whither Turkestan?* Santa Monica, California: Rand, 1992.

Hitchins, Keith. "Modern Tajik Literature." Pages 454-75 in E. Yarshater, ed., *Persian Literature*. Albany: Bibliotheca Persica, 1988.

Hooson, David. *The Soviet Union: People and Regions*. Belmont, California: Wadsworth, 1966.

Horton, Scott, and Tatiana Geller. "Investing in Uzbekistan's Natural Resources Sector," *Central Asia Monitor*, 1996, No. 1, 25-35.

Horton, Scott, and Tatiana Geller. "Secured Transactions in Uzbekistan," *Central Asia Monitor*, 1996, No. 2, 21-7.

Hostler, Charles Warren. *The Turks of Central Asia*. Westport, Connecticut: Praeger, 1993.

Howard, G. "The Caspian Oil and Gas Oasis: Turkmenistan," *Russian Oil and Gas Guide*, 3, No. 1, 1994, 54-58.

Institute for National Strategic Studies. *Strategic Assessment 1995: U.S. Security Challenges in Transition*. Washington: GPO, 1995.

International Monetary Fund. *Economic Review: Turkmenistan*. Washington: 1992.

International Monetary Fund. *Turkmenistan*. Washington: 1994.

Irons, William. "The Turkmen of Iran: A Brief Research Report," *Iranian Studies*, 2, Winter 1969, 27-38.

Irons, William. *The Yomut Turkmen: A Study of Social Organization among a Central Asian Turkic-Speaking Population*. Ann Arbor: University of Michigan Press, 1975.

Istoriya kul'turnogo stroitel'stva v Tadzhikistane, 1917-1977 gg (The History of Cultural Construction in Tajikistan, 1917-1977, 2.) Dushanbe: Donish, 1983.

Istoriya Turkmenskoy SSR (History of the Turkmen SSR). Ashgabat: Akademiya nauk Turkmenskoy SSR, 1957.

Janabel, Jiger. "When National Ambition Conflicts with Reality: Studies on Kazakhstan's Ethnic Relations," *Central Asian Survey*, 15, No. 1, March 1996, 5-22.

Jane's Sentinel Regional Security Assessment: Commonwealth of Independent States. Ed., Paul Beaver. Coulsdon, United Kingdom: Jane's Information Group, 1994.

Kaiser, Robert J. *The Geography of Nationalism in Russia and the USSR*. Princeton: Princeton University Press, 1994.

Karasik, Theodore, ed. *USSR Facts and Figures Annual 1992*. Gulf Breeze, Florida: Academic International Press, 1992.

Karasik, Theodore. *Azerbaijan, Central Asia, and Future Persian Gulf Security*. Santa Monica, California: Rand, 1993.

Karpat, Kemal. "The Foreign Policy of the Central Asian States, Turkey, and Iran," *OSCE Bulletin*, 3, No. 1, Winter 1994-95, 17-30.

Katz, Zev, ed. *Handbook of Major Soviet Nationalities*. New York: Free Press, 1975.

Kedzie, Christopher R. *Stumbling Blocks and Stepping Stones: The Crossing from Soviet Domination to Self Rule in the Republics of Central Asia*. Santa Monica, California: Rand, 1994.

Keller, S. "Islam in Soviet Central Asia, 1917-1930: Soviet Policy and the Struggle for Control," *Central Asian Survey* [Abingdon, United Kingdom], 11, No. 1, 1992, 25-50.

Khrushchev, Anatoliy Timofeyevich, and O.D. Chuvilkin. "Resursy gaza gosudarstv Tsentral'noy Azii: Ekonomiko-geograficheskiye aspekty" (Gas Resources of the States of Central Asia: Economic-Geographic Aspects), *Vestnik Moskovskogo universiteta: Geografiya* [Moscow], 1994, No. 4, 51-57.

Kirpichenko, V. "Khozyaystvennyye svyazi stran-chlenov SNG" (Economic Relations of CIS Member States). *Ekonomist* [Moscow], 1993, No. 4, 53-62.

Kojaoglu, T. "The Existence of a Bukharan Nationality in the Recent Past." Pages 151-8 in Edward Allworth, ed., *The Nationality Question in Soviet Central Asia*. New York: Praeger, 1973.

Konyukhov, V.G. *Ekologicheskaya obstanovka v Uzbekistanskoy SSR i mery po yeye uluchsheniyu* (The Ecological Situation in the Uzbek SSR and Measures to Improve It). Tashkent: State Committee on Environmental Protection, 1990.

Korsunskiy, L. "Podzemnyy atomnyy gulag deystvuyet" (An Underground Atomic Gulag Is in Operation). *Stolitsa* [Moscow] 1992, No. 35, 22-6.

Krader, Lawrence. *Peoples of Central Asia*. Uralic and Altaic Series, No. 26. Bloomington: Indiana University Press, 1963.

Landau, Jacob M. *Pan-Turkism: From Irredentism to Cooperation*. Bloomington: Indiana University Press, 1995.

Lawyers' Committee for Human Rights. Freedom of Association Project. *Karimov's Way: Freedom of Association and Assembly in Uzbekistan*. Briefing Paper No. 1. New York: 1994.

Lipski, Andrei. "The Community of Central Asia: Inside or Outside the CIS?" *International Affairs* [Moscow], October 1993, 51-5.

Lubin, Nancy. "Islam and Ethnic Identity in Central Asia: A View from Below." Pages 53-70 in Yaacov Ro'i, ed., *Muslim Eurasia: Conflicting Legacies*. London: Frank Cass, 1995.

Lubin, Nancy. "Leadership in Uzbekistan and Kazakhstan: The Views of the Led." Pages 217-34 in Timothy J. Colton and Robert C. Tucker, eds., *Patterns in Post-Soviet Leadership*. Boulder, Colorado: Westview Press, 1995.

Lubin, Nancy. "Uzbekistan." Pages 289-306 in Philip R. Pryde, ed., *Environmental Resources and Constraints in the Former Soviet Republics*. Boulder, Colorado: Westview Press, 1995.

Lubin, Nancy. "Uzbekistan: The Challenges Ahead," *Middle East Journal*, 43, No. 4, Autumn 1989, 619-34.

Lubin, Nancy. *Central Asians Take Stock*. Washington: United States Institute of Peace Press, 1995.

Lubin, Nancy. *Labour and Nationality in Soviet Central Asia: An Uneasy Compromise*. Princeton: Princeton University Press, 1985.

Maier, Frith. *Trekking in Russia and Central Asia: A Traveler's Guide*. Seattle: Mountaineers Books, 1994.

Maksudov, Sergey. "On Infant Mortality in Turkmenistan," *Central Asia Monitor*, 1992, No. 1, 26-30.

Malik, Hafeez, ed. *Central Asia: Its Strategic Importance and Future Prospects*. New York: St. Martin's Press, 1994.

Mandelbaum, Michael, ed. *Central Asia and the World: Kazakhstan, Uzbekistan, Tajikistan, Kyrgyzstan, and Turkmenistan*. New York: Council on Foreign Relations Press, 1994.

Manz, Beatrice F., ed. *Central Asia in Historical Perspective*. Boulder, Colorado: Westview Press, 1994.

Martin, Keith. "Environment: Central Asia's Forgotten Tragedy," *RFE/RL Research Report* [Munich], 3, No. 29, July 29, 1994, 35-48.

Mesbahi, Mohiaddin, ed. *Central Asia and the Caucasus after the Soviet Union: Domestic and International Dynamics*. Gainesville: University Press of Florida, 1994.

Micklin, Philip. "The Aral Sea Crisis: Introduction to the Special Issue," *Post-Soviet Geography*, 33, No. 5, May 1992, 269-82.

Micklin, Phillip P. *The Water Management Crisis in Soviet Central Asia*. The Carl Beck Papers in Russian and East European Studies, No. 905. Pittsburgh: University of Pittsburgh Press, 1992.

Migranyan, Andranik. "Russia and the Near Abroad," *Current Digest of the Post-Soviet Press*, 47, March 9, 1994, 1-4 and March 16, 1994, 6-11.

Monogarova, L.F. "Evolyutsiya natsional'nogo samosoznaniya pripamirskikh narodnostey" (The Evolution of National Self-Awareness of the Pamiri Peoples). Pages 125-35 in *Etnicheskiye protsessy u natsional'nykh grupp Sredney Azii i Kazakhstana*. Moscow: Nauka, 1980.

Nahaylo, Bohdan, and Viktor Swoboda. *Soviet Disunion*. New York: The Free Press, 1990.

Narody mira: Etnograficheskiye ocherki (Peoples of the World: Ethnographic Sketches). Moscow: Nauka, 1963.

Naumkin, Vitaly. *State, Religion, and Society in Central Asia: A Post-Soviet Critique*. London: Ithaca Press, 1993.

Nissman, David B. "Iran and Soviet Islam: The Azerbaijan and Turkmen SSRs," *Central Asia Survey* [Abingdon, United Kingdom], 2, No. 4, 1983, 45-60.

Olcott, Martha Brill. "Central Asia's Islamic Awakening," *Current History*, 93, April 1994, 150-54.

Olcott, Martha Brill. "The Basmachi or Freemen's Revolt in Turkestan 1918-1924," *Soviet Studies*, 33, No. 3, July 1981, 352-69.

Olcott, Martha Brill. "The Myth of 'Tsentral'naia Aziia'," *Orbis*, 38, No. 3, Summer 1995, 549-66.

Olcott, Martha Brill. *Central Asia's New States: Independence, Foreign Policy, and Regional Security*. Washington: United States Institute of Peace Press, 1996.

Olcott, Martha Brill. *The Kazakhs*. 2d ed. Studies of Nationalities in the USSR. Stanford, California: Hoover Institution Press, 1995.

Paksoy, G.B., ed. *Central Asia Reader: The Rediscovery of History*. Armonk, New York: M.E. Sharpe, 1994.

Park, A.G. *Bolshevism in Turkestan, 1917-1927*. New York: Columbia University Press, 1957.

Pierce, Richard A. *Russian Central Asia, 1867-1917*. Berkeley: University of California Press, 1960.

Pilkington, John. "Kyrgyzstan: A Tale of Two Journeys," *Geographical Magazine*, 65, April 1993, 8-12.

Pipes, Daniel. "The Politics of the 'Rip Van Winkel' States: The Southern Tier States of the Ex-Soviet Union Have Moved the Borders of the Middle East North," *Middle East Insight*, 10, November-December 1993, 30-40.

PlanEcon. *Review and Outlook for the Former Soviet Republics*. Washington: 1995.

Plyshevskiy, B. "Ekonomicheskoye polozheniye gosudarstv SNG" (The Economic Situation of the CIS States), *Ekonomist* [Moscow], 1993, No. 4, 63-75.

Polat, Abdumannob. "Uzbekistan: Does the Government Want a Dialogue with the Opposition," *Caspian Crossroads*, Winter 1995, 26-28.

Polyakov, Sergey Petrovich. *Etnicheskaya istoriya severo-zapadnoy Turkmenii v sredniye veka* (The Ethnic History of Northwest Turkmenia in the Middle Ages). Ashgabat: 1973.

Pomfret, Richard. *The Economies of Central Asia*. Princeton: Princeton University Press, 1995.

Posner, Michael. *Human Rights and Legal Issues in Uzbekistan*. New York: Lawyers' Committee for Human Rights, 1993.

Potter, William C. "The 'Sapphire' File: Lessons for International Nonproliferation Cooperation," *Transition*, 1, November 17, 1995, 14-19.

Pryde, Ian. "Kyrgyzstan: Secularism vs. Islam," *World Today*, 48, November 1992, 208-11.

Pryde, Ian. "Kyrgyzstan: The Trials of Independence," *Journal of Democracy*, 5, January 1994, 109-20.

Pryde, Philip R., ed. *Environmental Resources and Constraints in the Former Soviet Republics*. Boulder, Colorado: Westview Press, 1995.

Rakowska-Harmstone, Teresa. *Russia and Nationalism in Central Asia: The Case of Tadzhikistan*. Baltimore: Johns Hopkins Press, 1970.

Rashid, Ahmed. *The Resurgence of Central Asia: Islam or Nationalism?* Karachi: Oxford University Press, 1994.

Rashid, Ahmed. *The Resurgence of Central Asia: Islam or Nationalism?* Atlantic Highlands, New Jersey: Zed Books, 1994.

Ro'i, Yaacov, ed. *Muslim Eurasia: Conflicting Legacies*. London: Frank Cass, 1995.

Rotor, Igor. "Kyrgyzstan: Capitalist Experiment in Central Asia," *Current Digest of the Post-Soviet Press*, 44, April 8, 1992, 4-5.

Rubin, Barry M. "The Fragmentation of Tajikistan," *Survival*, 35, No. 4, Winter 1993-1994, 71-91.

Rubinstein, Alvin Z. "The Geopolitical Pull on Russia," *Orbis*, 38, No. 3, Summer 1995, 567-84.

Rubinstein, Alvin Z., and Oles M. Smolansky, eds. *Regional Power Rivalries in the New Eurasia: Russia, Turkey, and Iran*. Armonk, New York: M.E. Sharpe, 1995.

Rumer, Boris Z. *Soviet Central Asia: "A Tragic Experiment."* Winchester, Massachusetts: Unwin Hyman, 1990.

Rumer, Boris Z. *Soviet Central Asia: A "Tragic Experiment."* Boston: Unwin Hyman, 1989.

Rywkin, Michael. *Moscow's Muslim Challenge: Soviet Central Asia*. Armonk, New York: M.E. Sharpe, 1990.

Sagers, Matthew J. "News Notes," *Post-Soviet Geography*, 33, No. 3, 1992, 190.

Saray, Mehmet. *The Turkmens in the Age of Imperialism: A Study of the Turkmen People and Their Incorporation into the Russian Empire*. Ankara: Turkish Historical Society, 1989.

Sharipov, I. *Zakonomernosti formirovaniya sotsialisticheskikh obshchestvennykh otnosheniy v Tadzhikistane* (The Regularity of the Formation of Socialist Social Relations in Tajikistan). Dushanbe: Donish, 1983.

Shlapentokh, Vladimir, Munir Sendich, and Emil Payin, eds. *The New Russian Diaspora: Russian Minorities in the Former Soviet Republics*. Armonk, New York: M.E. Sharpe, 1994.

Shome, Parthasarathi, and Julio Escolano. "The State of Tax Policy in the Central Asian and Transcaucasian Newly Independent States," *Bulletin of International Fiscal Documentation*, 48, April 1994, 159-66.

Shukurov, E., ed. *Discovery of Kyrghyzstan*. Bishkek: International Foundation "A Discovery of Kyrghyzstan," 1993.

Shukurov, Maksud Rakhmatullayevich. *Kul'turnaya zhizn' Tadzhikistana* (The Cultural Life of Tajikistan). Dushanbe: Irfon, 1980.

Simon, Gerhard. *Nationalism and Policy Toward the Nationalities in the Soviet Union*. Trans., K. Forster and O. Forster. Boulder, Colorado: Westview Press, 1991.

Sizov, Andrey Yevgen'yevich. "Ekonomika Rossii i drugikh stran SNG v nachale 90-kh godov" (The Economy of Russia and the Other Countries of the CIS at the Beginning of the 1990s). *Mirovaya ekonomika i mezhdunarodnyye otnosheniya* [Moscow], 1993, No. 7, 20-29.

Smirnov, Yu. "Strannyy Islam" (Strange Islam), *Pamir*, No. 2, 1988, 104-25.

Soviet Union. Central Statistical Administration. *Chislennost' i sostav naseleniy SSSR* (Size and Composition of the Populations of the USSR). Moscow: Finansy i statistika, 1984.

Soviet Union. State Committee on Statistics. *Chislennost' naseleniya soyuznykh respublik po gorodskim poseleniyam i rayonam* (Size of the Population of the Union Republics by Urban Settlement and District). Moscow: Informatsionno-izdatel'skiy tsentr Goskomstata SSSR, 1991.

Soviet Union. State Committee on Statistics. *Demograficheskiy yezhegodnik SSSR 1990* (Demographic Yearbook of the USSR 1990). Moscow: Finansy i statistika, 1990.

Soviet Union. State Committee on Statistics. *Soyuznyye respubliki: Osnovnyye ekonomicheskiye i sotsial'nyye pokazateli* (The Union Republics: Basic Economic and Social Indicators). Moscow: Informatsionno-izdatel'skiy tsentr Goskomstata SSSR, 1991.

Sparks, John. *Realms of the Russian Bear: A Natural History of Russia and the Central Asian Republics*. Waltham, Massachusetts: Little Brown, 1992.

Staar, S. Frederick. "Making Eurasia Stable," *Foreign Affairs*, 75, January-February 1996, 80-92.

Starr, S. Frederick, ed. *The Legacy of History in Russia and the New States of Eurasia*. Armonk, New York: M.E. Sharpe, 1994.

Subtelny, E. "The Cult of Holy Places: Religious Practices among Soviet Muslims," *Middle East Journal*, 43, No. 4, 1989, 593-604.

Symon, L. "Tadzhikistan: A Developing Country in the Soviet Union," *Asian Affairs*, 61, pt. 3, October 1974, 249-56.

Szporluk, Roman, ed. *National Identity and Ethnicity in Russia and the New States of Eurasia*. Armonk, New York: M.E. Sharpe, 1994.

Tadjbakhsh, Shahrbanou. "Causes and Consequences of the Civil War," *Central Asia Monitor*, 1993, No. 1, 10-14.

Tadjbakhsh, Shahrbanou. "The 'Tajik Spring' of 1992," *Central Asia Monitor*, No. 2, 1993, 21-9.

Tadzhikistan. Tashkent: Obshchestvo dlya izucheniya Tadzhikistana i iranskikh narodnostey za yego predelami, 1925.

Tajik SSR. Supreme Soviet. Presidium. "Soobshcheniye komissii Prezidiuma Verkhovnogo Soveta Tadzhikskoy SSR po proverke sobytiy 12-14 fevralya 1990 g. v Dushanbe" (Report of the Commission of the Presidium of the Supreme Soviet of the Tajik SSR on Examining the Events of February 12-14, 1990, in Dushanbe), *Sogdiana* [Dushanbe],1990. No. 3, entire issue.

The Europa World Year Book 1993, 2. London: Europa, 1993.

The Europa World Year Book 1994, 2. London: Europa, 1994.

The Europa World Year Book 1995, 2. London: Europa, 1995.

The Europa World Year Book 1996, 2. London: Europa, 1996.

The FirstBook [sic] *of Demographics for the Republics of the Former Soviet Union, 1951-1990*. Shady Side, Maryland: New World Demographics, 1992.

The Military Balance 1992-1993. London: International Institute for Strategic Studies, 1992.

The Military Balance 1993-1994. London: International Institute for Strategic Studies, 1993.

The Military Balance 1994-1995. London: International Institute for Strategic Studies, 1994.

The Military Balance 1995-1996. London: International Institute for Strategic Studies, 1995.

The Statesman's Year-Book 1992-1993. Ed., Brian Hunter. New York: St. Martin's Press, 1992.

The Statesman's Year-Book 1993-1994. Ed., Brian Hunter. New York: St. Martin's Press, 1993.

The Statesman's Year-Book 1994-1995. Ed., Brian Hunter. New York: St. Martin's Press, 1994.

The Statesman's Year-Book 1995-1996. Ed., Brian Hunter. New York: St. Martin's Press, 1995.

Thomas, Paul. *The Central Asian States: Tajikistan, Uzbekistan, Kyrgyzstan, Turkmenistan*. Brookfield, Connecticut: Millbrook Press, 1992.

Turkmenenforschung (Research on the Turkmen), 1-15. Hamburg and Berlin: Reinhold Schletzer Verlag, 1979-93.

Tyson, David, and Larry Clark. *Turkmen: Language Competencies for Peace Corps Volunteers in Turkmenistan*. Washington: GPO, 1994.

Undeland, Charles, and Nicholas Platt. *The Central Asian Republics: Fragments of Empire, Magnets of Wealth*. New York: Asia Society, 1994.

United Nations. Department for Economic and Social Information and Policy Analysis. *Demographic Yearbook 1993*. New York: 1995.

United Nations. Department for Economic and Social Information and Policy Analysis. *Demographic Yearbook 1994*. New York: 1996.

United States. Agency for International Development. Center for Health Information. *USAID Health Profile: Turkmenistan*. Arlington, Virginia: USAID, 1992.

United States. Bureau of International Narcotics Matters. *International Narcotics Strategy Report March 1996*. Washington: GPO, 1996.

United States. Central Intelligence Agency. *Handbook of International Economic Statistics 1995*. Washington: GPO, 1995.

United States. Central Intelligence Agency. *Handbook of International Economic Statistics 1992*. Washington: GPO, 1992.

United States. Central Intelligence Agency. *Kazakhstan: An Economic Profile*. Springfield, Virginia: National Technical Information Service, 1993.

United States. Central Intelligence Agency. *Piecing Together Central Asia: A Look at Key Leaders*. Washington: GPO, 1993.

United States. Central Intelligence Agency. *The World Factbook 1994*. Washington: GPO, 1994.

United States. Central Intelligence Agency. *The World Factbook 1995*. Washington: GPO, 1995.

United States. Central Intelligence Agency. *Turkmenistan: An Economic Profile.* Springfield, Virginia: National Technical Information Service, 1993.

United States. Congress. 103d, 2d Session. House of Representatives. Foreign Affairs Subcommittee on Europe and the Middle East. Prepared testimony of Holly Burkhalter of Human Rights Watch/Helsinki, Sept. 22, 1994. Washington: GPO, 1994.

United States. Congress. 103d, 2d Session. House of Representatives. Subcommittee on International Security, International Operations, and Human Rights. Testimony from Pamela B. Cohen, National President, and Micah H. Naftalin, National Director of the Union of Councils, April 26, 1994. Washington: GPO, 1994.

United States. Congress. Commission on Security and Cooperation in Europe. *Report on the Helsinki Commission Visit to Armenia, Azerbaijan, Tajikistan, Uzbekistan, Kazakhstan, and Ukraine.* Washington: GPO, 1992.

United States. Congress. Commission on Security and Cooperation in Europe. *Human Rights and Democratization in the Newly Independent States of the Former Soviet Union.* Washington: GPO, 1993.

United States. Department of Agriculture. Economic Research Service. *Former USSR: Agriculture and Trade Report 1991.* Washington: GPO, 1992.

United States. Department of Agriculture. Economic Research Service. *Former USSR: Agriculture and Trade Report 1992.* Washington: GPO, 1993.

United States. Department of Commerce. Business Information Service for the Newly Independent States. *Commercial Overview of Turkmenistan.* Washington: 1993.

United States. Department of State. Bureau of International Narcotics Matters. *International Narcotics Strategy Report March 1996.* Washington: GPO, 1996.

United States. Department of State. *Country Reports on Human Rights Practices for 1993.* (Report submitted to United States Congress, 103d, 2d Session, House of Representatives, Committee on Foreign Affairs, and Senate, Committee on Foreign Relations.) Washington: GPO, 1994.

Uzbekistan. State Committee on Projections and Statistics. *Chislennost', sostav i dvizheniye naseleniya Respubliki Uzbekistan* (The Size, Composition, and Movement of the Population of the Republic of Uzbekistan). Tashkent: 1992.

Uzbekistan. State Committee on Projections and Statistics. *Okhrana zdorov'ya v respublike Uzbekistana* (Health Protection in the Republic of Uzbekistan). Tashkent: 1991.

Vaisman, Demian. "Regionalism and Clan Loyalty in the Political Life of Uzbekistan." Pages 105-22 in Yaacov Ro'i, ed., *Muslim Eurasia: Conflicting Legacies.* London: Frank Cass, 1995.

Veselovskiy, Vladimir Glebovich, et al. *Arkhitektura sovetskogo Tadzhikistana* (The Architecture of Soviet Tajikistan). Moscow: Stroyizdat, 1987.

Vinnikov, Ya. R. "Natsional'nyye i etnograficheskiye gruppy Sredney Azii po dannym etnicheskoy statistiki" (The National and Ethnographic Groups of Central Asia According to Ethnic Statistical Data). Pages 11-42 in R. Sh. Dzharylgasimova and L.S. Tolstova, eds., *Etnicheskiye protsessy u natsional'nykh grupp Sredney Azii i Kazakhstana.* Moscow: Nauka, 1980.

WEFA Group. *Eurasia Economic Outlook February 1996.* Eddystone, Pennsylvania: 1996.

Wheeler, Geoffrey. *The Modern History of Soviet Central Asia.* New York: Praeger, 1964.

Wixman, Ronald. *Peoples of the USSR: An Ethnographic Handbook.* Armonk, New York: M.E. Sharpe, 1984.

Wolfson, Zeev. "Central Asian Environment: A Dead End," *Environmental Policy Review*, 4, No. 1, January 1990, 29-46.

World Bank. *Kazakhstan: Agricultural Sector Review*. Washington: 1994.

World Bank. *Kazakhstan: The Transition to a Market Economy*. Washington: 1993.

World Bank. *Kyrgyz Republic: Agricultural Sector Review*. Washington: 1995.

World Bank. *Kyrgyz Republic: Economic Report*. Washington: 1994.

World Bank. *Kyrgyz Republic: Energy Sector Review*. Washington: 1995.

World Bank. *Kyrgyz Republic: National Environmental Action Plan*. Washington: 1995.

World Bank. *Kyrgyz Republic: Poverty Assessment and Strategy*. Washington: 1995.

World Bank. *Kyrgyzstan: Social Protection in a Reforming Economy*. Washington: 1993.

World Bank. *Kyrgyzstan: The Transition to a Market Economy*. Washington: 1993.

World Bank. *Statistical Handbook 1995: States of the Former USSR*. Washington: 1995.

World Bank. *Turkmenistan*. World Bank Country Study. Washington: 1994.

World Bank. *Uzbekistan: An Agenda for Economic Reform*. Washington: 1993.

World Radio TV Handbook 1996. Ed., Andrew G. Sennitt. Amsterdam: Billboard, 1996.

Worldwide Directory of Defense Authorities, 1996, 1. Ed., Kenneth Gause. Bethesda, Maryland: Worldwide Government Directories, 1996.

Worldwide Directory of Defense Authorities, 2. Ed., Kenneth Gause. Bethesda, Maryland: Worldwide Government Directories, 1996.

Wright, R. "Report from Turkestan," *New Yorker*, April 6, 1992, 53-75.

Yarshater, Ehsan, ed. *Persian Literature*. Albany: Bibliotheca Persica, 1988.

Yekayev, Orazpolat. *Turkmenistan i turkmeny v kontse XV-pervoy polovine XVI v* (Turkmenistan and the Turkmen at the End of the Fifteenth-First Half of the Sixteenth Centuries). Ashgabat: Ylym, 1981.

Chapter 8

AFGHANISTAN: CURRENT ISSUES AND U.S. POLICY

Kenneth Katzman

SUMMARY

Afghanistan is stabilizing after more than 22 years of warfare, including a U.S.-led war that brought the current government to power. Before the U.S. military campaign against the Taliban movement began on October 7, 2001, Afghanistan had been mired in conflict since the Soviet invasion of Afghanistan in 1979. The Taliban ruled most of Afghanistan from 1996 until its collapse in December 2001 at the hands of the U.S. and Afghan opposition military campaign.

The defeat of the Taliban enabled the United States and its coalition partners to send forces throughout Afghanistan to search for Taliban and Al Qaeda fighters and leaders that remain at large, including Al Qaeda founder Osama bin Laden. Since the fall of the Taliban, Afghan citizens are enjoying new personal freedoms that were forbidden under the Taliban, about 2 million Afghan refugees have returned, and women have returned to schools, the workforce, and participation in politics.

As U.S.-led combat activity against remaining Al Qaeda and Taliban elements has diminished, the United States has been shifting its military focus toward stabilizing and extending the writ of the central government. Stabilization measures include training a new Afghan national army, supporting an international security force (ISAF), and setting up regional enclaves to protect aid and reconstruction workers. To help foster development, the United Nations and the Bush Administration have lifted most sanctions imposed on Afghanistan since the Soviet occupation. The United States gave Afghanistan a total of over $620 million in aid during FY2002.

There are some indications that Afghanistan's different ethnic and political factions are working together at the national level, although each faction exerts substantial influence in its home region. Although the minority coalition Northern Alliance emerged from the war as the dominant force in the country, the United States and United Nations mediators persuaded the Alliance to share power with Pashtun representatives in a broad-based interim government. On December 5, 2001, major Afghan factions, meeting under U.N. auspices in Bonn, signed an agreement to form an interim government that ran Afghanistan until a traditional national assembly ("loya jirga") was held June 11-19, 2002. The loya jirga delegates selected a new government to run Afghanistan for the next 18 months and approved Hamid Karzai, a Pashtun, to continue as leader for that time, but the assembly adjourned without establishing a new parliament. Karzai is said to be highly popular throughout Afghanistan, including among non-Pashtuns.

BACKGROUND TO RECENT DEVELOPMENTS

Afghanistan became unstable in the 1970s as both its Communist Party and its Islamic movement grew in strength and became increasingly bitter opponents of each other.[3] The instability shattered the relative peace and progress that characterized the rule of King Mohammad Zahir Shah, who reigned during 1933 - 1973. Zahir Shah was the last King in Afghanistan's monarchy, which was founded in 1747 by Ahmad Shah Durrani. Prior to the founding of the monarchy, Afghanistan did not exist as a distinct political entity, but was a territory inhabited by tribes and tribal confederations often linked to neighboring nations. Zahir Shah was the only surviving son of King Mohammad Nadir Shah (1929-1933), whose rule followed that of King Amanullah Khan (1919-1929), after a brief rule in 1919 by a Tajik strongman named Bacha-i-Saqqo. King Amanullah Khan launched attacks on British forces in Afghanistan shortly after taking power and won complete independence from Britain as recognized in the Treaty of Rawalpindi (August 8, 1919). He was considered a secular modernizer and who presided over a government in which all ethnic minorities participated.

Zahir Shah is remembered fondly by many older Afghans for promulgating a constitution in 1964 that established a national legislature and promoting freedoms for women, including freeing them from the veil. However, possibly believing that doing so would enable him to limit Soviet support for communist factions in Afghanistan, Zahir Shah also entered into a significant political and arms purchase relationship with the Soviet Union.

While undergoing medical treatment in Italy, Zahir Shah was overthrown by his cousin, Mohammad Daoud, a military leader. Daoud established a dictatorship characterized by strong state control over the economy. After taking power in 1978 by overthrowing Daoud, the communists, first under Nur Mohammad Taraki and then under Hafizullah Amin (leader of a rival communist faction who overthrew Taraki in 1979), attempted to impose radical socialist change on a traditional society. The communists tried to redistribute land and bring more women into government positions. These moves spurred recruitment for Islamic parties and their militias opposed to communist ideology. The Soviet Union sent troops into Afghanistan on December 27, 1979 to prevent a seizure of power by the Islamic-oriented militias that later became known as "mujahedin"[4] (Islamic fighters), and thereby keep Afghanistan pro-Soviet. Upon their invasion, the Soviets ousted Hafizullah Amin and installed its local ally, Babrak Karmal, as Afghan president.

After the Soviets occupied Afghanistan, the U.S.-backed mujahedin fought them effectively, and Soviet occupation forces were never able to pacify all areas of the country.

---

[3] For more information, see CRS Report RL31389, *Afghanistan: Challenges and Options for Reconstructing a Stable and Moderate State*, by Richard Cronin; and CRS Report RL31355, *Afghanistan's Path to Reconstruction: Obstacles, Challenges, and Issues for Congress*, by Rhoda Margesson.

[4] The term refers to an Islamic guerrilla; literally "one who fights in the cause of Islam."

The Soviets held major cities, but the outlying mountainous regions remained largely under mujahedin control. The mujahedin benefitted from U.S. weapons and assistance, provided through the Central Intelligence Agency, working closely with Pakistan's Inter-Service Intelligence directorate (ISI). That weaponry included man-portable shoulder-fired anti-aircraft systems called "Stingers," which proved highly effective against Soviet aircraft. The Islamic guerrillas also hid and stored weaponry in a large network of natural and manmade tunnels and caves throughout Afghanistan. The Soviet Union's losses mounted, and domestic opinion shifted against the war. In 1986, perhaps in an effort to signal some flexibility on a possible political settlement, the Soviets replaced Babrak Karmal with the more pliable former director of Afghan intelligence (Khad), Najibullah Ahmedzai (who went by the name Najibullah or, on some occasions, the abbreviated Najib).

On April 14, 1988, the Soviet Union, led by reformist leader Mikhail Gorbachev, agreed to a U.N.-brokered accord (the Geneva Accords) requiring it to withdraw. The Soviet Union completed the withdrawal on February 15, 1989, leaving in place a weak communist government facing a determined U.S. backed mujahedin. A warming of superpower relations moved the United States and Soviet Union to try for a political settlement to the internal conflict. From late 1989, the United States pressed the Soviet Union to agree to a mutual cutoff of military aid to the combatants. The failed August 1991 coup in the Soviet Union reduced Moscow's capability for and interest in supporting communist regimes in the Third World, leading Moscow to agree with Washington on September 13, 1991, to a joint cutoff of military aid to the Afghan combatants.

The State Department has said that a total of about $3 billion in economic and covert military assistance was provided by the U.S. to the Afghan mujahedin from 1980 until the end of the Soviet occupation of Afghanistan in 1989. Press reports and independent experts believe the covert aid program grew from about $20 million per year in FY1980 to about $300 million per year during fiscal years 1986 - 1990. Even before the 1991 U.S.-Soviet agreement on Afghanistan, the Soviet withdrawal had decreased the strategic and political value of Afghanistan and made the Administration and Congress less forthcoming with funding. For FY1991, Congress reportedly cut covert aid appropriations to the mujahedin from $300 million the previous year to $250 million, with half the aid withheld until the second half of the fiscal year. Although the intelligence authorization bill was not signed until late 1991, Congress abided by the aid figures contained in the bill.[5]

With Soviet backing withdrawn, on March 18, 1992, Afghan President Najibullah publicly agreed to step down once an interim government was formed. His announcement set off a wave of regime defections, primarily by Uzbek and Tajik ethnic militias that had previously been allied with the Kabul government, including that of Uzbek militia commander Abdul Rashid Dostam.

Joining with the defectors, prominent mujahedin commander Ahmad Shah Masud (of the Islamic Society, a largely Tajik party headed by Burhannudin Rabbani) sent his fighters into Kabul, paving the way for the installation of a mujahedin regime on April 18, 1992. Masud, nicknamed "Lion of the Panjshir," had earned a reputation as a brilliant strategist by successfully preventing the Soviets from occupying his power base in the Panjshir Valley of northeastern Afghanistan. After failing to flee, Najibullah, his brother, and a few aides

[5] See "Country Fact Sheet: Afghanistan," in *U.S. Department of State Dispatch*. Volume 5, No. 23, June 6, 1994. Page 377.

remained at a U.N. facility in Kabul until the Taliban movement later seized control and hanged them.

Population: 25.8 million
Ethnic Groups: Pashtun 38%; Tajik 25%; Uzbek 6%; Hazara 19%; others 12%
Religions: Sunni Muslim 84%; Shiite Muslim 15%; other 1%
Per Capita Income: $280/yr (World Bank figure)
External Debt: $5.5 billion (1996 est.)
Major Exports: fruits, nuts, carpets
Major Imports: food, petroleum
Source: CIA World Factbook, 2000.

The fall of Najibullah brought the mujahedin parties to power in Afghanistan but also exposed the serious differences among them. Under an agreement among all the major mujahedin parties, Burhannudin Rabbani became President in June 1992, with the understanding that he would leave office in December 1994. His refusal to step down at the end of that time period–on the grounds that political authority would disintegrate in the absence of a clear successor–led many of the other parties to accuse him of monopolizing power. His government faced daily shelling from another mujahedin commander, Pakistan-backed Gulbuddin Hikmatyar, a radical Islamic fundamentalist who headed a faction of Hizb-e-Islami (Islamic Party) and who was nominally the Prime Minister. Hikmatyar was later ousted by the Taliban from his powerbase around Jalalabad despite sharing the Taliban's ideology and Pashtun ethnicity, and he fled to Iran before returning to Afghanistan in early 2002. Four years (1992-1996) of civil war among the mujahedin followed, destroying much of Kabul and creating popular support for the Taliban. In addition, the dominant Pashtun ethnic group accused the Rabbani government of failing to represent all of Afghanistan's ethnic groups, and many Pashtuns allied with the Taliban.

The Rise of The Taliban

The Taliban movement was formed in 1993-1994 by Afghan Islamic clerics and students, many of them former mujahedin who had become disillusioned with continued internal conflict and moved into the western areas of Pakistan to study in Islamic seminaries ("madrassas"). They were mostly ultra-orthodox Sunni Muslims who practice a form of Islam, "Wahhabism," similar to that practiced in Saudi Arabia. The Taliban was composed overwhelmingly of ethnic Pashtuns (Pathans) from rural areas of Afghanistan. Pashtuns constitute a plurality in Afghanistan, accounting for about 38% of Afghanistan's population of about 26 million. Taliban members viewed the Rabbani government as corrupt and responsible for continued civil war in Afghanistan and the deterioration of security in the major cities. With the help of defections by sympathetic mujahedin fighters, the Taliban seized control of the southeastern city of Qandahar in November 1994 and continued to gather strength. The Taliban's early successes encouraged further defections, and by February 1995, it had reached the gates of Kabul, after which an 18-month stalemate around the capital ensued. In September 1995, the Taliban captured Herat province, on the border with Iran, and expelled the pro-Iranian governor of the province, Ismail Khan. In September 1996, a string of Taliban victories east of Kabul led to the withdrawal of the Rabbani government to the Panjshir Valley north of Kabul with most of its heavy weapons; the Taliban took control of Kabul on September 27, 1996.

The Taliban lost much of its international support as its policies unfolded. It imposed strict adherence to Islamic customs in areas it controls, and used harsh punishments, including executions, on transgressors. The Taliban regime made extensive use of its Ministry for the Promotion of Virtue and the Suppression of Vice, a force of religious police officers that often used violence and physical punishments to enforce Islamic laws, customs, and moral regulations. It banned television, popular music, and dancing, and required males to wear beards. It prohibited women from attending school or working outside the home, except in health care.

Mullah Muhammad Umar/Taliban Leaders

During the war against the Soviet Union, Taliban founder Mullah Muhammad Umar fought in the Hizb-e-Islam (Islamic Party) mujahedin party led by Yunis Khalis. During Taliban rule, Mullah Umar held the title of Head of State and Commander of the Faithful. He lost an eye during the anti-Soviet war, rarely appeared in public, and did not take an active role in the day-to-day affairs of governing. However, in times of crisis or to discuss pressing issues, he summoned Taliban leaders to meet with him in Qandahar. Considered a hardliner within the Taliban regime, Mullah Umar forged a close personal bond with bin Laden and was adamantly opposed to handing him over to another country to face justice. Born near Qandahar, Umar is about 52 years old. His ten year old son, as well as his stepfather, reportedly died at the hands of U.S. airstrikes in early October 2001. Umar, having reportedly fled Qandahar city when the Taliban surrendered the city on December 9, 2001, is still at large and believed alive, possibly in his native Uruzgan Province.

Coalescence of the Northern Alliance

The rise of the Taliban movement caused other power centers to make common cause with ousted President Rabbani and commander Ahmad Shah Masud. The individual groups allied with them in a "Northern Alliance." The Persian-speaking core of the Northern Alliance was located not only in the Panjshir Valley of the northeast but also in largely Persian-speaking western Afghanistan near the Iranian border. The fighters in the west were generally loyal to the charismatic Ismail Khan, who regained the governorship of his former stronghold in Herat and surrounding provinces after the Taliban collapse of mid-November 2001.

One non-Tajik component of the Northern Alliance was the ethnic Uzbek militia force (the Junbush-Melli, or National Islamic Movement of Afghanistan) of General Abdul Rashid Dostam. Uzbeks constitute about 6% of the population, compared with 25% that are Tajik. Dostam was best known for his break with Najibullah in early 1992, the key defection that paved the way for the overthrow of the Najibullah regime. He subsequently fought against Rabbani during his presidency in an effort to persuade him to yield power, but then allied with Rabbani and the Northern Alliance when the Taliban took power in Kabul. Dostam once commanded about 25,000 troops, significant amounts of armor and combat aircraft, and even some Scud missiles, but infighting within his faction left him unable to hold off Taliban forces. The Taliban captured his power base in August 1998, leaving him in control of only small areas of northern Afghanistan near the border with Uzbekistan. During the U.S.-led war against the Taliban, he, in concert with a Tajik commander Atta Mohammad and a Shiite Hazara commander Mohammad Mohaqqiq, recaptured Mazar-e-Sharif from the Taliban. There have been tensions among the three in governing the city and its environs since, often resulting in minor clashes. Clashes escalated in July 2002 but were calmed after mediation by the U.N. personnel in Afghanistan (UNAMA, U.N. Assistance Mission in Afghanistan).

Shiite Muslim parties, generally less active against the Soviet occupation than were the Sunni parties, constituted another part of the Northern Alliance. The main Shiite Muslim party is Hizb-e-Wahdat (Unity Party, an alliance of eight Hazara tribe Shiite Muslim groups), which was part of Rabbani's government for most of his rule during 1992-1996. Hizb-e-Wahdat has traditionally received some material support from Iran, which practices Shiism and has an affinity for the Hazaras. Hizb-e-Wahdat forces occasionally retook Bamiyan city from the Taliban but were unable to hold it, until the Taliban collapse of November 2001 in the U.S.-led war.

Another mujahedin party leader, Abd-i-Rab Rasul Sayyaf, heads a Pashtun-dominated faction called the Islamic Union for the Liberation of Afghanistan. Sayyaf lived many years in and is politically close to Saudi Arabia, which shares his interpretation of Sunni Islam. This interpretation ("Wahhabism") was also shared by the Taliban, which partly explains why many of Sayyaf's fighters originally defected to the Taliban movement when that movement was taking power. Although he is a Pashtun, Sayyaf was allied with the Northern Alliance and placed his forces at Alliance disposal. Sayyaf is considered personally close to Rabbani and is reputedly maneuvering in concert with Rabbani for a future leadership role.

Operation Enduring Freedom and Other U.S. Military Activities

The political rivalries among opposition groups long hindered their ability to shake the Taliban's grip on power. In the few years prior to the beginning of the U.S.-led war, the opposition had steadily lost ground, even in areas outside Taliban's Pashtun ethnic base. The losses extended to the point at which the Taliban controlled at least 75% of the country and almost all major provincial capitals. The Northern Alliance suffered a major setback on September 9, 2001, two days before the September 11 attacks that led to the U.S. intervention in Afghanistan, when Ahmad Shah Masud, the undisputed, charismatic military leader of Northern Alliance forces, was assassinated at his headquarters by suicide bombers allegedly linked to Al Qaeda. His successor was his intelligence chief, Muhammad Fahim, who is a veteran commander but lacked the overarching authority or charisma of Masud.

The U.S.-led war in Afghanistan began on October 7, 2001 (Operation Enduring Freedom). The campaign consisted of U.S. airstrikes on Taliban and Al Qaeda forces, coupled with targeting by U.S. special operations forces working in Afghanistan with the Northern Alliance and other anti-Taliban forces. Taliban control of the north collapsed first, followed by its control of southern Afghanistan, which it progressively lost to pro-U.S. Pashtun forces, such as those of Hamid Karzai, who is now President. Karzai, the 46 year old leader of the powerful Popolzai tribe of Pashtuns, had entered Afghanistan in October 2001 to organize Pashtun resistance to the Taliban, and he was supported in that effort by U.S. special forces. By the time the Taliban had been defeated, Northern Alliance forces controlled about 70% of Afghanistan, including Kabul, which they captured on November 12, 2001. Groups of Pashtun commanders took control of cities and provinces in the east and south. One example is Ghul Agha Shirzai, now the governor of Qandahar province and environs.

Despite the overwhelming defeat of the Taliban, small Taliban and Al Qaeda groups reportedly continue to operate throughout Afghanistan. The United States has about 9,000 troops in and around Afghanistan, and coalition forces are contributing another 8,000, including those in the International Security Assistance Force (ISAF). In late September 2002, the top U.S. commander in Afghanistan said that as many as 1,000 Al Qaeda might still be active inside Afghanistan, suggesting there is still substantial work left to do to eliminate the Al Qaeda presence. The United States and its Afghan allies conducted "Operation Anaconda" in the Shah-i-Kot Valley south of Gardez during March 2 - 19, 2002, to eliminate a pocket of as many as 800 Al Qaeda and Taliban fighters. In late March 2003, about 1,000 U.S. troops launched a raid on suspected Taliban or Al Qaeda fighters in villages around Qandahar. There were also reports in early March 2003 that U.S. special forces were conducting a hunt in Afghanistan and over the border into Pakistan to search for Al Qaeda leader Osama Bin Laden, identified by the Bush Administration as the main organizer of the September 11 attacks. He escaped the U.S.-Afghan offensive against the Al Qaeda stronghold of Tora Bora in eastern Afghanistan in December 2001, but new reports of his possible locations surfaced following the arrest on March 2, 2003 of top Al Qaeda planner Khalid Shaikh Mohammed.

U.S. forces are increasingly focused on locating and combating forces loyal to former mujahedin leader Gulbuddin Hikmatyar (see above). Hikmatyar has allied with and tried to rally Taliban and Al Qaeda remnants against U.S. forces and the Karzai government. On February 19, 2003, the U.S. government formally designated Hikmatyar as a "Specially Designated Global Terrorist," under the authority of Executive Order 13224. That order subjected named terrorists and terrorist-related institutions to financial and other U.S. sanctions.

Provincial Reconstruction Teams

As the frequency and intensity of combat has decreased since early 2002, the U.S. military is increasingly focusing its operations on ensuring political stability. In mid-December 2002, the Defense Department said it would focus increased attention to creating secure conditions for aid workers. The plan unveiled is to create 8-10 "Provincial Reconstruction Teams" (PRTs) composed of U.S. forces, Defense Department civil affairs officers, and representatives of U.S. aid and other agencies. The objective of the PRTs is to provide safe havens for international aid workers to help with reconstruction and to extend the writ of the Kabul government throughout Afghanistan. At least three PRTs have begun operations at Gardez, Bamiyan, and Konduz.

The creation of the PRTs appeared intended, in part, to deflect criticism that the United States is paying insufficient attention to reconstruction and as an alternative to expanding ISAF (see below). Fears of terrorism and instability were increased significantly on September 5, 2002. That day, there was a car bombing in a crowded marketplace in Kabul, and an assassination attempt against President Karzai. Karzai was unhurt and the assailant, a member of the security detail, was killed by U.S. special forces who serve as Karzai's protection unit. Afghan officials blamed Taliban/Al Qaeda remnants for both events. Employees of a private U.S. security contractor (Dyncorp) have taken over the Afghan leadership protection effort as of November 2002.

War-Related Casualties

No reliable Afghan casualty figures for the war on the Taliban and Al Qaeda have been announced, but estimates by researchers of Afghan civilian deaths generally cite figures of "several hundred" civilian deaths. On July 1, 2002, a U.S. airstrike on suspected Taliban leaders in Uruzgan Province, the home province of Taliban head Mullah Umar, mistakenly killed about 40 civilians. According to CENTCOM, as of May 24, 2002, 37 U.S. servicepersons were killed, including from enemy fire, friendly fire, and non-hostile deaths (accidents). Of coalition forces, 4 Canadian and 1 Australian military personnel were killed in hostile circumstances. In addition, according to CENTCOM, there have been ten U.S. deaths in the Philippines theater of Operation Enduring Freedom (operations against the Al Qaeda-affiliated Abu Sayyaf organization), all of which resulted from a helicopter crash.

Political Settlement Efforts and the Post-Taliban Government

The war against Al Qaeda and the Taliban paved the way for a pre-existing U.N. effort to form a broad-based Afghan government to bear fruit, although substantial instability remains.

Pre-September 11 U.N. Mediation

For the 8 years prior to the U.S.-led war, the United States worked primarily through the United Nations to end the Afghan civil conflict, because the international body was viewed as a credible mediator by all sides. It was the forum used for ending the Soviet occupation. However, some observers criticized U.S. policy as being insufficiently engaged in Afghan mediation to bring about a settlement. After the fall of Najibullah in 1992, a succession of U.N. mediators – former Tunisian Foreign Minister Mahmoud Mestiri (March 1994-July 1996); German diplomat Norbert Holl (July 1996- December 1997); and Algeria's former Foreign Minister Lakhdar Brahimi (August 1997-October 1999) – sought to arrange a ceasefire, and ultimately a peaceful transition to a broad-based government. The proposed process for arranging a transition incorporated many ideas advanced by former King Zahir Shah and outside experts, in which a permanent government was to be chosen through a traditional Afghan selection process, the hallmark of which was to be the holding of a *loya jirga*, a grand assembly of notable Afghans. These U.N. efforts, at times, appeared to make significant progress, but ceasefires and other agreements between the warring factions always broke down. Brahimi suspended his activities in frustration in October 1999, and another U.N. mediator, Spanish diplomat Fransesc Vendrell, was appointed.

The "Six Plus Two" and Geneva Contact Groups

In coordination with direct U.N. mediation efforts, the "Six Plus Two" contact group began meeting in early 1997; the group consisted of the United States, Russia, and the six states bordering Afghanistan: Iran, China, Pakistan, Turkmenistan, Uzbekistan, and

Tajikistan. The group was created following informal meetings of some of the key outside parties, in which the United States and others agreed not to provide weapons to the warring factions. (In June 1996, the Administration formally imposed a ban on U.S. sales of arms to all factions in Afghanistan, a policy already that had been already in place less formally.[6]) In 2000, possibly because of the lack of progress in the Six Plus Two process, another contact group began meeting in Geneva, and with more frequency than the Six Plus Two. The Geneva grouping included Italy, Germany, Iran, and the United States. Another Afghan-related grouping multilateral mediating grouping consisted of some Islamic countries operating under the ad-hoc "Committee on Afghanistan" under the auspices of the Organization of Islamic Conference (OIC). The countries in that ad-hoc committee include Pakistan, Iran, Guinea, and Tunisia.

King Zahir Shah and the Loya Jirga *Processes*

During the period of Taliban rule, the United States also supported initiatives coming from Afghans inside Afghanistan and in exile. During 1997, Afghans not linked to any of the warring factions began a new peace initiative called the Intra Afghan Dialogue. This grouping, consisting of former mujahedin commanders and clan leaders, held meetings during 1997 and 1998 in Bonn, Frankfurt, Istanbul, and Ankara. Another group, based on the participation of former King Zahir Shah, was centered in Rome ("Rome Grouping"), where the former King lived. A third grouping, calling itself the "Cyprus Process," consisted of former Afghan officials and other Afghan exiles generally sympathetic to Iran, including a relative of Gulbuddin Hikmatyar.

Post-September 11 Efforts

The September 11 attacks and the start of U.S. military action against the Taliban injected new urgency into the search for a government that might replace the Taliban. In late September 2001, Brahimi was brought back as the U.N. representative to help arrange an alternative government, an effort that, it was hoped, would encourage defections within Taliban ranks and hasten its demise. On November 14, 2001, the U.N. Security Council adopted Resolution 1378, calling for a "central" U.N. role in establishing a transitional administration and inviting member states to send peacekeeping forces to promote stability and secure the delivery of humanitarian assistance.

Many of the hopes for a post-Taliban government at first appeared to center on the former King. A 2-day (October 25-26, 2001) meeting of more than 700 Afghan tribal elders in Peshawar, Pakistan ("Peshawar Grouping") issued a concluding statement calling for the return of the former King. However, neither the King's representatives nor those of the Northern Alliance attended the gathering, instead airing suspicions that the meeting was orchestrated by Pakistan for its own ends.

Bonn Conference/Interim Government

In late November 2001, after Kabul had already fallen (November 12, 2001), delegates of the major Afghan factions – most prominently the Northern Alliance and representatives of

---

[6] *Federal Register*, Volume 61, No. 125, June 27, 1996. Page 33313.

the former King – gathered in Bonn, Germany, at the invitation of the United Nations. The Taliban was not invited. On December 5, 2001, the factions signed an agreement to form a 30-member interim administration, to govern until the holding in June 2002 of a *loya jirga*, to be opened by the former King. The *loya jirga* would then choose a new government to run Afghanistan for the next two years until a new constitution is drafted and national elections held. The *loya jirga* also would establish a 111- member parliament. According to the Bonn agreement, the new government was to operate under the constitution of 1964 until a new constitution is adopted. The last *loya jirga* that was widely recognized as legitimate was held in 1964 to ratify a constitution. Communist leader Najibullah convened a *loya jirga* in 1987 largely to approve his policies; that gathering was widely viewed by Afghans as illegitimate.

The Bonn agreement also provided for an international peace keeping force to maintain security, at least in Kabul. Northern Alliance forces were to withdraw from Kabul, according to the Bonn agreement, but forces under the command of Defense Minister Fahim have remain garrisoned there. The Bonn conference's conclusions were endorsed by U.N. Security Council Resolution 1385 (December 6, 2001), and the international peacekeeping force was authorized by Security Council Resolution 1386, adopted December 20, 2001. (For text of the Bonn agreement, see [http://www.uno.de/frieden/afghanistan/talks/agreement.htm].)

At the Bonn meeting, Hamid Karzai was selected chairman of the interim administration, which governed from December 22, 2001, until the end of the *loya jirga*. However, Karzai presided over a cabinet in which a slight majority (17 out of 30) of the positions were held by the Northern Alliance, with this block holding the key posts of Defense (Mohammad Fahim), Foreign Affairs (Dr. Abdullah Abdullah), and Interior (Yunus Qanuni). The three are ethnic Tajiks, with the exception of Dr. Abdullah, who is half Tajik and half Pashtun. This trio, all of whom are in their mid- 40s and were close aides to Ahmad Shah Masud, was considered generally well disposed toward the United States, although they also have ties to Iran and Russia, and all three are suspicious of Pakistan.

The Loya Jirga

In late January 2002, the 21 members of the commission, including two women, were chosen to prepare for the *loya jirga*. In preparation for the assembly, the former King returned to Afghanistan on April 18, 2002, and he conducted meetings with Afghan notables and local leaders. By the beginning of June, 381 districts of Afghanistan had chosen the 1,550 delegates to the *loya jirga*. About two hundred of the delegates were women.

On the first day of the *loya jirga* (June 11, 2002), the former King and Burhannudin Rabbani withdrew from leadership consideration and endorsed interim government chairman Hamid Karzai to continue as Afghanistan's leader. Their withdrawals, reportedly urged or supported by the United States, paved the way for Karzai's selection as leader by the *loya jirga* delegates over two other candidates, one of whom was a woman. On June 13, 2002, by an overwhelming margin, the *loya jirga* selected Karzai to lead Afghanistan until the elections by June 2004. On its last day, June 19, 2002, the assembly approved Karzai's new cabinet, which included three vice presidents and several "presidential advisors" in an effort to balance the ethnic and factional composition of the government. However, the *loya jirga* adjourned without establishing the new parliament; a group of experts has remained in Kabul to continue working on the parliament, with no decision to date. The experts reportedly are considering forming a 93-member national assembly, with no party affiliations represented.

The assembly will be temporary, and would be replaced by a new body chosen in June 2004 national elections.

In the cabinet endorsed by the *loya jirga*, Karzai moved Yunus Qanooni to head the Ministry of Education and serve as an adviser on security. He was replaced as Interior Minister by Taj Mohammad Wardak, a Pashtun. Abdullah and Fahim retained their positions, with Fahim acquiring the additional title of vice president.

Other notable changes to the government made by the *loya jirga* include the following:

- Ashraf Ghani replaced Hedayat Amin Arsala as Finance Minister (see below). Ghani is a Pashtun with ties to international financial institutions.
- The new Minister of Women's Affairs is Habiba Sorabi, replacing Sima Samar.
- Hajji Abdul Qadir, a Pashtun, who is also governor of Nangahar Province, switched portfolios to head the Ministry of Public Works. He had headed the Ministry of Urban Affairs in the interim government. He was also appointed a vice president. However, Abdul Qadir was assassinated by unknown gunmen on July 6. Hedayat Amin Arsala was appointed a Vice President to replace Qadir. Arsala, a former World Bank official, is a supporter of the former King and a relative of Pir Ahmad Gaylani, leader of a pro-King mujahedin faction during the anti-Soviet war.
- The third vice president appointed was Karim Khalili, the leader of a faction of the Hazara Shiite party Hizb-e-Wahdat.
- Herat leader Ismail Khan was given no formal post; he preferred to remain in his locality rather than take a position in the central government in Kabul. His son, Mir Wais Saddiq was retained in the new cabinet, heading the Ministry of Civil Aviation and Tourism. (He headed the Ministry of Labor and Social Affairs in the interim government.)
- Dostam was given no formal post, although he served as deputy Defense Minister in the interim administration. Dostam said in early August 2002 that he prefers to remain in his northern stronghold rather than accept a post that would bring him to Kabul.
- A national security council was formed as an advisory body to Karzai. The intention in establishing this council is to increase Kabul's decisionmaking power and extend central government influence. The national security adviser is Zalmai Rasool.

There have been reports of strain between Karzai and Fahim, who continues to dominate most of the armed force in Afghanistan. U.S. envoy Khalilzad visited Kabul in August 2002 to try to ease these tensions, with some signs of success, at least for the current time. Some of the reports of strains surfaced after Karzai replaced his Afghan bodyguard force with U.S. special forces, shortly after the assassination of Abd al Qadir. The bodyguard switch suggested to some Afghans that Karzai did not trust Fahim's forces to protect him or the interests of Afghanistan as a whole. As noted above, Fahim did not withdraw his forces from Kabul and was said to oppose the formation of a national army, although he now reportedly accepts that army. U.S. officials have said they are trying to persuade Fahim to pull his forces out of Kabul, as required in the Bonn agreement.

International Security Force (ISAF)

The International Security Assistance Force (ISAF) created by the Bonn agreement has reached its agreed strength of over 4,900. It was headed until December 20, 2002 by Turkey, which replaced Britain as the lead force following the *loya jirga*. Since then, Germany and the Netherlands have assumed command for the December 20, 2002- December 20, 2003 period. The force is operating in conjunction with Afghan security forces in Kabul and is coordinating, to an extent, with U.S. military forces in and immediately around Afghanistan.

As of August 2002, ISAF has forces from the following 18 countries: Austria (71 troops), Belgium (19), Bulgaria (32), Czech Republic (132), Denmark (36), Finland (31), France (520), Germany (1121), Greece (163), Ireland (7), Italy (403), the Netherlands (232), New Zealand (8), Norway (17), Romania (155), Spain (349), Sweden (38), Turkey (1322), and the United Kingdom (426). Germany will roughly double its troop commitment now that it has assumed co-command of ISAF.

Because of several threats to Afghanistan's internal security since the interim government was constituted, Afghan officials wanted ISAF to be expanded and deploy to other major cities. The Bush Administration favored its own alternative plan to help build an Afghan national army rather than expand ISAF, but the Administration has recently expressed support for an expansion if enough troops are contributed to it.

Afghan National Army

U.S. special forces have begun training the new national army, and the first 3,000 have completed training as of late March 2003. In early December 2002, the first recruits began training as a battalion, according to the Defense Department, and deployed to eastern Afghanistan to fight alongside U.S. and coalition forces. They performed well, by all accounts, and were welcomed by the local population as a symbol of a unified future for Afghanistan. Afghan officials say the desired size of the army is 70,000, a level that will likely not be reached for several more years, at the current rate of U.S.-led training, but the Department of Defense envisions training up to 14,400 Afghan troops by the end of 2003 at a cost, including establishing a general staff and a headquarters staff, of about $135 million.[7] Thus far, its weaponry has come primarily from Defense Ministry weapons stocks, with the concurrence of Defense Minister Fahim who controls those stocks. The United States plans to provide some additional U.S. arms and/or defense services to the national army, according to statements by U.S. officials. In November 2002, at U.S. urging, Albania sent surplus light weaponry to the national army.

There has been some concern that Vice President/Defense Minister General Fahim has weighted the recruitment of the national army to favor his Tajik ethnic base. In the early stages of the training program, many Pashtuns, in reaction, refused recruitment or left the national army program, although U.S. officials say this problem has been alleviated recently

[7] Briefing Slides Prepared by the National Defense University, Institute for National Strategic Studies, for J-5 of the Department of Defense Joint Staff. June 2002.

with somewhat better pay and more involvement by U.S. special forces.[8] Fully trained recruits are paid about $70 per month.

New Governmental Authority

The Afghan national army is one key component in the attempts by the U.S. government and the Afghan government to expand central governmental capabilities, guide reconstruction efforts, and bring security to all parts of Afghanistan. The U.S. is hoping to attract to the national army young fighters who are now part of regional militias not linked to the central government. Japan is the government assisting the effort to demobilize regional and ethnic-affiliated militias. Afghan officials say that a key to demobilization is to find Afghanistan's young men alternate employment so that they no longer need to rely on the pay they receive to serve in armies maintained by the regional leaders around Afghanistan. In August 2002, Karzai threatened to send Afghan central government forces to combat a rebellious local leader in Paktia province, Padsha Khan Zadran, but no fighting ensued. In early November 2002, Karzai fired 15 provincial officials, partly in an attempt to establish the primacy of the central government, although many remain at their jobs. That same month, police in Kabul suppressed student riots at Kabul University; they were protesting poor dormitory facilities.

Karzai has sought and received some international funds to pay government workers who had not been paid in many months. At a meeting on October 13, 2002, international donors applauded Afghanistan's budgetary and reconstruction plans. The national airline, Ariana, also has resumed some operations, although its fleet is very small. On March 23, 2002, schools reopened following the Persian/Afghan new year (Nowruz). Girls returned to the schools for the first time since the Taliban came to power, and a total of 3 million children have returned to school since the fall of the Taliban.

Since the establishment of the interim government, several countries have reopened embassies in Kabul, including the United States. In conjunction with the formation of the interim administration, NSC official Zalmay Khalilzad was appointed a special envoy to Afghanistan in December 2001 and has made several extended visits there. In late March 2002, a U.S. Ambassador to Afghanistan, Robert Finn, was sworn in Kabul. The new Afghan government has reopened the Afghan embassy in Washington and a new ambassador, U.S.-educated and U.S.-based energy entrepreneur Ishaq Shahryar, has taken office. He previously was an adviser to former King Zahir Shah.

REGIONAL CONTEXT[9]

Even before September 11, several of Afghanistan's neighbors were becoming alarmed about threats to their own security interests emanating from Afghanistan. All of these governments endorsed the Bonn agreement, but some experts believe that the neighboring governments will likely attempt, over the long term, to manipulate Afghanistan's factions and

[8] Gall, Carlotta. In a Remote Corner, an Afghan Army Evolves From Fantasy to Slightly Ragged Reality. *New York Times*, January 25, 2003.

[9] For further information, see CRS Report RS20411, *Afghanistan: Connections to Islamic Movements in Central and South Asia and Southern Russia*. December 7, 1999, by Kenneth Katzman.

its political structure to their advantage. On December 23, 2002, Afghanistan and its six neighbors signed a non-interference pledge (Kabul Declaration).

Pakistan[10]

Pakistan reversed its position on the Taliban in the aftermath of the September 11 attacks. Pakistan initially saw the Taliban movement as an instrument with which to fulfill its goals. Those goals traditionally have been to seek an Afghan central government strong enough to prevent calls for unity between ethnic Pashtuns in Afghanistan and Pakistan, while at the same time sufficiently friendly and pliable to provide Pakistan strategic depth against rival India. In the wake of the Soviet pullout in 1989, Pakistan was troubled by continued political infighting in Afghanistan that was enabling drug trafficking to flourish and to which Afghan refugees did not want to return. Pakistan saw Afghanistan as essential to opening up trade relations and energy routes with the Muslim states of the former Soviet Union.

Pakistan was the most public defender of the Taliban movement and was one of only three countries (Saudi Arabia and the United Arab Emirates are the others) to formally recognize it as the legitimate government. Prior to the September 11 attacks, the government of General Pervez Musharraf, who took power in an October 1999 coup, resisted U.S. pressure to forcefully intercede with the Taliban leadership to achieve bin Laden's extradition. Pakistan's links to the Taliban, and the Taliban's hosting of Al Qaeda terrorist leader Osama bin Laden, were a major focus of a visit to Pakistan by Undersecretary of State Thomas Pickering in May 2000, but Pakistan made no commitments to help the United States on that issue. U.N. Security Council Resolution 1333, of December 19, 2000, was partly an effort by the United States and Russia to compel Pakistan to cease military advice and aid to the Taliban. Pakistan did not completely cease military assistance, but it abided by some provisions of the resolution, for example by ordering the Taliban to cut the staff at its embassy in Pakistan.[11] Prior to the September 11 terrorist attacks in the United States, Pakistan had said it would cooperate with a follow-on U.N. Security Council Resolution (1363 of July 30, 2001) that provided for U.N. border monitors to ensure that no neighboring state was providing military equipment or advice to the Taliban.

Pakistan's modest pre-September 11 steps toward cooperation with the United States reflected increasing wariness that the Taliban movement was radicalizing existing Islamic movements inside Pakistan. Pakistan also feared that its position on the Taliban was propelling the United States into a closer relationship with Pakistan's arch-rival, India. These considerations, coupled with U.S. pressure as well as offers of economic benefit, prompted Pakistan to cooperate with the U.S. response to the September 11 attacks. Pakistan provided the United States with requested access to Pakistani airspace, ports, airfields. Pakistan also arrested hundreds of Al Qaeda fighters fleeing Afghanistan and turned them over to the United States and deployed substantial forces to the Afghan border to capture Al Qaeda fighters attempting to flee into Pakistan. Pakistani authorities helped the United States track and capture top bin Laden aide Abu Zubaydah in early April 2002, alleged September 11 plotter Ramzi bin Al Shibh (captured September 11, 2002), and top Al Qaeda planner Khalid

[10] For further discussion, see Rashid, Ahmed. "The Taliban: Exporting Extremism." *Foreign Affairs,* November - December 1999.

[11] Constable, Pamela. New Sanctions Strain Taliban-Pakistan Ties. *Washington Post*, January 19, 2001.

Shaikh Mohammed (March 2, 2003). Pakistani forces reportedly are helping the United States track and fight Al Qaeda forces along the Pakistan-Afghanistan border.

At the same time, Pakistan has sought to protect its interests by fashioning a strong Pashtun-based component for a post-Taliban government. Pakistan was wary that a post-Taliban government dominated by the Northern Alliance, which is backed by India, and it is. Some Afghan officials are concerned about the implications for the new Afghan government of the election gains of some pro-Taliban parties in Pakistan's October 2002 parliamentary elections; those parties did well in districts that border Afghanistan.

As of October 2002, about 1.75 million Afghan refugees have returned from Pakistan since the Taliban fell. About 300,000 Afghan refugees remain in Pakistan.

Iran

Iran's key national interests in Afghanistan are to exert influence over western Afghanistan, which Iran borders and was once part of the Persian empire, and to protect Afghanistan's Shiite minority. Iran strongly supported the Northern Alliance and its Tajik (Persian-speaking) leaders who have traditionally been strong in western Afghanistan as well as northern Afghanistan. Since Taliban forces ousted Ismail Khan from Herat (the western province that borders Iran) in September 1995, Iran has seen the Taliban movement as a threat to its interests in Afghanistan. After that time, Iran provided fuel, funds, and ammunition to the Northern Alliance[12] and hosted fighters loyal to Khan, who was captured by the Taliban in 1998 but escaped and fled to Iran in March 2000. In September 1998, Iranian and Taliban forces nearly came into direct conflict when Iran discovered that nine of its diplomats were killed in the course of Taliban's offensive in northern Afghanistan. Iran massed forces at the border and threatened military action, but the crisis cooled without a major clash, possibly because Iran lacked confidence in its military capabilities.

The United States and Iran have long had common positions on Afghanistan, despite deep U.S.-Iran differences on other issues. U.S. officials have long acknowledged working with Tehran, under the auspices of the Six Plus Two contact group and Geneva group. Iran has confirmed that it offered search and rescue assistance in Afghanistan, and it also allowed U.S. humanitarian aid to the Afghan people to transit Iran. On the other hand, some Iranian leaders were harshly critical of U.S. military action against the Taliban.

Amid reports Iran seeks to exert influence over the new government by arming pro-Iranian Afghan factions, in early January 2002 President Bush warned Iran against meddling in Afghanistan. The President listed Iran as part of an "axis of evil" in his January 29, 2002 State of the Union message, partly because of Iran's actions in Afghanistan. Since then, the Bush Administration has continued to accuse Iran of trying to build influence over the interim government and of failing to attempt to locate or arrest Al Qaeda fighters who have fled to Iran from Afghanistan. Partly in response to the U.S. criticism, in February 2002 Iran expelled Karzai-opponent Gulbuddin Hikmatyar, although it did not arrest him and allowed him to return to Afghanistan. For his part, Karzai has said that Iran is an important neighbor of Afghanistan and visited Iran in late February 2002, pledging to build ties with the Islamic

[12] Steele, Jonathon, "America Includes Iran In Talks On Ending War In Afghanistan." *Washington Times*, December 15, 1997. A14.

republic. Saudi Arabia said in early August 2002 that Iran had turned over to Saudi Arabia several Al Qaeda fighters located and arrested in Iran.

As of October 2002, about 275,000 Afghan refugees have returned from Iran since the Taliban fell. About 1.2 million remain, many of which are integrated into Iranian society.

Russia

A number of considerations might explain why Russia supported the U.S. effort against the Taliban and Al Qaeda, including the use of bases in Central Asia to conduct the war. Russia's main objective in Afghanistan has been to prevent the further strengthening of Islamic or nationalist movements in the Central Asian states or Islamic enclaves in Russia itself, including Chechnya. Russia's fear became acute following an August 1999 incursion into Russia's Dagestan region by Islamic guerrillas from neighboring Chechnya. Some reports link at least one faction of the guerrillas to Al Qaeda.[13] This faction was led by a Chechen of Arab origin who is referred to by the name "Hattab" (full name is Ibn al-Khattab), although there are some reports Russia may have killed him in Chechnya in 2002. In January 2000, the Taliban became the only government in the world to recognize Chechnya's independence, and some Chechen fighters integrated into Taliban/Al Qaeda forces were captured or killed during Operation Enduring Freedom.

The U.S. and Russian positions on Afghanistan became coincident well before the September 11 attacks.[14] Even before the U.S.-led war, Russia was supporting the Northern Alliance with some military equipment and technical assistance.[15] U.S.- Russian cooperation led to the passage of U.N. Security Council Resolution 1267 and 1233 (see section on "Harboring of Al Qaeda"). On the other hand, the United States has not blindly supported Russia's apparent attempts to place a large share of the blame for the rebellion in Chechnya on the Taliban and Al Qaeda. Some outside experts believe that Russia exaggerated the threat emanating from Afghanistan in an effort to persuade the Central Asian states to rebuild closer defense ties to Moscow and to justify its actions in Chechnya.

Central Asian States[16]

During Taliban rule, leaders in Uzbekistan, Tajikistan, and Kyrgyzstan grew increasingly alarmed that Central Asian radical Islamic movements were receiving safe haven in Afghanistan. In 1996, several of these states banded together with Russia and China into a regional grouping called the Shanghai Cooperation Organization to discuss the threat emanating from Afghanistan's Taliban regime. The organization groups China, Russia, Uzbekistan, Tajikistan, Kazakhstan, and Kyrgyzstan. Of the Central Asian states that border Afghanistan, two of them – Uzbekistan and Tajikistan – had seen themselves as particularly vulnerable to militants harbored by the Taliban. Uzbekistan saw its ally, Abdul Rashid Dostam, the Uzbek commander in northern Afghanistan, lose most of his influence in 1998.

[13] Whittell, Giles. "Bin Laden Link To Dagestan Rebel Fightback." *London Times*, September 6, 1999.

[14] Constable, Pamela. "Russia, U.S. Converge on Warnings to Taliban." *Washington Post*, June 4, 2000.

[15] Risen, James. "Russians Are Back in Afghanistan, Aiding Rebels." *New York Times*, July 27, 1998.

[16] For further information, see CRS Report RL30294. *Central Asia's Security: Issues and Implications for U.S. Interests*. December 7, 1999.

Prior to the U.S. war on the Taliban and Al Qaeda, Uzbek officials had said that more active support from Uzbekistan would not necessarily have enabled Dostam to overturn Taliban control of the north.[17]

Uzbekistan has long asserted that the group Islamic Movement of Uzbekistan (IMU), allegedly responsible for four simultaneous February 1999 bombings in Tashkent that nearly killed President Islam Karimov, is linked to Al Qaeda.[18] One of its leaders, Juma Namangani, reportedly was killed while commanding Taliban/Al Qaeda forces in the battle for Mazar-e-Sharif in November 2001. Uzbekistan was highly supportive of the United States in the wake of the September 11 attacks and placed military facilities at U.S. disposal for use in the combat against the Taliban and Al Qaeda. About 1,000 U.S. troops from the 10th Mountain Division, as well as U.S. aircraft, have been based at the Khanabad/Karsi air base there. Following the fall of the Taliban, in December 2001 Uzbekistan reopened the Soviet-built "Friendship Bridge" over the Amu Darya river in order to facilitate the flow of aid into Uzbekistan. Uzbek officials in Tashkent told CRS in May 2002 that the defeat of the Taliban has made them less anxious about the domestic threat from the IMU, and press reports say the IMU has been severely weakened by its war defeats and Namangani's death.

Tajikistan feared that its buffer with Afghanistan would disappear if the Taliban defeated the Northern Alliance, whose territorial base borders Tajikistan. Some of the IMU members based in Afghanistan, including Namangani, fought alongside the Islamic opposition United Tajik Opposition (UTO) during the 1994-1997 civil war in that country. Tajikistan, heavily influenced by Russia, whose 25,000 troops guards the border with Afghanistan, initially sent mixed signals on the question of whether it would give the United States the use of military facilities in Tajikistan. However, on September 26, 2001, Moscow officially endorsed the use by the United States of three air bases in Tajikistan, paving the way for Tajikistan to open facilities for U.S. use, which it did formally offer in early November 2001.

Kazakhstan and Kyrgyzstan do not directly border Afghanistan. However, IMU guerrillas have transited Kyrgyzstan during past incursions into Uzbekistan.[19] Kazakhstan had begun to diplomatically engage the Taliban over the year prior to the September 11 attacks, but it publicly supported the U.S. war effort against the Taliban. In early December 2001, Kyrgyzstan offered to host U.S. warplanes, and U.S. and French aircraft, including U.S. Marine F-18 strike aircraft, have been using part of the international airport at Manas (Peter J. Ganci base) as a base for combat flights in Afghanistan.[20] Kyrgyzstan said in March 2002 that there is no time limit on the U.S. use of military facilities there; French aircraft withdrew in September 2002 as the war wound down. Kazakhstan signed an agreement with the United States in July 2002 to allow coalition aircraft to use Kazakhstan's airports in case of an emergency or short term need related to the ongoing war in Afghanistan.

Of the Central Asian states that border Afghanistan, only Turkmenistan chose to seek close relations with the Taliban leadership, possibly viewing engagement as a more effective means of preventing spillover of radical Islamic activity from Afghanistan. Turkmenistan's leadership also saw Taliban control as bringing the peace and stability that would permit construction of a natural gas pipeline from Turkmenistan through Afghanistan, which would help Turkmenistan bring its large gas reserves to world markets. However, the September 11

---

[17] CRS conversations with Uzbek government officials in Tashkent. April 1999.
[18] The IMU was named a foreign terrorist organization by the State Department in September 2000.
[19] *Patterns of Global Terrorism: 1999*, pp. 14, 92.
[20] Some information based on CRS visit to the Manas facility in Kyrgyzstan, May 2002.

events stoked Turkmenistan's fears of the Taliban and its Al Qaeda guests and the country politically supported the U.S. anti-terrorism effort. There are no indications the United States requested basing rights in Turkmenistan.

China

China has a small border with a sliver of Afghanistan known as the "Wakhan corridor" (see map) and had become increasingly concerned about the potential for Al Qaeda to promote Islamic fundamentalism among Muslims (Uighurs) in northwestern China. A number of Uighurs fought in Taliban and Al Qaeda ranks in the U.S.-led war. China expressed its concern through active membership in the Shanghai Cooperation Organization, as noted above. In December 2000, sensing China's increasing concern about Taliban policies, a Chinese official delegation met with Mullah Umar at the Taliban's invitation.

Although it has long been concerned about the threat from the Taliban and bin Laden, China did not, at first, enthusiastically support U.S. military action against the Taliban. Many experts believe this is because China, as a result of strategic considerations, was wary of a U.S. military buildup on its doorstep. China is an ally with Pakistan, in part to balance out India, which China sees as a rival. Pakistan's cooperation with the United States appears to have allayed China's opposition to U.S. military action, and President Bush has praised China's cooperation with the antiterrorism effort in his meetings with senior leaders of China.

Saudi Arabia

During the Soviet occupation, Saudi Arabia channeled hundreds of millions of dollars to the Afghan resistance, and particularly to hardline Sunni Muslim fundamentalist resistance leaders. Saudi Arabia, which itself practices the strict Wahhabi brand of Islam practiced by the Taliban, was one of three countries to formally recognize the Taliban government. (The others are Pakistan and the United Arab Emirates.) The Taliban initially served Saudi Arabia as a potential counter to Iran, with which Saudi Arabia has been at odds since Iran's 1979 revolution. However, Iranian-Saudi relations improved dramatically beginning in 1997, and balancing Iranian power ebbed as a factor in Saudi policy toward Afghanistan.

Instead, drawing on its intelligence ties to Afghanistan during the anti-Soviet war, Saudi Arabia worked with Taliban leaders to persuade them to suppress anti-Saudi activities by Al Qaeda. Saudi Arabia apparently believed that Al Qaeda's presence in Afghanistan drew Saudi Islamic radicals away from Saudi Arabia itself and thereby reduced their opportunity to destabilize the Saudi regime. Some press reports indicate that, in late 1998, Saudi and Taliban leaders discussed, but did not agree on, a plan for a panel of Saudi and Afghan Islamic scholars to decide bin Laden's fate. Other reports, however, say that Saudi Arabia refused an offer from Sudan in 1996 to extradite bin Laden to his homeland on the grounds that he could become a rallying point for opposition to the regime. In March 2000 and again in May 2000, the Saudi-based Organization of Islamic Conference (OIC) sponsored indirect peace talks in Saudi Arabia between the warring factions.

According to U.S. officials, Saudi Arabia has generally cooperated with the U.S. war effort. Along with the UAE, Saudi Arabia broke diplomatic relations with the Taliban in late

September 2001. It quietly permitted the United States to use a Saudi base for command of U.S. air operations over Afghanistan, but it did not permit U.S. aircraft to launch strikes on Afghanistan from Saudi bases. The Saudi position has generally been to allow the United States the use of its facilities as long as doing so is not publicly requested or highly publicized.

U.S. POLICY ISSUES

U.S. policy objectives in Afghanistan have long been multifaceted, although in the 3 years prior to the September 11 attacks, U.S. goals had largely narrowed to ending the presence of the Al Qaeda leadership and infrastructure there. Since the Soviet withdrawal, returning peace and stability to Afghanistan has also been a U.S. goal, pursued with varying degrees of intensity. Other longstanding U.S. goals have included an end to discrimination against women and girls, the eradication of narcotics production, and alleviating severe humanitarian difficulties.

The Clinton Administration diplomatically engaged the Taliban movement as it was gathering strength, but U.S. relations with the Taliban deteriorated sharply during the 5 years that the Taliban were in power in Kabul, to the point where the United States and the Taliban were largely adversaries well before the September 11 attacks. Despite the deterioration, Clinton Administration officials including Assistant Secretary of State for South Asian Affairs Karl Inderfurth met periodically with Taliban officials. At the same time, the United States withheld recognition of Taliban as the legitimate government of Afghanistan and formally recognized no faction as the government. Based on the lack of broad international recognition of Taliban, the United Nations seated representatives of the former Rabbani government, not the Taliban. The United States closed its embassy in Kabul in January 1989, just after the Soviet pullout from Afghanistan, and the State Department ordered the Afghan embassy in Washington, D.C. closed in August 1997 because of a power struggle within it between Rabbani and Taliban supporters.

Although press reports in May 2002 said the Bush Administration was considering a plan to give military aid to the Northern Alliance prior to the September 11 attacks, the Bush Administration continued the previous Administration's policy of maintaining a dialogue with the Taliban. In compliance with U.N. Security Council Resolution 1333, in February 2001 the State Department ordered the closing of a Taliban representative office in New York. The Taliban complied with the directive, but its representative, Abdul Hakim Mujahid, continued to operate informally. In March 2001, Bush Administration officials received a Taliban envoy, Rahmatullah Hashemi, to discuss bilateral issues. Three State Department officers visited Afghanistan in April 2001, the first U.S. visit since the August 1998 bombings of the Al Qaeda camps, although the purpose of the visit was described as assessing the humanitarian needs and not furthering U.S.-Taliban relations. As did the executive branch, Congress became highly critical of the Taliban well before the September 11 attacks. A sense of the Senate resolution (S.Res. 275) that resolving the Afghan civil war should be a top U.S. priority passed that chamber by unanimous consent on September 24, 1996. A similar resolution, H.Con.Res. 218, passed the House on April 28, 1998.

After September 11, legislative proposals became significantly more adversarial toward the Taliban. One bill, H.R. 3088, stated that it should be the policy of the United States to remove the Taliban from power and authorized a drawdown of up to $300 million worth of U.S. military supplies and services for the anti-Taliban opposition. The bill, as well as another bill (H.R. 2998, introduced October 2, 2001), established a "Radio Free Afghanistan" broadcasting service under RFE/RL. On February 12, 2002, the House passed the Senate version of H.R. 2998 providing $17 million funding for the radio broadcasts for FY2002. President Bush signed the bill into law on March 11, 2002 (P.L. 107-148).

The following sections discuss major issues in U.S. relations with Afghanistan.

Taliban Harboring of Al Qaeda

Even before the September 11, 2001 attacks, the Taliban's refusal to yield Al Qaeda leader Osama bin Laden to the United States (or a U.S. ally) for trial – and its protection of radical Islamic movements more broadly – had become the overriding bilateral agenda item in U.S. policy toward Afghanistan.[21] Particularly after the August 7, 1998 Al Qaeda bombings of the U.S. embassies in Kenya and Tanzania, the United States had been placing progressively more pressure on the Taliban to extradite bin Laden, adding sanctions, some military action, reported covert intelligence operations, and the threat of further punishments to ongoing diplomatic efforts.

- During his April 1998 visit, Ambassador Richardson asked the Taliban to hand bin Laden over to U.S. authorities, but he was rebuffed.
- On August 20, 1998, the United States fired cruise missiles at alleged bin Laden-controlled terrorist training camps in retaliation for the embassy bombings in Kenya and Tanzania.
- On July 4, 1999, because of the Taliban's hosting of bin Laden, President Clinton issued Executive Order 13129, imposing a ban on U.S. trade with Taliban-controlled portions of Afghanistan and blocking Taliban assets in U.S. financial institutions. The Taliban was not designated as a terrorist group, nor was Afghanistan named a state sponsor of terrorism. On August 10, 1999, the Clinton Administration determined that Ariana Airlines represents Taliban-controlled property, thereby preventing Americans from using the airline and triggering the blocking of about $500,000 in Ariana assets identified in the United States. (President George W. Bush revoked Executive Order 13129 on the grounds that the Taliban government had been dismantled.)
- On October 15, 1999, with Russian support, the United States achieved adoption of U.N. Security Council Resolution 1267, the first U.N. resolution sanctioning the Taliban regime. The resolution banned flights outside Afghanistan by Ariana airlines and directed U.N. member states to freeze Taliban assets. The resolution was in response to the Taliban's refusal to hand bin Laden over to justice, and it threatened further sanctions if it did not do so.

[21] For more information on bin Laden and his Al Qaeda organization, see CRS Report RL31119, *Terrorism: Near Eastern Groups and State Sponsors, 2001, September 10, 2001.* See also CRS Report RS20411, *Afghanistan: Connections to Islamic Movements in Central and South Asia and Southern Russia.*

On December 19, 2000, again by combining diplomatic forces with Russia, the United States achieved adoption of U.N. Security Council Resolution 1333, a followon to Resolution 1267, imposed even stricter sanctions against the Taliban. The major additional provisions of the Resolution included

1. a worldwide prohibition against the provision of arms or military advice to the Taliban and a requirement (directed against Pakistan) that all countries withdraw any military advisers that are helping the Taliban;
2. a call for all countries that recognize the Taliban to reduce the size of Taliban representative missions in their countries, and for all other countries to close completely all Taliban offices and Ariana Afghan airline offices and ban all nonhumanitarian assistance flights into or out of Taliban-controlled Afghanistan;
3. a requirement that all countries freeze any bin Laden/Al Qaeda assets that can be identified;
4. a prohibition on any supply to areas under Taliban control of the chemical acetic anhydride, which is used to produce heroin; and
5. a ban on foreign travel by all Taliban officials at or above the rank of Deputy Minister, except for the purposes of participation in peace negotiations, compliance with the resolution or 1267, or humanitarian reasons, including religious obligations.

On July 30, 2001, the U.N. Security Council adopted an implementing Resolution 1363. The resolution provided for the stationing of monitors in Pakistan, to ensure that no weapons or military advice was being provided by the Taliban. In the aftermath of the Taliban's ouster from power, these provisions were narrowed to focus on Al Qaeda, and not the Taliban, by U.N. Security Council Resolution 1390 of January 17, 2002.

Human Rights/Treatment of Women

Virtually all observers agree that Afghans are freer than they were under the Taliban, although the interim administration is relatively young, and many want to evaluate its human rights practices over a longer period of time. The groups that have assumed power from the Taliban are widely considered far less repressive of women than was the Taliban, although some of the factions now part of the ruling coalition, including the Northern Alliance, have been accused of significant human rights abuses in the past. Since the interim administration took office, there have been some reports of reprisals and other abuses based on ethnicity in certain parts of Afghanistan, particularly against Pashtuns living in largely Tajik and Uzbek northern Afghanistan. Some Afghans say that the Taliban brought order and peace to the areas it captured by disarming independent militiamen and that, to some extent, lawlessness has returned in certain parts of Afghanistan. U.S. officials believe that law and order will improve as the central government extends its writ throughout the country and as economic reconstruction expands.

Some observers say that the new government is reimposing some Islamic restrictions that characterized Taliban rule, including the code of criminal punishments stipulated in Islamic law.[22] Some have blamed the increased restrictions on chief justice Fazl Hadi Shinwari, a religious conservative. On January 21, 2003, Shinwari ordered shut down cable television in Kabul on the grounds it was un-Islamic, and called for an end to co-education. The U.S. government has generally refrained from advising the new government on these issues, lest the United States be accused of undue interference in Kabul's affairs.

Under the new government, women in Kabul are said to be reverting to the less restrictive behavior practiced before the Taliban fled. The burqa is no longer obligatory, although many women continue to wear it by tradition or because of fear or uncertainty of the new government's attitudes on the issue. Two women hold positions in the new government, and many women are returning to the jobs they held before the Taliban came to power. As noted above, girls returned to school March 23, 2002, for the first time since the Taliban took over, and many female teachers have resumed their teaching jobs.

Before the war, there was significant U.S. and U.N. pressure on the Taliban regime to moderate its treatment of women. Several U.N. Security Council resolutions, including 1193 (August 28, 1998), and 1214 (December 8, 1998), urged the Taliban to end discrimination against women. During a November 1997 visit to Pakistan, then Secretary of State Madeleine Albright attacked Taliban policies as despicable and intolerable. U.S. women's rights groups like Feminist Majority and the National Organization for Women (NOW) mobilized to stop the Clinton Administration from recognizing the Taliban government unless it altered its treatment of women. On May 5, 1999, the Senate passed S.Res. 68, a resolution calling on the President not to recognize any Afghan government that refuses to end discrimination against women. On November 27, 2001, the House unanimously adopted S. 1573, the Afghan Women and Children Relief Act, which had earlier passed the Senate. The law (signed December 12, 2001) calls for the use of supplemental funding (appropriated by P.L. 107-38) to fund educational and health programs for Afghan women and children. After the new government took office, the United States and the new Afghan government set up a U.S.-Afghan Women's Council to coordinate the allocation of resources so as to improve the future of Afghan women. It is chaired on the U.S. side by Undersecretary of State for Global Affairs Paula Dobriansky, and on the Afghan side by the Ministers of Foreign Affairs and of Women's Affairs.

Destruction of Buddha Statues/Hindu Badges

The Taliban's critics pointed to its March 2001 destruction of two large Buddha statues, dating to the 7th century, as evidence of the Taliban's excesses. The Taliban claimed it ordered the destruction of the statues, which it considered un-Islamic, after representatives of the United Nations Economic, Social, and Cultural Organization (UNESCO) offered to fund preservation of the statues. Others believe the move was a reaction to new U.N. sanctions imposed in December 2000 (see below). The destruction provoked widespread condemnation, even among other Islamic states, including Pakistan. Some international groups are looking at the possibility of rebuilding the statues, although at least one group has said doing so will be extremely difficult technically.

[22] Shea, Nina. "Sharia in Kabul?" *The National Review*, October 28, 2002.

Counternarcotics

The December 5, 2001 Bonn agreement mentions the need for a post-Taliban Afghanistan government to prevent Afghanistan's re-emergence as a haven for drug cultivation, and the Bush Administration is focusing some U.S. resources on counter-narcotics. The new government has banned poppy cultivation, although it has had difficulty enforcing the ban due to resource limitations and opposition from Afghan farmers who see few alternatives. The U.N. Drug Control Program estimated in August 2002 that 3,000 tons of opium crop would be produced in Afghanistan in 2002, restoring Afghanistan to its previous place as the world's top opium producer.[23] On the other hand, the U.S. military is opposed to its conducting poppy crop eradication in Afghanistan.[24] In mid-October 2002, the Afghan government burned 5,500 pounds of hashish and opium to demonstrate its determination to the counter-narcotics effort.

Narcotics trafficking control was perhaps the one issue on which the Taliban apparently satisfied much of the international community. The Taliban, for the most part, enforced its July 2000 ban on poppy cultivation; in February 2001, U.N. International Drug Control Program (UNDCP) officials said that surveys showed a dramatic drop in poppy cultivation in the areas surveyed.[25] The Northern Alliance did not issue a similar ban in areas it controlled. In April 2001, the United States began funding a UNDCP crop substitution program, contributing $1.5 million to that program in FY2001. On January 31, 2003, the Bush Administration determined that Afghanistan was a major drug transit or illicit drug producing country. However, the Administration did not include Afghanistan in the list of countries that had "failed demonstrably to make substantial efforts" during the past 12 months to adhere to international counter-narcotics agreements and take certain counter-narcotics measures set forth in U.S. law. Therefore, no sanctions against Afghanistan were triggered. (This is equivalent to the listing by the United States, as Afghanistan has been listed every year since 1987, as a state that is uncooperative with U.S. efforts to eliminate drug trafficking or has failed to take sufficient steps on its own to curb trafficking.)

Retrieval of U.S. Stingers

Beginning in late 1985 and following an internal debate, the Reagan Administration provided "hundreds" of man-portable "Stinger" anti-aircraft missiles to the mujahedin for use against Soviet combat helicopters and aircraft. Prior to the U.S.-led war against the Taliban and Al Qaeda, common estimates among experts suggested that 200-300 Stingers remained at large in Afghanistan out of about 1,000 provided during the war against the Soviet Union.[26] In the aftermath of the Soviet withdrawal from Afghanistan, the United States had tried to retrieve the at-large Stingers.[27] The United States feared that the missiles could fall into the hands of terrorist groups for possible use against civilian airliners. Iran bought 16 of the missiles in 1987 and fired one against U.S. helicopters; some reportedly were transferred to

[23] Armitage, Tom. U.N. Sees Afghan Opium Cultivation Soaring in 2002. *Reuters*, February 28, 2002.
[24] Gertz, Bill. Military Opposes Spraying Poppies. *Washington Times*, March 25, 2002.
[25] Crossette, Barbara. "Taliban Seem to Be Making Good on Opium Ban, U.N. Says." *New York Times*, February 7, 2001.
[26] Saleem, Farrukh. Where Are the Missing Stinger Missiles? Pakistan, *Friday Times*. August 17-23, 2001.
[27] Gertz, Bill. Stinger Bite Feared in CIA. *Washington Times*, October 9, 2000.

Lebanese Hizballah, according to press reports in January 2002. India claimed that it was a Stinger, supplied to Islamic rebels in Kashmir probably by sympathizers in Afghanistan, that shot down an Indian helicopter over Kashmir in May 1999.[28] It was not the Stinger but Soviet-made SA-7 "Strella" man portable launchers that were fired, allegedly by Al Qaeda, against a U.S. military aircraft in Saudi Arabia in June 2002 and against an Israeli passenger aircraft in Kenya on November 30, 2002. Both firings missed their targets. SA-7s have been discovered in Afghanistan by U.S.-led forces, most recently in December 2002.

The practical difficulties of retrieving the weapons had caused this issue to fade from the U.S. agenda for Afghanistan. In 1992, the United States reportedly spent about $10 million to buy the Stingers back, at a premium, from individual mujahedin commanders. The *New York Times* reported on July 24, 1993, that the buy back effort failed because the United States was competing with other buyers, including Iran and North Korea, and that the CIA would spend about $55 million in FY1994 in a renewed Stinger buy-back effort. On March 7, 1994, the *Washington Post* reported that the CIA had recovered only a fraction of the at-large Stingers. Many observers speculate that the CIA program retrieved perhaps 50 or 100 Stingers. According to Defense Intelligence Agency testimony in 1996,[29] an unspecified number of man-portable surface-to-air missiles (Stingers) remain in Afghanistan.[30]

The Stinger issue resurfaced in conjunction with the U.S. war effort. U.S. pilots reported that the Taliban fired some Stingers at U.S. aircraft during the war, but they recorded no hits. Any Stingers that survived the anti-Taliban war are likely controlled by Afghans now allied to the United States and would presumably pose less of a threat. In early February 2002, the interim government collected and returned to the United States "dozens" of Stingers and said it would continue to try to find and return additional Stingers.[31]

Land Mine Eradication

Land mines laid during the Soviet occupation constitute one of the principal dangers to the Afghan people. The United Nations estimates that 5 -7 million mines remain scattered throughout the country, although some estimates by outside organizations are significantly lower. An estimated 400,000 Afghans have been killed or wounded by land mines. U.N. teams have succeeded in destroying one million mines and are now focusing on de-mining priority-use, residential and commercial property, including land surrounding Kabul. As shown in the U.S. aid table for FY1999-FY2002, the United States Humanitarian Demining Program was providing about $3 million per year for Afghanistan demining activities, and the amount escalated to $7 million in the post-Taliban period. Most of the funds go to the HALO Trust, a British organization, and the U.N. Mine Action Program for Afghanistan.

[28] "U.S.-Made Stinger Missiles – Mobile and Lethal." *Reuters*, May 28, 1999.
[29] John Moore, before the House International Relations Committee. May 9, 1996.
[30] Common estimates in a variety of press reports suggest that 200-300 Stingers may remain at large in Afghanistan.
[31] Fullerton, John. "Afghan Authorities Hand in Stinger Missiles to U.S." *Reuters*, February 4, 2002.

Assistance and Reconstruction

Since the Soviet invasion, Afghanistan has faced major humanitarian difficulties, some of which deteriorated further under Taliban rule. In addition to 3.6 million Afghan refugees at the start of the U.S.-led war,[32] another 500,000 Afghans were displaced internally even before U.S. military action began, according to Secretary General Annan's April 19, 2001 report on Afghanistan. Many of the displaced persons had fled the effects of a major drought that affected the 85% of the population that directly depends on agriculture. About 2 million Afghan refugees have returned since January 2002. The conflicts in Afghanistan, including the war against the Soviet Union, have reportedly left about 2 million dead, 700,000 widows and orphans and about one million Afghan children who were born and raised in refugee camps outside Afghanistan.

As part of its military operations, the United States air-dropped food rations to help alleviate suffering. Following the Taliban collapse, aid routes via Uzbekistan and Pakistan reopened, largely eliminating the need for the airdrops. A variety of U.N. agencies and non-governmental organizations (NGOs) serve as the vehicles for international assistance to Afghanistan. The U.N. High Commission for Refugees (UNHCR) supervises Afghan refugee camps in Pakistan and Afghan repatriation.

U.S. Assistance Issues

The United States had become the largest single provider of assistance to the Afghan people, even before the crisis triggered by the September 11, 2001 attacks. In 1985, the United States began a cross-border aid program for Afghanistan, through which aid was distributed in Afghanistan, via U.S. aid workers in Pakistan. However, citing budgetary constraints and the difficulty of administering a cross-border program, there was no USAID mission for Afghanistan after the end of FY1994, and U.S. aid has been provided through various channels, mostly U.N. agencies and NGOs.

Primarily because of a drought and the widely publicized suffering of the Afghan people, U.S. aid to the Afghan people in FY2001 greatly exceeded that provided in FY2000 or FY1999, but no U.S. assistance went directly to the Taliban government. **Table 2** breaks down FY1999-FY2002 aid by program. For a history of U.S. aid to Afghanistan (FY1978-FY1998), see **Table 4**.

Post Taliban

On October 4, 2001, in an effort to demonstrate that the United States has an interest in the welfare of the Afghan people and not just the defeat of the Taliban, President Bush announced that humanitarian aid to the Afghan people would total about $320 million for FY2002. After the fall of the Taliban, at a donors' conference in Tokyo during January 20-21, 2002, the United States pledged $296 million in reconstruction aid for Afghanistan for FY2002. The amounts provided for FY2002 are listed in the table; the figures include both humanitarian and reconstruction aid, totaling over $620 million for FY2002, which includes

---

[32] About 1.5 million Afghan refugees were in Iran; 2 million in Pakistan; 20,000 in Russia; 17,000 in India, and 9,000 in the Central Asian states.

Foreign Military Financing (FMF) funds devoted to the establishment and training of an Afghan national army.

The conference report on the FY2002 foreign aid appropriations (H.Rept. 107- 354, P.L. 107-115) contained a sense of Congress provision that the United States should contribute substantial humanitarian assistance to Afghanistan, although no dollar figures were mentioned. The conference report on an FY2002 supplemental appropriations (H.R. 4775, P.L. 107-480) recommends $134 million in additional aid to Afghanistan.

FY2003 Plans

The Administration says it plans to spend about $820 million for Afghan programs in FY2003, a figure announced on March 17, 2003 at a donors forum for Afghanistan, held in Brussels. As part of the FY2003 plan, on September 12, 2002, the Administration pledged Afghanistan $80 million for road reconstruction, as part of an international pledge of $180 million. Table 3 covers FY2003 aid. The FY2003 foreign aid appropriations, contained in P.L. 108-7, an omnibus appropriations, stipulates that at least $295 million in aid be provided to Afghanistan. Earmarks in that law are as follows: $50 million for child survival programs; $40.5 million for Development Assistance (DA); $85 million for International Disaster Assistance; $10 million for transition initiatives; $50 million in Economic Support Funds (ESF); $5 million for non-proliferation, antiterrorism and de-mining (NADR); and $50 million for migration and refugee assistance. Other Administration documents say that an additional $21 million has been allocated for Foreign Military Financing (FMF) for FY2003 to continue training the Afghan national army.

The remaining funds in the planned $820 million are to come from an FY2003 supplemental appropriations. That request includes $25 million for anti-terrorism assistance, $150 million to reimburse DOD for funds spent to equip and train the Afghan national army; $170 million in new FMF for the Afghan national army; and $127 million in ESF.

An authorization bill, S. 2712, the Afghanistan Freedom Support Act of 2002, was passed by the Senate on November 14 and by the House on November 15, and signed on December 4, 2002 (P.L. 107-327). It authorizes $2.5 billion in reconstruction aid during FY2002-FY2005, of which $500 million would be for an enterprise fund, plus an additional $1 billion to expand ISAF if such an expansion takes place. It also authorizes $300 million in defense, crime control, and counternarcotics articles and services.

FY2004 Plans

The Administration has requested substantial funds for FY2004. The total request, according to specific categories in the congressional presentation, is about $532 million. The categories are as follows: $150 million in FMF (for the Afghan national army); $150 million for DA; $150 million in ESF; $21 million for child survival programs; $40 million for counter-narcotics; $20 million for peacekeeping; and $600,000 for International Military Education and Training Funds (IMET).

Additional Forms of U.S. Assistance

In addition to providing U.S. foreign assistance, the U.S. Treasury Department (Office of Foreign Assets Control, OFAC) has unblocked over $145 million in assets of Afghan government owned banking entities that were frozen under U.S. sanctions imposed on the Taliban in 1999 (see below). These funds have been used by the new government for currency stabilization, not for recurring costs of the interim government. Most of the funds consisted of gold that will be held in Afghanistan's name in the United States to back up Afghanistan's currency. Together with its allies, over $350 million in frozen funds have been released to the new government. In January 2002, the United States agreed to provide $50 million in credit for U.S. investment in Afghanistan, provided by the Overseas Private Investment Corporation (OPIC). On March 7, 2003, OPIC pledged an additional $50 million, bringing the total line of credit to $100 million. The United States also has successfully pressed the International Air Transport Association to pay Afghanistan $20 million in overflight fees that were withheld because of U.N. sanctions on the Taliban. In April 2002, OFAC unblocked $17 million in privately-owned Afghan assets. In May 2002, the World Bank reopened its office in Afghanistan after twenty years and, on March 12, 2003, it announced a $108 million loan to Afghanistan, the first since 1979.

International Reconstruction Pledges

Common estimates of reconstruction needs run up to about $10 billion. At the Tokyo donors' conference, mentioned above, the following international reconstruction pledges were announced: European Union - $495 million in 2002; Japan - $500 million over the next 30 months; Germany - $362 million over the next 4 years; Saudi Arabia - $220 million over the next 3 years; Iran - $560 million over the next 5 years; Pakistan - $100 million over the next 5 years; India - a $100 million line of credit; South Korea - $45 million over 30 months; and United Kingdom - $86 million in 2002. Total pledges in Tokyo for reconstruction amounted to $2 billion to be spent in 2002 and $4.5 billion over the next 5 years. Of the amounts pledged for 2002, about $1.9 billion has been spent, received, or about to be received, as of January 2003.

Promoting Long-Term Economic Development

In an effort to find a long-term solution to Afghanistan's acute humanitarian problems, the United States has, when feasible, tried to promote major development projects as a means of improving Afghan living standards and political stability over the long term. During 1996-98, the Administration supported proposed natural gas and oil pipelines through western Afghanistan as an incentive for the warring factions to cooperate. One proposal by a consortium led by Los Angeles-based Unocal

Corporation[33] was for a Central Asia Oil Pipeline (CAOP) that would originate at the Turkmenistan-Uzbekistan border and extend through the western region of Afghanistan to Pakistan. A $2.5 billion Central Asia Gas Pipeline (CentGas) would originate in southern Turkmenistan and pass through Afghanistan to Pakistan, with possible extensions into India.

The deterioration in U.S.-Taliban relations after 1998 largely ended hopes for the pipeline projects while the Taliban was in power. Immediately after the August 20,1998 U.S. strikes

[33] Other participants in the Unocal consortium include Delta of Saudi Arabia, Hyundai of South Korea, Crescent Steel of Pakistan, Itochu Corporation and INPEX of Japan, and the government of Turkmenistan. Some

on bin Laden's bases in Afghanistan, Unocal suspended all its Afghan pipeline-related activities, including a U.S.-based training program for Afghans who were expected to work on the project. With few prospects of improved U.S. relations with Taliban, Unocal withdrew from its consortium in December 1998. Saudi Delta Oil was made interim project leader, although Delta lacked the financing and technology to make the consortium viable. The rival consortium led by Bridas of Argentina reportedly continued to try to win approval for its proposal to undertake the project.

Prospects for the project have improved in the post-Taliban period. In a summit meeting in late May 2002 between the leaders of Turkmenistan, Afghanistan, and Pakistan, the three countries agreed to revive the gas pipeline project. Sponsors of the project held an inaugural meeting on July 9, 2002 in Turkmenistan, signing a series of preliminary agreements. However, financing for the project is unclear.

Table 1. Major Factions in Afghanistan

Party/Commander	Leader	Ideology/Ethnicity	Areas of Control
Taliban	Mullah (Islamic cleric) Muhammad Umar	ultra-orthodox Islamic, Pashtun	Small groups hiding throughout Afghanistan. No presence in government.
Northern Alliance/Islamic Society (dominant party in the Northern Alliance)	Burhannudin Rabbani (political leader), Muhammad Fahim (military leader)	conservative Islamic, mostly Tajik	Most of northern and western Afghanistan, including Kabul. Fahim is Vice President and Defense Minister. Dr. Abdullah is Foreign Minister. Rabbani holds no official position.
Forces of Ismail Khan (part of Northern Alliance)	Ismail Khan	Tajik	Herat Province and environs; Khan's son in cabinet.
Eastern Shura (loosely allied with Northern Alliance)	No clear leader, following death of Abdul Qadir; Qadir's son appointed Jalalabad governor after Qadir's death	moderate Islamic, Pashtun	Jalalabad and environs; Qadir was vice president.
National Islamic Movement of Afghanistan (part of Northern Alliance)	Abdul Rashid Dostam	secular, Uzbek	Mazar Sharif and environs; Dostam was deputy defense minister in interim government.
Hizb-e-Wahdat (part of Northern Alliance)	Karim Khalili	Shiite, Hazara tribes	Bamiyan province. Khalili is a vice president.
Pashtun Commanders	Ghul Agha Shirzai, and other tribal leaders	mostly orthodox Islamic, Pashtun	Southern Afghanistan, including Qandahar.

accounts say Russia's Gazprom would probably receive a stake in the project. Moscow Nezavisimaya Gazeta, October 30, 1997. Page 3.

Table 2. U.S. Aid to Afghanistan in FY1999-FY2003
($ in millions)

	FY1999	FY2000	FY2001	FY2002(final)
U.S. Department of Agriculture (DOA) and USAID Food For Peace (FFP), via World Food Program(WFP)	$42.0 worth of wheat (100,000 metric tons under "416(b)" program.	$68.875 for 165,000 metric tons. (60,000 tons for May 2000 drought relief)	$131.0 (300,000 metric tonsunder P.L.480, Title II, and 416(b))	$198.12 (for food commodities)
State/Bureau of Population, Refugees and Migration (PRM) via UNHCR and ICRC	$16.95 for Afghan refugees in Pakistan and Iran, and to assist their repatriation	$14.03 for the same purposes	$22.03 for similar purposes	$136.54 (to U.N. agencies)
State Department/Office of Foreign Disaster Assistance (OFDA)	$7.0 to various NGOs to aid Afghans inside Afghanistan	$6.68 for drought relief and health, water, and sanitation programs	$18.934 for similar programs	$113.36 (to various U.N. agencies and NGOs)
State Department/HDP (Humanitarian Demining Program)	$2.615	$3.0	$2.8	$7.0 to Halo Trust/other demining
Aid to Afghan Refugees in Pakistan (through various NGOs)	$5.44 (2.789 for health, training – Afghan females in Pakistan	$6.169, of which $3.82went to similar purposes	$5.31 for similar purposes	
Counter-Narcotics			$1.50	$63.0
USAID/Office of Transition Initiatives			$0.45 (Afghan women in Pakistan)	$24.35 for broadcasting/media
Dept. of Defense				$50.9 (2.4 million rations)
Foreign Military Financing				$57.0 (for Afghan national army)
Anti-Terrorism				$36.4
Economic Support Funds (E.S.F)				$105.2
Peacekeeping				$24.0
Totals	**$76.6**	**$113.2**	**$182.6**	**$815.9**

Table 3. U.S. Aid Provided to Afghanistan, FY2003
($ in millions, same acronyms as above table)
(figures as of March 13, 2002)

USAID/OFDA	$14.95 (mostly for urban shelter)
USAID/FFP	$26.7 (for wheat)
State/PRM	$23.5 (mostly refugee assistance)
Total	$65.15

Table 4. U.S. Assistance to Afghanistan FY1978-1998
($ in millions)

Fiscal Year	Devel. Assist.	Econ. Supp. (ESF)	P.L. 480 (Title I and II)	Military	Other (Incl. regional refugee aid)	Total
1978	4.989	–	5.742	0.269	0.789	11.789
1979	3.074	–	7.195	–	0.347	10.616
1980	–	(Soviet invasion - December 1979)			–	–
1981	–	–	–	–	–	–
1982	–	–	–	–	–	–
1983	–	–	–	–	–	–
1984	–	–	–	–	–	–
1985	3.369	–	–	–	–	3.369
1986	–	–	8.9	–	–	8.9
1987	17.8	12.1	2.6	–	–	32.5
1988	22.5	22.5	29.9	–	–	74.9
1989	22.5	22.5	32.6	–	–	77.6
1990	35.0	35.0	18.1	–	–	88.1
1991	30.0	30.0	20.1	–	–	80.1
1992	25.0	25.0	31.4	–	–	81.4
1993	10.0	10.0	18.0	–	30.2	68.2
1994	3.4	2.0	9.0	–	27.9	42.3
1995	1.8	–	12.4	–	31.6	45.8
1996	–	–	16.1	–	26.4	42.5
1997	–	–	18.0	–	31.9*	49.9
1998	–	–	3.6	–	49.14**	52.74

Source: U.S. Department of State.
* Includes $3 million for demining and $1.2 million for counternarcotics.
** Includes $3.3 million in projects targeted for Afghan women and girls, $7 million in earthquake relief aid, 100,000 tons of 416B wheat worth about $15 million, $2 million for demining, and $1.54 for counternarcotics.

U.S. and International Sanctions

Shoring up a post-Taliban government of Afghanistan with financial and other assistance has required waivers of restrictions or the permanent modification of U.S. and U.N. sanctions previously imposed on Afghanistan. Most of the sanctions discussed below have now been lifted.

- On May 2, 1980, Afghanistan was deleted from the list of designated beneficiary countries under the U.S. Generalized System of Preferences (GSP), denying Afghanistan's exports duty free treatment, by Executive Order 12204 (45 F.R. 20740). This was done under the authority of Section 504 of the Trade Act of 1974, as amended [P.L. 93-618; 19 U.S.C. 2464]. *On January 10, 2003, the President signed a proclamation making Afghanistan a beneficiary of GSP, eliminating U.S. tariffs on 5,700 Afghan products.*

- On June 3, 1980, as part of the sanctions against the Soviet Union for the invasion of Afghanistan, the United States imposed controls on exports to Afghanistan of agricultural products, oil and gas exploration and production equipment, and phosphates. This was implemented at 15 CFR Part 373 et seq (45 F.R. 37415) under the authority of Sections 5 and 6 of the Export Administration Act of 1979 [P.L. 96-72; 50 U.S.C. app. 2404, app. 2405]. On April 24, 1981, these sanctions were modified to terminate controls on U.S. exports to Afghanistan of agricultural products and phosphates.

- In mid-1992, the George H.W. Bush Administration determined that Afghanistan no longer had a "Soviet-controlled government." This opened Afghanistan to the use of U.S. funds made available for the U.S. share of U.N. organizations that provide assistance to Afghanistan.

- On October 7, 1992, President George H.W. Bush issued Presidential Determination 93-3 that Afghanistan is no longer a Marxist-Leninist country. The designation as such a country had prohibited Afghanistan from receiving Export-Import Bank guarantees, insurance, or credits for purchases under Sec. 8 of the 1986 Export-Import Bank Act, which amended Section 2(b)(2) of the Export-Import Bank Act of 1945 (P.L. 79-173, 12 U.S.C. 635). However, President George H.W. Bush's determination was not implemented before he left office.

- President George H.W. Bush's October 7, 1992 determination (93-3) also found that assistance to Afghanistan under Section 620D of the Foreign Assistance Act is in the national interest of the United States because of the change of regime in Afghanistan. The presidential determination, had it been implemented in regulations, would have waived restrictions on assistance to Afghanistan provided for in the Act, as amended [P.L. 87-195; 22 U.S.C. 2374]; as added by Section 505 of the International Development Cooperation Act of 1979 [P.L. 96-53]. These provisions prohibit foreign assistance to Afghanistan until it apologizes for the death of U.S. Ambassador to Afghanistan Adolph Dubs, who was kidnapped in Kabul in 1979 and killed when Afghan police stormed the hideout where he was held, unless the President determines that such assistance is in the national interest because of changed circumstances in Afghanistan. *The restrictions on U.S. aid to the government of Afghanistan have been lifted in light of the change of government there.*

- Section 552 of the Foreign Assistance Appropriations for FY1986 [P.L. 99-190] authorized the President to deny any U.S. credits or most-favored-nation (MFN) tariff status for Afghanistan. Under that law, on February 18, 1986, the height of the Soviet occupation, President Reagan had issued Presidential Proclamation 5437, suspending (MFN) tariff status for Afghanistan (51 F.R. 4287). *On May 3, 2002, President Bush restored normal trade treatment to the products of Afghanistan.*

- On March 31, 1993, President Clinton, on national interest grounds, waived restrictions provided for in Section 481 (h) of the Foreign Assistance Act of 1961, as amended [P.L. 87-195]; as amended and restated by Section 2005(a) of the Anti-Drug Abuse Act of 1986 [P.L. 99-570]. The waiver was renewed in 1994. Mandatory sanctions include bilateral aid cuts and suspensions, including denial of Ex-Im Bank credits; the casting of negative U.S. votes for multilateral development bank loans;

and a non-allocation of a U.S. sugar quota. Discretionary sanctions included denial of GSP; additional duties on country exports to the United States; and curtailment of air transportation with the United States. *On February 25, 2002, President Bush waived restrictions on FY2002 aid to Afghanistan under this Act.*

- On June 14, 1996, Afghanistan was formally added to the list of countries prohibited from receiving exports or licenses for exports of U.S. defense articles and services. This amended the International Traffic in Arms Regulations (22 CFR Part 121 et seq.) under the authority of Section 38 of the Arms Export Control Act, as amended (P.L. 90-629; 22 U.S.C. 2778) by adding Afghanistan at Section 126.1 of 22 CFR Part 126. *On July 2, 2002, the State Department amended U.S. regulations (22 CFR Part 126) to allow arms sales to the new Afghan government.*

- In a ruling largely redundant with the one above, on May 15, 1997, the State Department designated Afghanistan under the Antiterrorism and Effective Death Penalty Act of 1996 (P.L. 104- 132), as a state that is not cooperating with U.S. anti-terrorism efforts. The designation, made primarily because of Taliban's harboring of bin Laden, makes Afghanistan ineligible to receive U.S. exports of items on the U.S. Munitions List. The designation was repeated every year since 1997. *Afghanistan was deleted from the list of non-cooperative states when the list was reissued on May 15, 2002, thereby eliminating this sanction on Afghanistan.*

- On July 4, 1999, the President declared a national emergency with respect to Taliban because of its hosting of bin Laden, and issued Executive Order 13129 that imposed sanctions. The sanctions include the blocking of Taliban assets and property in the United States, and a ban on U.S. trade with Taliban-controlled areas of Afghanistan. On August 10, 1999, the Administration determined that Ariana Afghan Airlines was a Taliban entity. That determination triggered a blocking of Ariana assets (about $500,000) in the United States and a ban on U.S. citizens' flying on the airline. *On January 29, 2002, the State Department issued a determination that the Taliban controls no territory within Afghanistan, thus essentially ending this trade ban. On July 2, 2002, President Bush formally revoked this Executive order.*

- On October 15, 1999, the U.N. Security Council adopted Resolution 1267; on December 19, 2000, it adopted U.N. Security Council Resolution 1333, imposed a number of new sanctions against the Taliban. For the provisions of these sanctions, see the section on the harboring of bin Laden. *As noted, these sanctions were narrowed to penalize only Al Qaeda by virtue of the adoption of U.N. Security Council Resolution 1390 of January 17, 2002.*

Chapter 9

CENTRAL ASIA'S NEW STATES: POLITICAL DEVELOPMENTS AND IMPLICATIONS FOR U.S. INTERESTS

James P. Nichol

SUMMARY

After the collapse of the Soviet Union in 1991, the United States recognized the independence of all the former Central Asian republics and established diplomatic relations with each by mid-March 1992. The United States also supported their admission to the Organization on Security and Cooperation in Europe (OSCE) and other Western organizations, and elicited Turkish support in countering Iranian influence in the region. Congress was at the forefront in urging the formation of coherent U.S. policies for aiding these and other Eurasian states of the former Soviet Union, and approved the Freedom Support Act and other legislation for this purpose.

Soon after the terrorist attacks on America on September 11, 2001, all the Central Asian states offered overflight and other support to coalition anti-terrorist efforts in Afghanistan. Kyrgyzstan, Tajikistan, and Uzbekistan have hosted coalition troops and provided access to airbases. After 9/11, the United States boosted its security assistance throughout the region for anti-terrorism, counter-narcotics, non-proliferation, border and customs, and defense cooperation programs, while also increasing aid for democratization and free market reforms.

U.S. policy goals in Central Asia include fostering stability, democratization, free market economies, free trade and transport throughout the Eurasian corridor, denuclearization in the non-Russian states, and adherence to international human rights standards. An over-arching U.S. priority is to discourage attempts by extremist regimes and groups to block or subvert progress toward these goals. Administration policy also aims to integrate these states into the international community so that they follow responsible security and other policies, and to discourage xenophobic and anti-Western orientations that threaten peace and stability. The Administration is concerned about human rights and civil liberties problems in all the states. The Administration's policy goals in Central Asia reflect the differing characteristics of these states. U.S. interests in Kazakhstan include the security and elimination of Soviet-era nuclear and biological weapons materials and facilities. In Tajikistan, U.S. aid increasingly focuses on economic reconstruction. U.S. energy firms have invested in oil and natural gas development in Kazakhstan, Turkmenistan, and Uzbekistan.

Some observers call for different emphases or levels of U.S. involvement in Central Asia. Some have called for strengthening conditions linking aid to progress in improving human rights or in making adequate progress in democratization and the creation of free markets. Some have disputed the importance of energy resources to U.S. national security. Others point to civil and ethnic tensions in the region as possibly endangering U.S. lives and investments. Heightened congressional interest in Central Asia was reflected in passage of "Silk Road" language in late 1999 (P.L.106-113) authorizing enhanced U.S. policy attention and aid to support conflict amelioration, humanitarian needs, economic development, transport (including energy pipelines) and communications, border controls, democracy, and the creation of civil societies in the South Caucasian and Central Asian states.

Most Recent Developments

Uzbekistan is the only Central Asian state so far to have joined the coalition of the willing supporting operations in Iraq. Uzbek President Islam Karimov on March 6 stated that the Iraq operation was a continuation of "efforts to break the back of terrorism," and the government has agreed to provide post-war medical and construction aid to Iraq. The Uzbek Muslim Spiritual Board at the end of March assured Muslims that coalition operations in Iraq were neither aimed against the Iraqi people nor against Islam. Among other Central Asian states, Kazakh Foreign Minister Kasymzhomart Tokayev on March 28 voiced general support for disarming Iraq. Tajik President Emomaliy Rakhmanov reportedly on March 13 refused Russia's request to denounce coalition actions in Iraq. However, Sayed Abdullo Nuri, head of Tajikistan's Islamic Renaissance Party, on March 26 termed the Iraq conflict a "disgraceful" humanitarian disaster, and warned that it might trigger a domino effect of instability in Afghanistan and Tajikistan. He rejected talk of an anti-coalition jihad, instead urging the peaceful resolution of the conflict. Kyrgyzstan's Legislative Assembly (lower chamber) issued a statement on March 24 calling for the United States to cease "gross violations" of international law and to allow the return of U.N. weapons inspectors to Iraq.

The U.N. Rapporteur on Torture in March 2003 completed a draft report on his late 2002 visit to Uzbekistan that concludes that police and prison officials systematically employ torture and other coercive means to obtain confessions and as punishment. It also states that evidence frequently is planted on suspects. The Uzbek government denied that human rights problems in the prisons are systematic, while admitting that some instances of abuse have occurred and are being fully addressed.

Background and Analysis

Historical Background

Central Asia consists of the former Soviet republics of Kazakhstan, Kyrgyzstan, Tajikistan, Turkmenistan, and Uzbekistan, and borders Russia, China, the Middle East, and

South Asia. The major peoples of all but Tajikistan speak Turkic languages (the Tajiks speak an Iranian language), and most are Sunni Muslims (some Tajiks are Shiia Muslims). Most are closely related historically and culturally. By the late 19th century, Russian tsars had conquered the last independent khanates and nomadic lands of Central Asia. After the breakup of the tsarist empire, Central Asia was at first included within Soviet Russia, but by 1936 five "union republics" had been created. Soviet communist rule resulted in massive loss of life from collectivization and purges, though economic development took place. Upon the collapse of the Soviet Union in December 1991, the five republics gained worldwide diplomatic recognition.

Central Asia: Basic Facts

Area: 1.6 million sq. mi., larger than India; Kazakhstan: 1.1 m. sq. mi.; Kyrgyzstan: 77,000 sq. mi.; Tajikistan: 55,800 sq. mi.; Turkmenistan: 190,000 sq. mi.; Uzbekistan: 174,500 sq. mi.
Population: 56.4 million (2001 est., *Economist Intelligence Unit*), somewhat less than France; Kazakhstan: 14.8 m.; Kyrgyzstan: 4.9 m.; Tajikistan: 6.3 m.; Turkmenistan: 5.3 m.; Uzbekistan: 25.1 m.
Gross Domestic Product: $41.6 billion in 2001; per capita GDP is about $740; poverty is rampant. Kazakhstan: $22.0b.; Kyrgyzstan: $1.5b.; Tajikistan: $1.0b.; Turkmenistan: $6.0 b.; Uzbekistan: $11.1b. (*EIU*, current prices)

OVERVIEW OF U.S. POLICY CONCERNS

After the collapse of the Soviet Union at the end of 1991, the United States recognized the independence of all the former Central Asian republics. Citing the dangers they faced from Iranian-sponsored Islamic fundamentalism, U.S. diplomatic relations were established with all five new states by mid-March 1992. Faced with calls in Congress and elsewhere that the Administration devise a policy on aiding the new Eurasian states, former President Bush sent the Freedom Support Act to Congress, which was amended and signed into law in October 1992 (P.L. 102-511). In 1999, Congressional concerns led to passage of the "Silk Road Strategy Act" authorizing language (contained in Consolidated Appropriations for FY2000; P.L. 106-113) calling for enhanced policy and aid to support conflict amelioration, humanitarian needs, economic development, transport and communications, border controls, democracy, and the creation of civil societies in the South Caucasus and Central Asia.

Post-9/11

Since the terrorist attacks on the United States on September 11, 2001, the Administration has stated that U.S. policy toward Central Asia focuses on three inter-related activities: the promotion of security, domestic reforms, and energy development. The 9/11 attacks led the Administration to realize that "it was critical to the national interests of the United States that we greatly enhance our relations with the five Central Asian countries" to prevent them from becoming harbors for terrorism, according to Deputy Assistant Secretary of State B. Lynn Pascoe in testimony in June 2002.

Immediately after 9/11, the Central Asian governments condemned the attacks, but over the next two weeks, as U.S. attention focused on Afghanistan, none unambiguously offered to permit overflight rights or U.S. military airbase access. At first, Turkmenistan's foreign minister reiterated its policy of neutrality and its friendship with the Taliban in refusing to cooperate in a U.S.-led military campaign. Tajikistan, host to the largest Russian military presence in Central Asia and largely dependent on Russia to police its border with Afghanistan, was hesitant to cooperate with the United States without permission from Moscow. However, since Tajikistan and Uzbekistan had long supported the Northern Alliance's combat against the Taliban, they were predisposed to welcome U.S.-led backing for the Northern Alliance. These Central Asian states, along with Kyrgyzstan, also had suffered from incursions by the IMU and other terrorists, who were harbored by the Taliban.

On September 24, 2001, Turkmenistan's President Niyazov gave his consent for ground transport and overflights to deliver humanitarian aid to support U.S. anti-terrorism efforts in Afghanistan because "evil must be punished." Kazakhstan's President Nazarbayev also offered airfields, military bases, and airspace. That evening, President Putin stated that Russia would support U.S. efforts by providing intelligence, overflight rights for humanitarian cargoes, access to Central Asian airbases, and support for the Northern Alliance. The next day, Kyrgyz President Akayev indicated that he had received the backing of the other members of the Commonwealth of Independent States' (CIS's) Collective Security Treaty for U.S. use of Kyrgyz airspace for anti-terrorism in Afghanistan. Many Uzbek officials were offended by a warning from the Taliban "foreign minister" on September 24, 2001, against permitting U.S. use of Uzbek territory to attack Afghanistan. Two days later, Uzbek President Karimov permitted U.S. use of Uzbek airspace against Afghan-based terrorists for "humanitarian and security purposes" if Uzbekistan's security was guaranteed. This condition was met with a U.S.-Uzbek agreement signed on October 7, a Joint Statement issued on October 12, 2001, and a Declaration on the Strategic Partnership signed on March 12, 2002 (see below, *Security*).

The United States and Kazakhstan signed a memorandum of understanding on July 10, 2002, permitting U.S. military aircraft to use Kazakhstan's airport in Almaty for emergency military landings. The accord was needed in part because military flights out of Kyrgyzstan's Ganci airbase at Manas Airport, 120 miles away, can be disrupted by harsh weather. Sensitive to some Kazakh, Russian, and Chinese concerns, the Kazakh Foreign Ministry stressed that there would be no "permanent" U.S. military presence. A few days later, the United States and Kazakhstan reached another agreement providing increased U.S. military training and equipment for the Kazakh armed forces. The United States is refurbishing a military base at Atyrau on the Caspian Sea to help Kazakhstan provide security for its energy resources (see also below, *Security*).

While a consensus appears to exist among most U.S. policymakers and others on these interests, there are various views on the types and levels of U.S. involvement in the region. Many of those who endorse continued or enhanced U.S. support for Central Asia argue that political instability and the growth of terrorist groups in Central Asia can produce spillover effects both in important nearby states, including U.S. allies and friends such as Turkey, and worldwide. They also argue that the United States has a major interest in preventing terrorist regimes or groups from illicitly acquiring nuclear weapons-related technology in the region. They maintain that U.S. interests do not perfectly coincide with those of its allies and friends, that Turkey and other actors possess limited aid resources, and that the United States is in the strongest position as the superpower to influence democratization and respect for human rights. They stress that U.S. leadership in world aid efforts to foster reform will help alleviate the social distress exploited by anti-Western Islamic extremist groups to gain new members. Although many U.S. policymakers acknowledge a role for a democratizing Russia in the region, they stress that U.S. and other Western aid and investment strengthen the independence of the states and forestall Russian attempts to re-subjugate the region.

Some views of policymakers and academics who previously objected to a more forward U.S. policy toward Central Asia appeared less salient after 9/11, but aspects of these views could gain more credence once Afghanistan appears less unstable. These observers argued that the United States historically had few interests in this region and that developments there were largely marginal to U.S. interests. They advocated limited U.S. contacts undertaken with Turkey and other friends and allies to ensure U.S. interests. They discounted fears that anti-Western Islamic extremism would make enough headway to threaten secular regimes or otherwise harm U.S. interests. They were dubious of claims of sizeable oil and gas resources in these new states and argued that, in any event, such resources could not be economically developed and delivered to Western markets. Other still topical arguments include whether the United States should continue to try to foster democratization among cultures some view as historically attuned to authoritarianism. Some observers urge reducing or cutting off most aid to repressive governments that widely violate human rights, arguing that such aid provides tacit support for these regimes, and might even unwittingly be fueling the rise of Islamic fundamentalism as an alternative channel of dissent. These observers reject arguments that U.S. interests in anti-terrorism, nonproliferation, regional cooperation, trade, and investment outweigh concerns over democratization and human rights. They warn that the populations of these states may come to view U.S. engagement as propping up authoritarian leaders. Some observers point to civil problems in the region as another reason for the United States to eschew major involvement such as military access that might place more U.S. personnel and citizens in danger. Some of these observers still call for the United States to accord major deference to China's and Russia's interests in the region.

Fostering Pro-Western Orientations

The United States has encouraged the Central Asian states to become responsible members of the international community, and supported their admission to the Organization for Security and Cooperation in Europe (OSCE), NATO bodies, and other Western organizations. The United States has supported these integrative goals through bilateral aid and through coordination with other aid donors, including regional powers such as Turkey. These and other means are used to discourage radical regimes, groups, and Islamic fundamentalists — who use repression or violence to oppose democratization — from attempts to gain influence. All the Central Asian leaders publicly embrace Islam, but display hostility toward Islamic fundamentalism. At the same time, they have established some trade and aid ties with Iran. While they have had greater success in attracting development aid from the West than from the East, some observers argue that, in the long run, their foreign policies will probably not be anti-Western, but may more closely reflect the concerns of other Islamic states.

Russia's Role

The events of 9/11 may weaken Russia's influence over the Central Asian states, though long-term impacts depend on the duration and scope of U.S. and coalition presence in the region, Russia's countervailing polices, and the fate of Afghanistan. Prior to 9/11, the Putin Administration had tried to strengthen Russia's interests in the region while opposing the growth of U.S. and other influence. On the other hand, while calling Central Asia an important or even "vital" interest of the United States, U.S. Administrations had generally deferred to Russia on regional security issues and had refused major U.S. military assistance to the states to combat terrorism. Russia's other reasons for permitting the increased U.S. and coalition presence included its interests in boosting some economic and other ties to the West and its hope of regaining influence in a post-Taliban Afghanistan. Russia cooperated with Central Asia in supporting U.S. and coalition efforts, including by quickly sending military equipment and advisors to assist the Northern Alliance in attacks on the Taliban. On September 19, 2001, Russian Foreign Minister Igor Ivanov indicated that the nature of support given by the Central Asian states to the U.S.-led coalition was up to each state, and President Putin reiterated this point on September 24, 2001, giving Russia's accedence to cooperation between these states and the United States.

In accord with long-standing U.S. policy, the Bush Administration generally views a democratizing Russia as able to play a traditional stabilizing role in Central Asia, though emphasizes that Russia should not seek to dominate the region or exclude Western and other involvement. Assistant Secretary of State Jones most recently reiterated this policy on February 11, 2002, stating that "our goal with the Russians is to make sure they understand that ... we're not trying to take over Central Asia from them, but we have ... international common interests that we will be transparent about as they play out in Central Asia." While some observers continue to warn that Russia seeks to reabsorb Central Asia into a new empire, most discount Russia's capabilities, if not intentions, because of what they view as Russia's deep economic, political, ethnic, and military disorder. Virtually all U.S. analysts agree, however, that Russia's actions should be monitored to ensure that they do not infringe on the independence of the Central Asian states.

Russian officials have variously emphasized interests in strategic security and economic ties with Central Asia, and concerns over the treatment of ethnic Russians. Strategic concerns have focused on drug trafficking and regional conflict, and the region's role as a buffer to Islamic extremism. By the late 1990s, Russia's economic decline and demands by Central Asia caused it to reduce its security presence, a trend that President Putin may be seeking to reverse. About 12,000 Russian Border Troops (mostly ethnic Tajiks under Russian command) still defend "CIS borders" in Tajikistan, but were largely phased out in Kyrgyzstan in 1999. Russia justified a 1999 military basing accord with Tajikistan for its estimated 7,800 Russian troops of the 201st motorized rifle division stationed there by citing the Islamic extremist threat to the CIS. In late 1999, the last Russian military advisors left Turkmenistan. In 1999, Uzbekistan withdrew from the Collective Security Treaty, citing its ineffectiveness and obtrusiveness.

In an apparent shift toward a more activist Russian role in Central Asia, in January 2000, then-Acting President Putin approved a "national security concept" that termed foreign efforts to "weaken" Russia's "position" in Central Asia a security threat. In April 2000, Russia called for the members of the Collective Security Treaty (CST) to approve the creation of rapid reaction forces, including in Central Asia, to combat terrorism emanating from Afghanistan, and hinted that such a force might launch pre-emptive strikes on Afghan terrorist bases. These hints elicited U.S. calls for Russia to exercise restraint and consult the UN. A May 2001 CST summit approved the creation of a Central Asian force composed of Kazakh, Kyrgyz, and Tajik country-based battalions and a headquarters in Bishkek. This initiative seemed in part aimed to protect Russian regional influence in the face of nascent U.S. and NATO anti-terrorism moves in the region against Afghanistan. CIS members in 2001 also approved the creation of a regional Anti-Terrorist Center (composed of intelligence agencies). Russia's threats of pre-emptive strikes caused the Taliban in May 2000 to warn the Central Asian states of reprisals if they permitted Russia to use their bases for strikes. At the June 2000 U.S.-Russia summit, the two presidents agreed to set up a working group to examine Afghan-related terrorism, and the group held two meetings prior to 9/11. These events prior to 9/11 helped to ease the way for Russian and Central Asian assistance to the U.S.-led coalition in Afghanistan.

Soon after 9/11, Russia demonstrably reversed its policy of drawing down its military presence in Central Asia by increasing its troop presence in Tajikistan. In mid-June 2002, Russia also signed military accords with Kyrgyzstan extending leases on military facilities to fifteen years (including, amazingly, a naval test base), opening shuttered Kyrgyz defense industries, and training Kyrgyz troops. Most significantly, Kyrgyzstan also agreed that its Kant airfield outside its capital of Bishkek could be used as a base for the Central Asian rapid reaction force. In signing the accords, Russian Defense Minister Sergey Ivanov declared that they marked Russia's help – along with the U.S.-led coalition and China – in combating terrorism, were necessary for Russia to monitor the proliferation of weapons of mass destruction, and marked Russia's intention to maintain a military presence in the region. According to some reports, Ivanov also pressed Kyrgyz authorities to announce that all U.S. and coalition use of the Manas airport had to end by mid-2003.

Economically, Russia seeks to counter Western business interests and gain substantial influence over oil and gas resources in the region through participation in joint ventures and by insisting that pipeline routes transit Russian territory. At the same time, Russia has avoided large economic subsidies to the region. Russia's motives in the post-9/11 environment vis-a-vis a Western role in energy development in the Caspian remain complex and it does not appear that a coherent regional energy policy is being followed. The Russian Ministry of Foreign Affairs has softened but not reversed its attitude against construction of the Baku-Tbilisi-Ceyhan (BTC) pipeline post-9/11, and the Russian government generally remains less willing than are Russian energy firms to accept a role for Western energy firms in the region. During Turkmen President Niyazov's Moscow visit in January 2002, President Putin called for Central Asian states to form a Eurasian Gas Alliance to "export through a single channel." Russian media speculate that Putin advocates the alliance to protect Russia's influence over the world gas market against the possibility of more U.S. energy influence in the region.

The safety of Russians in Central Asia is a populist concern in Russia, but has in practice mainly served as a political stalking horse for those in Russia advocating the "reintegration" of former "Russian lands." Ethnic Russians residing in Central Asia have had rising concerns about employment, language, and other policies or practices they deem discriminatory and many have emigrated, contributing to their decline from 20 million in 1989 to 6.6 million in 2001. They now constitute 12% of the population of Central Asia, according to the *CIS*

Statistics Agency. Remaining Russians tend to be elderly or low-skilled. In Kazakhstan, ethnic Kazakhs have again become the majority.

OBSTACLES TO PEACE AND INDEPENDENCE

The presidents of four out of five of the Central Asian states have been in power since independence, and were previous communist party heads or officials during the Soviet period. They have remained in place by orchestrating extensions of their terms and by limiting political freedoms. U.S. policymakers have warned, however, that political repression ultimately harms stability. The lack of obvious successors to the present leaders raises concern among many observers. Kyrgyzstan's Constitutional Court in 1999 ruled that President Askar Akayev could run for a third term as president, although the constitution set a two-term limit, and Niyazov orchestrated a constitutional change in late 1999 naming him president for life. Nazarbayev too in 2000 gained some official powers for life. A referendum in early 2002 extended Karimov's term to 2007. Belying the appearance of stability, Uzbekistan's capital of Tashkent was shaken in February 1999 by explosions that Karimov denounced as a coup attempt (see below, *Bombings*), Turkmenistan's President Niyazov supposedly faced an attempted coup in November 2002, and Karimov's, Niyazov's, and Akayev's regimes face rising popular protests (see below, *Democratization*).

Regional Tensions and Conflicts

The legacies of co-mingled ethnic groups, convoluted borders, and vague national identities pose serious problems to stability in all the Central Asian states. With the Soviet collapse, most in Central Asia support national identities, but also are emphasizing identifications with clan, family, region, and Islam. Some in the four Turkic-language states (Kazakhstan, Kyrgyzstan, Turkmenistan, and Uzbekistan) promote a pan-Turkic identity. Most analysts conclude that in the foreseeable future, the term Central Asia will denote a geographic area more than a region of shared identities and aspirations, although it can be argued that the land-locked, poverty-stricken, and non-populous region will need to embrace economic integration in order to develop.

Central Asia's borders, described as among the world's most convoluted, fail to accurately reflect ethnic distributions and are hard to police, hence contributing to potential instability. Ethnic Uzbeks make up sizeable minorities in the other Central Asian countries and Afghanistan. In Tajikistan, they make up almost a quarter of the population. More ethnic Turkmen reside in Iran and Afghanistan — over three million — than in Turkmenistan. Sizeable numbers of ethnic Tajiks reside in Uzbekistan, and seven million in Afghanistan. Many Kyrgyz and Tajiks live in China's Xinjiang province. The fertile Ferghana Valley was divided by Stalin among Tajikistan, Kyrgyzstan, and Uzbekistan, leaving large numbers of people outside their "national" borders. Criss-crossing mountains thwart Tajikistan's integrity. Akayev has faced popular criticism over a border accord with China that ceded some territory, and Tajikistan and China continue to wrangle over borders.

In 1996, Russia, Kazakhstan, Kyrgyzstan, and Tajikistan, signed the "Shanghai treaty" with China pledging the sanctity and substantial demilitarization of mutual borders, and in

1997 they signed a follow-on treaty demilitarizing the 4,300 mile former Soviet-Chinese border. China has used the treaty to pressure the Central Asian states to deter their ethnic Uighur minorities from supporting separatism in China's Xinjiang province, and to get them to extradite Uighurs fleeing China. In 2001, Uzbekistan joined the group, re-named the Shanghai Cooperation Organization (SCO). The SCO played no real role in U.S.-led coalition actions in Afghanistan. Reportedly, the United States attempted to contact the SCO right after 9/11, but discovered that its "headquarters" in Bishkek was dormant (it is now staffed). China and Russia have appeared to move slowly in bolstering the SCO, since some of the reasons for forming it – to counter terrorism and limit U.S. presence – appear less salient since the United States moved militarily into the region after 9/11. Some Chinese officials have acknowledged that U.S. anti-terrorism efforts in the region have increased stability along China's borders. Nonetheless, the two states retain long term interests in limiting the U.S. presence and in gaining influence in the region.

The Bombings in Tashkent, Uzbekistan

After the February 16, 1999, explosions, which by various reports killed 16-28 and wounded 100-351, Uzbek officials detained dozens of suspects, including political dissidents. Karimov in April 1999 accused Mohammad Solikh (former Uzbek presidential candidate and head of the banned Erk Party) of masterminding the plot, along with Tohir Yuldashev (former leader of the banned Uzbek Adolat social movement) and the Taliban. The first trial of 22 suspects in June 1999 resulted in six receiving the death sentence. The suspects were described in court proceedings as Islamic terrorists who received training in Afghanistan (by the Taliban), Tajikistan, Pakistan, and Russia (by the terrorist Khattab in Chechnya), and were led by Solikh, Yuldashev, and militia head Jama Namanganiy. Testimony alleged that Solikh had joined the Islamic Movement of Uzbekistan (IMU), led by Yuldashev and Namanganiy, in mid-1997, and that Solikh, Yuldashev, Namanganiy, and others had agreed that Solikh would be president and Yuldashev defense minister after Karimov was overthrown and a caliphate established. In November 2000, the Uzbek Supreme Court convicted twelve persons of terrorism, nine of whom were tried in absentia. The absent Yuldashev and Namanganiy were given death sentences and the absent Solikh, 15.5 years in prison. U.S. officials criticized the apparent lack of due process during the trial. Solikh has rejected accusations of involvement in the bombings or membership in the IMU. Yuldashev too has eschewed responsibility for the bombings but warned that more might occur if Karimov does not step down.

In September 2000, the State Department designated the IMU as a Foreign Terrorist Organization, stating that the IMU resorts to terrorism, actively threatens U.S. interests, and attacks American citizens. The "main goal of the IMU is to topple the current government in Uzbekistan," it warned, linking the IMU to bombings and attacks on Uzbekistan in 1999-2000. The IMU is being aided by Afghanistan's Taliban and by Osama bin Laden, according to the State Department, and it stressed that the "United States supports the right of Uzbekistan to defend its sovereignty and territorial integrity from the violent actions of the IMU," in ways that respect basic human rights. According to *Patterns of Global Terrorism 2001*, IMU forces assisting the Taliban against coalition actions in Afghanistan suffered major losses, and Namanganiy was probably killed, but the IMU remains a regional threat.

The Incursions into Kyrgyzstan

Several hundred Islamic extremists and others first invaded Kyrgyzstan in July-August 1999. Namanganiy headed the largest guerrilla group. They seized hostages and several villages, allegedly seeking to create an Islamic state in south Kyrgyzstan as a springboard for a jihad in Uzbekistan. With Uzbek and Kazakh air and other support, Kyrgyz forces finally forced the guerrillas out in October 1999. According to some observers, the incursion indicated both links among terrorism in Kyrgyzstan, Uzbekistan, Russia (Chechnya), and elsewhere and the weakness of Kyrgyzstan's security forces. Dozens of IMU and other insurgents again invaded Kyrgyzstan and Uzbekistan in August 2000. Uzbekistan provided air and other support, but Kyrgyz forces were largely responsible for defeating the insurgents by late October 2000, reporting the loss of 30 Kyrgyz troops. According to the State Department, the IMU did not invade the region in the summer before September 11, 2001, in part because bin Laden had secured its aid for the Taliban offensive against the Afghan Northern Alliance.

Civil War in Tajikistan

State Department officials served as observers at the U.N.-sponsored inter-Tajik peace talks and pledged to help Tajikistan rebuild after a peace settlement, indications of the Administration's efforts to ease ethnic and civil tensions in the Eurasian states. The United States has been the major humanitarian donor to alleviate the effects of the Tajik civil war. The United States supported the presence of U.N. observers in Tajikistan, and urged Russian-CIS "peacekeeping" forces to cooperate fully with them and to abide by international law. U.S. programs in Tajikistan have been complicated by the U.S. closure of its embassy in Dushanbe in 1998, and relocation of personnel to Kazakhstan, because of inadequate security. Beginning in 2000, some diplomatic personnel have traveled back and forth to Dushanbe. A site has been leased where a secure chancery will be built.

Tajikistan was among the Central Asian republics least prepared and inclined toward independence when the Soviet Union broke up. In September 1992, a loose coalition of nationalist, Islamic, and democratic parties and groups – largely consisting of members of Pamiri and Garmi regional elites who had long been excluded from political power – tried to take over. Kulyabi and Khojenti regional elites, assisted by Uzbekistan and Russia, launched a successful counteroffensive that by the end of 1992 had resulted in 20,000-40,000 casualties and up to 800,000 refugees or displaced persons, about 80,000 of whom fled to Afghanistan. These United Tajik Opposition (UTO) rebels variously received help from Iran and the IMU. In 1993, the CIS authorized "peacekeeping" in Tajikistan, consisting of Russian and token Kazakh, Kyrgyz, and Uzbek troops. After the two sides agreed to a cease-fire, the U.N. Security Council established a small U.N. Mission of Observers in Tajikistan (UNMOT) in December 1994. In June 1997, Tajik President Emomali Rakhmanov and UTO leader Seyed Abdullo Nuri signed a *comprehensive peace agreement*, under which Rakhmanov remained president but 30% of ministerial posts were allotted to the opposition. Benchmarks of the peace process were largely met, including the return of refugees, demilitarization of rebel forces, legalization of rebel parties, and the holding of elections. In March 2000, the NRC disbanded. UNMOT pulled out in May 2000, and a small U.N. Tajikistan Office of Peace-Building (UNTOP) was set up to facilitate aid. The CIS declared its peacekeeping mandate fulfilled in June 2000, but Russian troops remain under a 25-year basing agreement.

DEMOCRATIZATION AND HUMAN RIGHTS

A major concern of U.S. policy in Central Asia has been to foster the long-term development of democratic institutions and policies upholding human rights. U.S. democratization support has been provided for political parties, voter education and electoral laws, legal and constitutional reform, media, structuring the division and balance of governmental powers, and parliamentary and educational exchanges. At the same time, the United States has worked with the ex-Communist Party officials who have led in the five states (even in Tajikistan, the current president was once a low-level party official) since before independence, recognizing that they may continue to hold power for some time.

Scenarios of political development in Central Asia include continued rule in most of the states by former Soviet elites, gradual transitions to more nationalistic elites who are at least somewhat democratic and Western-oriented, or large-scale and perhaps violent transitions to Islamic fundamentalist or xenophobic rule. All the Central Asian leaders have given assurances to the United States that they support democratization, but all have continued to rule largely as they did during the communist period, with minimal adaptations. During Nazarbayev's 1994 U.S. visit, he and then-President Clinton signed a Charter on Democratic Partnership recognizing Kazakhstan's commitments to the rule of law, respect for human rights, and economic reform. During his December 2001 visit, Nazarbayev repeated these pledges in a joint statement with President Bush. In March 2002, Uzbek Foreign Minister Abdulaziz Komilov and Secretary Powell signed a Strategic Partnership Declaration pledging Uzbekistan to "intensify the democratic transformation" and improve freedom of the press. During previous visits in 1997 and 1999 to Washington, D.C., Tajikistan's President Emomali Rakhmanov was not received at the presidential level as a protest against failures in democratization, but during his December 2002 visit he met with President Bush and other top officials, and the Administration highlighted Tajikistan's recent "significant progress" in democratization and its support for U.S.-led coalition actions in Afghanistan.

According to the State Department's *Country Reports on Human Rights Practices for 2001*, presidential power in all the Central Asian states overshadows legislative and judicial power, and all the states have lost ground in democratization. Turkmenistan and Uzbekistan are generally viewed as the most repressive, while Kazakhstan and Kyrgyzstan permit some limited free expression and other rights. Tajikistan experienced many conflict-related human rights abuses in the course of its 1992-1997 civil war, but during its fragile peace there have been a few human rights improvements. In most of the states, religious freedom is threatened by repression against nonfavored faiths, missionaries, and pious Muslims who tend to be viewed as extremists. Unfair elections and unseemly extensions of presidential terms increase political alienation and frustration among the populations and contribute to the formation of clandestine groups seeking to overthrow the regimes. In its 2002 *Trafficking in Persons Report*, the State Department categorized Kyrgyzstan and Tajikistan as having serious problems with human trafficking for labor or prostitution. If the states do not make serious efforts to reduce trafficking by the time of issuance of the 2003 report, they could be subject to aid sanctions (however, there is a presidential waiver provision).

In Turkmenistan, a late November 2002 failed coup resulted in dozens of arrests and trials, the first of which resulted in the quick conviction in late December of former Turkmen foreign minister Boris Shikhmuradov and two other opposition leaders (tried in absentia) for organizing the coup attempt. The trial was beamed to a session of the quasi-legislative

People's Council, led by Niyazov, that quickly changed the sentences from 25 years to life in prison. Subsequent trials have resulted in over 60 convictions. Many of the accused "admitted" their guilt on state television, and even begged to be executed, causing human rights organizations and others to raise allegations of torture. The U.S. State Department has strongly protested violations of legal due process and "credible reports" of forced confessions and other human rights abuses. A U.S. citizen remains in custody. Concerns about human rights led OSCE members to call for a fact-finding mission. Although Niyazov refused to let the mission into the country, it drew up an as-yet unreleased assessment by late February 2003. *Reuters* reported in early March that the mission had concluded that "large-scale violations of all the principles of due process of law" took place after the coup attempt, including arbitrary detentions, "show trials," and the use of torture and drugs to obtain confessions.

Some critics who argue that there have been stepped-up human rights abuses in Kazakhstan and Uzbekistan – despite U.S.-led coalition actions in Afghanistan that helped to ease terrorist threats to the regimes – surmise that leaders of these states have viewed post-9/11 U.S. policy as being less interested in human rights. Others surmise that regional populations have pressed democratization demands, emboldened by the U.S. presence. Countering the argument of less attention to human rights, Assistant Secretary of State Lorne Craner in testimony to Congress on June 27, 2002, referred to Central Asia in stating that "even while we ramp up our military cooperation with governments that have troubling human rights records, we also see this as an opportunity to enhance our engagement and impact on issues of democracy and human rights." He also repeated past Administration vows that "any deepening and broadening of our cooperation will depend on continual progress in respecting human rights and democracy."

In Congress, conferees on H.R. 4775 (H.Rept.107-593; an emergency supplemental for FY2002; P.L. 107-206) called for added Foreign Military Financing (FMF) aid to Uzbekistan to be conditioned on a report by the Secretary of State that it is making progress in meeting its human rights commitments under the "Strategic Partnership" agreement. Omnibus Appropriations for FY2003 (P.L. 108-7; signed into law on February 20, 2003) goes further, forbidding FREEDOM Support Act assistance to the government of Uzbekistan unless the Secretary of State determines and reports that Uzbekistan is making substantial progress in meeting its Strategic Partnership Declaration commitments to democratize and respect human rights. P.L. 108-7 also forbids assistance to the government of Kazakhstan unless the Secretary of State determines and reports that Kazakhstan has significantly improved its human rights record during the preceding six-month period. Unlike the case with Uzbekistan, the legislation permits the Secretary to waive this requirement on national security grounds. These provisions in P.L. 108-7 reflect the similar concerns of S.J.Res. 3, introduced January 14, 2003, which criticizes Central Asian governments for human rights abuses, and calls on the President to condition U.S. political, economic and military relations with the regional governments on their respect for human rights and democracy.

Security and Arms Control

Since 9/11, U.S. and coalition action in Operation Enduring Freedom (OEF) to halt the export of terrorism from Afghanistan has greatly increased the security of Central Asia. The development of U.S. security ties with Central Asia pre-9/11 facilitated the cooperation of the states in OEF. Reportedly, such pre-9/11 ties included Uzbek permission for U.S. clandestine efforts against al Qaeda in Afghanistan. According to Assistant Secretary of Defense Crouch in testimony in June 2002, "our military relationships with each [Central Asian] nation have matured on a scale not imaginable prior to September 11th." Kyrgyzstan, he relates, is a "critical regional partner" in OEF, providing basing for combat and combat support units at Manas Airport (at the U.S.-designated Ganci airbase) for U.S., French, Italian, Norwegian, Canadian, and South Korean forces. Uzbekistan provides a base for U.S. operations at Karshi-Khanabad and a base for German units at Termez, and a land corridor to Afghanistan for humanitarian aid via the Friendship Bridge at Termez. Kazakhstan has provided overflight rights and expedited rail transhipment of supplies. Turkmenistan has permitted blanket overflight and refueling privileges for humanitarian flights. Tajikistan has permitted use of its international airport in Dushanbe for U.S., British, and French refueling and basing. While the Administration has rejected the idea of permanent military bases in these states, Crouch stated in June 2002 that "for the foreseeable future, U.S. defense and security cooperation in Central Asia must continue to support actions to deter or defeat terrorist threats" and to build effective armed forces under civilian control.

Among recent accords, on March 12, 2002, a U.S.-Uzbekistan Declaration on the Strategic Partnership was signed that includes a nonspecific security guarantee. The United States affirms that "it would regard with grave concern any external threat" to Uzbekistan's security and would consult with Uzbekistan "on an urgent basis" regarding a response. The two states pledge to intensify military cooperation, including "re-equipping the Armed Forces" of Uzbekistan. Similarly, visiting Kyrgyz President Askar Akayev and President Bush issued a joint statement on September 23, 2002, pledging to deepen the strategic partnership, including cooperation in counter-terrorism. In early October 2002, Kyrgyzstan's Deputy Prime Minister praised the economic benefits of Ganci, stressing that coalition forces already had spent up to $35 million, about 15% of Kyrgyzstan's yearly budget.

A small but increasing amount of U.S. security assistance was provided to the region pre-9/11, and much more after 9/11. All the states receive FMF and International Military Education and Training (IMET) assistance, and are eligible to receive Excess Defense Articles (EDA) on a grant basis. U.S. Central Command in 1999 became responsible for U.S. military engagement activities, planning, and operations in Central Asia. It states that its peacetime strategy aims to foster "apolitical, professional militaries capable of responding to regional peacekeeping and humanitarian needs" in the region. USCENTCOM Commanders visited the region regularly, setting the stage for more extensive military ties post-9/11. Defense Secretary Donald Rumsfeld visited the region in December 2001 and April-May 2002. During his August 2002 visit, USCENTCOM Commander Tommy Franks stated that the U.S. military presence would continue in Afghanistan and Central Asia for some time and that military-to-military ties with regional states would increase.

Efforts to foster military cooperation were furthered when all the Central Asian states except Tajikistan joined NATO's PFP by mid-1994. Tajikistan decided to join PFP before 9/11, and signed accords on admission in February 2002. Central Asian officers and troops have participated in PFP exercises in the United States since 1995, and U.S. troops participated in exercises in Central Asia in 1997, 1998, and 2000. Many in Central Asia viewed these exercises as "sending a message" to Islamic extremists and others in

Afghanistan, Iran, and elsewhere against fostering regional instability. Central Asian PFP command exercises termed "Regional Cooperation" were held in Germany in mid-2001.

Weapons of Mass Destruction

Major U.S. security interests have included elimination of nuclear weapons remaining in Kazakhstan after the breakup of the Soviet Union and other efforts to control nuclear proliferation in Central Asia. The United States has tendered aid aimed at bolstering their export and physical controls over nuclear technology and materials, including because of concerns that Iran is targeting these countries. In December 2002, Harlan Strauss, the head of Counterproliferation Programs at the U.S. Defense Department, reported that U.S. aid had assisted Central Asian states during 2002 in halting the smuggling of radioactive materials out of the region that could have been used in so-called "dirty bombs" (radioactive materials mixed with conventional explosives).

After the Soviet breakup, Kazakhstan was on paper a major nuclear weapons power (in reality Russia controlled these weapons). Though some in Kazakhstan urged "retaining" the weapons, it pledged to become a non-nuclear weapons state. All bombers and their air-launched cruise missiles were removed by late February 1994. On April 21, 1995, the last of about 1,040 nuclear warheads had been removed from the SS-18 missiles and transferred to Russia, and Kazakhstan announced that it was nuclear weapons-free. The SS-18s were eliminated by late 1994 and most silos were blown up in 1995-1996. In December 1993, the United States and Kazakhstan signed a CTR umbrella agreement for the "safe and secure" dismantling of 104 SS-18s, the destruction of their silos, and related purposes. In June 2002, the United States and Kazakhstan signed an extension accord to destroy six remaining silos at the Leninsk testing ground in the Kyzyl-Orda region.

Besides the Kazakh nuclear weapons, there are active research reactors, uranium mines, and milling facilities in Kazakhstan, Kyrgyzstan, and Uzbekistan that pose proliferation concerns. Kazakhstan is reported to possess one-fourth of the world's uranium reserves, and Kazakhstan and Uzbekistan are among the world's top producers of low enriched uranium. Kazakhstan had a fast breeder reactor at Aktau, the world's only nuclear desalinization facility. Shut down in April 1999, it has nearly 300 metric tons of enriched uranium and plutonium spent fuel in storage pools. Kazakhstan and Kyrgyzstan report that their mining and milling activities have resulted in massive and hazardous waste dumps. In 1997 and 1999, U.S.-Kazakh accords were signed on safeguarding and mothballing the Aktau reactor and eventually removing its weapons-grade plutonium.

Kazakhstan and Uzbekistan hosted major chemical and biological warfare (CBW) facilities during the Soviet era. CTR and Energy Department funds are being used to eliminate infrastructure at a former biological weapons production facility in Stepnogorsk, Kazakhstan, and for retraining scientists. At the U.S.-Uzbek Joint Commission meeting in May 1999, the two sides signed a CTR agreement on securing, dismantling, and decontaminating the Soviet-era Nukus chemical research facility. Other aid will help keep Uzbek weapons scientists employed in peaceful research. U.S. aid has been used to eliminate active anthrax spores and other hazards at a Soviet-era CBW testing site on an island in the Aral Sea belonging to Kazakhstan and Uzbekistan.

TRADE AND INVESTMENT

The Administration and others stress that U.S. support for free market reforms directly serves U.S. national interests by opening new markets for U.S. goods and services, and sources of energy and minerals. U.S. private investment committed to Central Asia has greatly exceeded that provided to Russia or most other Eurasian states except Azerbaijan, although the region is relatively isolated and the states lag behind Russia in accommodating commercial ties. However, corruption is stifling the emergence of the rule of law, as exemplified by allegations that both Nazarbayev and Niyazov siphoned energy revenues into bank accounts they controlled. Currency convertibility problems in Uzbekistan and Turkmenistan stymie investment, business growth, and trade. In October 2002, U.S. Ambassador to Kazakhstan Larry Napper announced a "Houston Initiative" of U.S. aid to support enhanced U.S. investment in both energy and non-energy sectors to foster diverse economic development. However, a foreign investment law signed in Kazakhstan in January 2003 appears to lower safeguards against contractual violations by the Kazakh government.

U.S. trade agreements have been signed and entered into force with all the Central Asian states. Permanent normal trade relations with Kyrgyzstan were established by law in June 2000, so that Jackson-Vanik trade provisions calling for presidential reports and waivers no longer apply. The Export-Import Bank (Eximbank) has obligated funds for short-term insurance, loans, or guarantees for export sales of industrial and agricultural equipment and bulk agricultural commodities to all the states except Tajikistan. The Overseas Private Investment Corporation (OPIC) has signed agreements with all the Central Asian states on insuring U.S. private investments overseas, and has obligated funds for financing or insurance in all the states except Tajikistan. The Central Asian American Enterprise Fund, authorized by Congress to lend up to $150 million, has been bedeviled by convertibility problems and major defaults on its joint venture loans and has halted operations.

All the states of the region possess large-scale resources that could yield export earnings, but major investments are needed to revamp, develop, or market the resources in most cases. The Kazakh and Turkmen economies are dependent on energy exports but need added foreign investment for production and transport. Uzbekistan's cotton and gold production rank among the highest in the world and much is exported. It also has moderate energy reserves. Kyrgyzstan owns major gold mines and strategic mineral reserves, is a major wool producer, and could benefit from tourism. Tajikistan has one of the world's largest aluminum processing plants and is a major cotton grower.

Energy Resources

U.S. policy goals regarding energy resources in the Central Asian and South Caucasian states have included supporting their sovereignty and ties to the West, supporting U.S. private investment, breaking Russia's monopoly over oil and gas transport routes by encouraging the building of pipelines that do not traverse Russia, promoting Western energy security through diversified suppliers, assisting ally Turkey, and opposing the building of pipelines that transit "energy competitor" Iran or otherwise give it undue influence over the region. Security for Caspian region pipelines and energy resources also has been a recent interest. President Bush's May 2001 *National Energy Policy* report suggests that greater oil production in the

Caspian region could not only benefit regional economies, but also help mitigate possible world supply disruptions. It recommends U.S. support for building Baku-Ceyhan oil and gas pipelines, coaxing oil companies operating in Kazakhstan to use the oil pipeline, and otherwise encouraging the regional states to provide a stable and inviting business climate for energy development. It avers that the building of the pipelines will enhance energy supply diversification, including for Georgia and Turkey. In August 2002, U.S. Coordinator of Assistance to Eurasia William Taylor resurrected U.S. support (dropped during Taliban rule) for construction of a gas pipeline from Turkmenistan through Afghanistan to Pakistan and possibly to India. While touted by Niyazov, energy firms have so far viewed such a route as too risky.

According to the U.S. Department of Energy (DOE), the Caspian region is emerging as a significant source of oil and gas for world markets. Oil resources, DOE reports, are comparable to those of the North Sea, and Turkmenistan, Uzbekistan, and Kazakhstan rank among the top countries in terms of proven and probable gas reserves. DOE reports estimates of 10-17.6 billion barrels of proven oil reserves and 53-83 trillion cubic feet of natural gas in Kazakhstan, and 98-155 trillion cubic feet of proven gas reserves in Turkmenistan. Kazakhstan's Tengiz oil field began to be exploited by Chevron-Texaco and Kazakhstan during 1993 in a consortium called TengizChevoil (U.S. Exxon-Mobil, ARCO, and Russia's LUKoil later joined). The non-Kazakh partners balked in late 2002 at a Kazakh demand for higher taxes, but the dispute seemed to be resolved in early 2003. In July 2002, another consortium led by Italy's Agip oil firm reported findings from its test wells and research that Kazakhstan's Kashagan offshore Caspian oil field had between 7-9 billion barrels of oil in proven reserves and up to 38 billion barrels in probable reserves, comparable to those of Tengiz. Kazakhstan's oil exports currently are over 630,000 barrels per day (bpd), compared to 3 million bpd for Russia.

The Central Asian states have been pressured by Russia to yield portions of their energy wealth to Russia, in part because Russia controls most existing pipelines to export markets. In a strategy similar to one Russia has used in other CIS and in Eastern Europe, where it restricted energy supplies until given commercial concessions, Russia's restrictions on Tengiz oil exports to Europe were eased slightly in 1996 after the consortium admitted LUKoil, and after Gazprom was admitted to another consortium. Russian shareholders have a controlling interest, 44 percent, in the Caspian pipeline consortium (CPC), which completed construction in late 2001 on a 930-mile oil pipeline from Kazakhstan to Russia's Black Sea port of Novorossiysk – the region's first new large-capacity pipeline – that initially carries 560,000 bpd, and eventually will carry 1.3 million bpd. President Bush hailed the opening of the pipeline as an example "that the United States, Russia, and Kazakhstan are cooperating to build prosperity and stability in this part of the world." He stated that the CPC project also "advances my Administration's National Energy Policy by developing a network of multiple Caspian pipelines ... [that] help diversify U.S. energy supply and enhance our energy security." The Administration has urged Kazakhstan to pledge to use the oil pipeline being built from Baku, Azerbaijan, to Ceyhan, Turkey.

In the late 1980s, Turkmenistan was the world's fourth largest natural gas producer. It is now largely dependent on Russian export routes. In 1993, Russia had halted Turkmen gas exports to Western markets through its pipelines, diverting Turkmen gas to other Eurasian states that had trouble paying for the gas. In 1997, Russia cut off these shipments because of transit fee arrears and other problems. In 1998 and every year thereafter, Turkmenistan has tried to get higher prices for its gas but has capitulated to Russia's natural gas firm Gazprom (or its subsidiary Itera). Putin's talks in January, 2002 with Niyazov on long-term gas supplies were unproductive because Niyazov balked at the low prices offered. Seeking other export routes, Turkmenistan in December 1997 opened the first pipeline from Central Asia to the outside world beyond Russia, a 125-mile pipeline linkage to Iran's pipeline system, but disputes have limited exports. Some oil is also sent to Iran in a swap arrangement. Swiss and Chinese firms are modernizing Iran's infrastructure to boost its ability to process Turkmen and Kazakh oil.

AID OVERVIEW

The Bush Administration provided added security and other assistance to the Central Asian states in FY2002 in response to the events of September 11, 2001. Some observers characterized this assistance as a U.S. *quid pro quo* for the use of military facilities and an incentive for continued cooperation. The Administration has argued that the safer environment in the Central Asian states fostered by security assistance and the U.S. military presence should permit greater democratization, respect for human rights, and economic liberalization in the region, and the development of Caspian energy resources.

For much of the 1990s and until 9/11, U.S. assistance to Central Asian states was far less than that to Russia, Ukraine, Armenia, and Georgia (most such aid was funded from the FREEDOM Support Act account in Foreign Operations Appropriations, but some derived from other program and agency budgets). Cumulative foreign aid budgeted to Central Asia for FY1992 through FY2002 amounted to $2.76 billion, about 12% of the amount obligated to all the Eurasian states of the former Soviet Union, reflecting the lesser priority given to these states prior to 9/11. The amount of aid provided to Central Asia usually but not always tracked with the "roller coaster" of declining (FY1994-FY1997), increasing (FY1998-FY1999), and declining (FY2000-FY2001) aid provided to the rest of the Eurasian states. In FY1998, the previous Administration called for added civil society assistance, particularly for the Central Asian countries and Russia. Although congressional earmarks fenced off much of the FREEDOM Support Act aid, Central Asia benefitted from other program and agency spending. Increased appropriations in FY1999 for Eurasia also benefitted Central Asia. In FY2000, despite declining FREEDOM Support Act assistance, budgeted support for Central Asia increased to $222.57 million (including other program and Agency funding). The same situation occurred in FY2001. Estimated spending for FY2002 for Central Asia, during OEF, was greatly boosted in absolute amounts and as a percent of total aid to Eurasia. Aid amounts for FY2003 and proposed for FY2004 appear less in absolute amounts than in FY2002, but aid to Central Asia planned for FY2004 looms larger as a percent (27%) of the total FREEDOM Support Act aid to Eurasia (see Table 1).

Besides bilateral and regional aid, the United States contributes to international financial institutions and nongovernmental organizations that aid Central Asia. Policy issues regarding U.S. aid include whether the states are properly using it (is the aid subject to corruption or is the aid conditioned on reforms), what it should be used for, and who should receive it.

Table 1. U.S. Foreign Assistance to Central Asia
(in millions of dollars)

Central Asian Country	Cumulative Funds Budgeted FY1992-FY2002*	FY2001 Budgeted*	FY2002 Budgeted*	FY2003 Budgeted***	FY2004 Request***
Kazakhstan	885.95	74.87	89.34	42.72	32
Kyrgyzstan	635.03	41.46	95.66	37.85	40
Tajikistan	489.96	56.48	141.29	25.8	35
Turkmenistan	218.2	12.57	18.06	7.8	8
Uzbekistan	530.59	57.22	239.78	38.75	42
Total	2,759.73**	242.6	584.13	152.92	157
Percent of Eurasian Aid	13%	21%	25%	20%	27%

Source: State Department, Office of the Coordinator for U.S. Assistance to Europe and Eurasia.
*FREEDOM Support Act and Agency funds.
**In addition, $22.61 million in region-wide funds were budgeted FY1992-FY2002.
***FREEDOM Support Act and other Function 150 funds, not including Defense or Energy Department funds; the FY2004 request excludes funding for exchanges.

Map: Central Asia's New States

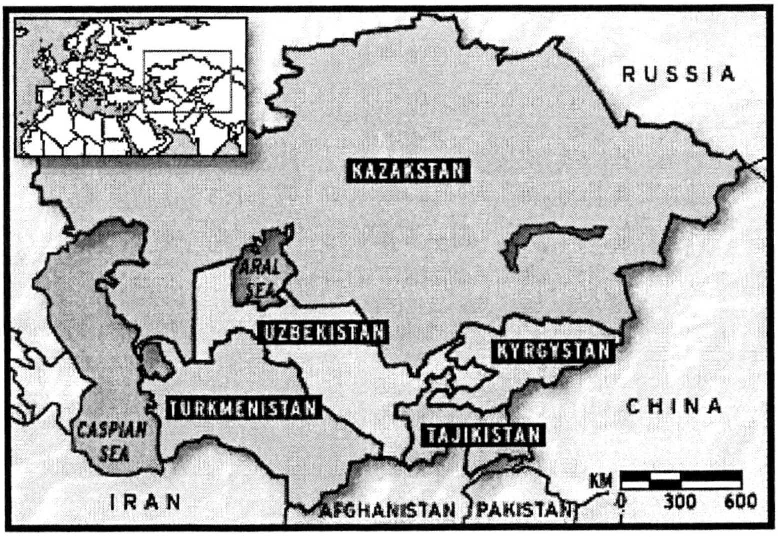

INDEX

#

A

B

C

D

E

F

O

P

R

S

T

U

V

W

Y